CHEMICAL THERMODYNAMICS

Benson · The Foundations of Chemical Kinetics

Dean · Flame Photometry

Djerassi · Optical Rotatory Dispersion

Fitts · Nonequilbrium Thermodynamics

Hill · Statistical Mechanics

Hine · Physical Organic Chemistry

Kirkwood and Oppenheim · Chemical Thermodynamics

Laitinen · Chemical Analysis

Lewis and Randall · Thermodynamics

Pople, Schneider, and Bernstein · High-resolution Nuclear Magnetic Resonance

Roberts · Nuclear Magnetic Resonance

Rossotti & Rossotti · The Determination of Stability Constants

Wiberg · Laboratory Technique in Organic Chemistry

CHEMICAL THERMODYNAMICS

JOHN G. KIRKWOOD

Late Sterling Professor and
Chairman of the Department of Chemistry
Yale University

IRWIN OPPENHEIM

Heat Division, National Bureau of Standards
Physics Section, Convair, San Diego
Department of Chemistry
Massachusetts Institute of Technology

McGRAW-HILL BOOK COMPANY, INC.

New York Toronto London

1961

CHEMICAL THERMODYNAMICS

 Library of Congress Catalog Card Number 60-16946

34860

II

THE MAPLE PRESS COMPANY, YORK, PA.

PREFACE

The main purpose of this book is to present a rigorous and logical discussion of the fundamentals of thermodynamics and to develop in a coherent fashion the application of the basic principles to a number of systems of interest to chemists. The concept of temperature is carefully discussed, and special emphasis is placed on the appropriate method for the introduction of molecular weights into thermodynamics. A new treatment of the second law of thermodynamics is presented which demonstrates that Carathéodory's principle is a necessary and sufficient consequence of the physical statements of Clausius and Kelvin.

The analysis of the application of thermodynamics to various systems is carried out in terms of measurable quantities wherever possible. Operational treatments of gas mixtures and electrochemical systems are discussed. In particular, we note that the concept of single-electrode potential can be made operational.

A detailed and general study of heterogeneous equilibrium is made. Surface phenomena are discussed from the point of view of Gibbs which seems to us to provide the best connection with molecular theory. The treatment of dielectrics utilizes a form of the first law which is more general than those usually used.

This book is based on lectures by Professor Kirkwood in a graduate course in thermodynamics at the California Institute of Technology. Most of the presentations were developed by Professor Kirkwood during the course of 20 years of teaching and active research in the field and reflect his ability to provide a logical and thorough treatment of the subject. The lecture notes were written up by one of the authors (I. Oppenheim) and by Prof. M. Karplus and A. Rich. The notes have attained a large circulation in mimeographed form and have been used in a large number of universities.

This book is meant to be a textbook and is primarily intended to serve as the basis of a senior or graduate course in thermodynamics.

It is a pleasant task to acknowledge the large contributions of M. Karplus and A. Rich at the early stages of this project. Many scientists have contributed advice on parts of the manuscript, but special thanks are due to Profs. Z. Salsburg and E. Montroll who have read the manuscript with care and have made a number of valuable suggestions.

Irwin Oppenheim

CONTENTS

I NOMENCLATURE AND TEMPERATURE

Thermodynamics is a discipline that involves a formalization of a large number of intuitive concepts derived from common experience. As such, it employs a number of terms which are used loosely in everyday language. Before beginning the presentation of thermodynamics as an exact science, it is essential to define the terms utilized with some exactitude. In this chapter we present detailed definitions of many of the most frequently employed terms and discuss the fundamental concept of temperature. In addition, we demonstrate how molecular weights can be introduced into thermodynamics in an unambiguous fashion.

1-1. DEFINITIONS

Thermodynamics is a macroscopic phenomenological discipline concerned with a description of the gross properties of systems of interest. A *system* is that part of the physical world which is under consideration. The *surroundings* are the rest of the physical world. Systems can be classified in terms of their interactions with the surroundings. An *open system* may exchange mass, heat, and work between system and surroundings. In a *closed system* no exchange of mass can occur; transfer of heat and work is still possible. An *isolated system* has no interactions with the surroundings.

A system may be further characterized in terms of the properties which describe its macroscopic coordinates. A *macroscopic coordinate* is one whose determination requires only measurements which are averages over regions containing many molecules, over times long with respect to periods of thermal motion, and which involve energies large with respect to individual quanta. *Thermodynamic properties* are the properties of the system which describe its macroscopic coordinates. An *intensive property* is a thermodynamic property which is independent of the mass of the system. An *extensive property* is a thermodynamic property which is dependent on the mass of the system. A system can be classified in terms of its intensive properties. A *homogeneous system* is one in which the intensive properties are continuous functions of position throughout the system. A *heterogeneous system* is one in which the intensive properties are not continuous functions of position throughout the system; i.e., surfaces of discontinuity exist. A heterogeneous system is composed of two or more homogeneous regions; each of these is called a *phase*. The number of phases is equal to the number of distinct homogeneous regions.

A system can be further described in terms of its components. *The number of independent components of a system* is the minimum number of chemical substances from which the system can be prepared by a specified set of procedures. Implicit in this statement is the definition of component. Some care is required in the application of this definition. For example, a system containing $CuSO_4$, $CuSO_4 \cdot 5H_2O$, and H_2O in equilibrium is composed of only two components as it can be prepared by mixing $CuSO_4$ and H_2O. *Pure systems* contain only a single component. *Mixed systems* contain more than one component. A system composed of *n*-butane and isobutane is a mixed, two-component system since each of the isomers can be prepared separately. However, a system containing various isomers of 1-2-dichloroethane is considered pure, owing to the high speed of isomerization at room temperature which prevents separation of the isomers.

States of a system are defined with respect to a specified class of properties by the statement: Two states are identical or agree if each member of the specified class of properties is identical or agrees in the two states. The *thermodynamic states* of a system are defined by the class of its intensive properties. A system is in a state of *thermodynamic equilibrium* if, during the time period allotted for experimentation, (*a*) its intensive properties are independent of time and (*b*) no current of matter or energy exists in its interior or at its boundaries with the surroundings. If a system satisfies only criterion *a*, it is said to be in a *steady state*. For two systems in a state of thermodynamic equilibrium, it is an experimental fact that, when all members of a small subclass of intensive properties agree, all other intensive properties also agree. Thus, states of thermodynamic equilibrium may be defined by this subclass. In a homogeneous open system of r independent components, $r + 1$ intensive properties must be specified to describe the equilibrium state. This assumes that we restrict ourselves to the case of no external electric, magnetic, or gravitational fields and that the only force which may act on the system is a uniform normal pressure.

The subclass of intensive properties which might be employed to describe a system is temperature t, pressure p, and $r - 1$ composition variables, x_i = mole fraction, $i = 1, \ldots, r - 1$. All intensive properties are, then, functions of $t, p, x_1, \ldots, x_{r-1}$, while the extensive properties are functions of $t, p, m_1, \ldots, m_r$, where m_i is the mass of the ith component. In a homogeneous system of one component, p and v (the molar volume) or t and v are usually sufficient to specify equilibrium states.

1-2. TEMPERATURE

The thermodynamic property temperature is used to formalize intuitive ideas concerning hotness and coldness. In this section, we develop an exact concept of temperature by considering the behavior of systems in thermal contact. Thermal contact exists between two systems when the interactions between them involve only heat transfer. No exchange of matter may occur between them, nor may one do work on the other.

If two homogeneous closed systems, both in states of thermodynamic equilibrium, are placed in thermal contact, either they remain in equilibrium from the instant of contact or they do not. *Temperature* t is that property of a system which determines whether it will remain in equilibrium on thermal contact with other systems. The temperatures of two systems are defined as equal if they remain in equilibrium on thermal contact; if equilibrium is not maintained, the temperatures are unequal. When two closed systems at unequal temperatures are brought into thermal contact, both undergo changes resulting in a final state of thermodynamic equilibrium, in which the temperatures of the two systems are equal. These changes consist of an alteration in the temperature of at least one of the systems *and* changes in the pressure (or volume) of the systems or a redistribution of matter among the phases of either system.

If a system C exhibits identical properties when allowed to come to equilibrium in successive thermal contacts with two systems A and B, it is found that A and B remain in equilibrium when placed in contact with each other. This fact permits a quantitative definition of temperature in terms of measurement by a suitably selected test body C, a thermometer.

The quantitative definition of temperature is completed by establishing a partially arbitrary functional relationship between the temperature t and a suitably selected property P of the thermometer. The thermometric property P and those other properties of the thermometer which are held constant in the operation of measurement must determine the thermodynamic state of the thermometer. The care necessary in choosing the variables to be held constant is illustrated by the fact that p and v are not always sufficient to determine the thermodynamic states of a pure system. Thus, for example, in water at temperatures between 0°C and 8°C, the dielectric constant may have two different values at the same values of p and v. The relationship between t and P, $t = t(P)$, though partially arbitrary, must be such that $t(P)$ is a continuous, monotonic, and single-valued function of P. Single-valuedness is required so that a set of systems with the same value of P remain in equilibrium on contact with each other, i.e., there is only one value of t for each P; monotonicity is necessary so that two systems with different values of P cannot be in equilibrium with each other. The function $t(P)$ is also invariably chosen in such a way that dissipation of mechanical energy produces a positive or zero increment in temperature.

A large variety of thermometers are employed for the measurement of temperature. Among these are the following:

Thermometer	*Thermometric property*
Pure gas at constant volume	Pressure
Pure gas at constant pressure	Volume
Platinum wire at constant pressure and tension	Electrical resistance
Thermocouple at constant pressure and tension	Thermal electromotive force
Crystal	Magnetic susceptibility

The choice of a temperature scale and the exact measurement of temperature are, in general, extremely difficult tasks. As yet, although much progress has been made, no scale for very low temperatures has been found to be universally acceptable. The situation for high temperatures is even worse since the problem of measurement of high temperatures has, at best, been only partially solved. It was pointed out above that the choice of a temperature scale is partly arbitrary. For convenience, a linear scale is usually employed. Use of a linear scale requires selection of an arbitrary zero and of an arbitrary scale unit. We shall discuss in detail the definitions of the centigrade, ideal gas, and absolute temperature scales.

Centigrade (Celsius) Scale. In the centigrade scale, the zero point P_0 is the value of P at the ice point, i.e., the freezing point of water at 1 atm pressure when all phases are saturated with air. The scale unit α is determined by the equation

$$\alpha = \frac{P_{100} - P_0}{100P_0} \tag{1-1}$$

where P_{100} is the value of P at the steam point, i.e., the boiling point of water at 1 atm pressure. Thus, the temperature t is given by

$$t(P) = \frac{1}{\alpha}\frac{P - P_0}{P_0} = \frac{100(P - P_0)}{P_{100} - P_0} \tag{1-2}$$

One of the possible choices of a thermometer is a pure gas or liquid at constant pressure. In this case, the volume V of the fluid is the thermometric property, and Eqs. (1-1) and (1-2) become

$$\alpha = \frac{V_{100} - V_0}{100V_0} \qquad p = \text{const} \tag{1-3}$$

and

$$t(V) = \frac{1}{\alpha}\frac{V - V_0}{V_0} \qquad p = \text{const} \tag{1-4}$$

Equation (1-4) is used for the mercury or alcohol thermometer, as well as for gas thermometers containing H_2 or He. It is found experimentally that the numerical value of the temperature, except the values at the ice and steam points which are fixed, depends upon the particular system and thermometric property employed. Because there is less variation among gas thermometers, a gas is usually chosen as the standard thermometric substance.

Ideal Gas Scale. It is found experimentally that the temperature measured in the constant-pressure gas thermometer, with V as the thermometric property, has a limiting value as the pressure tends to zero:

$$\lim_{p\to 0} t = t^* \tag{1-5}$$

which exists for every gas. The temperature scale t^* is the same for *all* gases and is called the ideal gas scale. A centigrade ideal gas scale is readily defined, by the use of Eqs. (1-3) and (1-4), by the relations

$$t^* = \lim_{p\to 0} \frac{1}{\alpha} \frac{V - V_0}{V_0} \tag{1-6}$$

and

$$\alpha^* = \lim_{p\to 0} \frac{V_{100} - V_0}{100 V_0} \tag{1-7}$$

The existence of the ideal gas temperature scale and the fact that it is the same for all gases are consequences of two laws which express conclusions drawn from a large number of experimental observations. One of these laws is Boyle's law which, in a modified form, states that for any given gas

$$\lim_{p\to 0} pV = \beta \tag{1-8}$$

where β is a function of temperature alone. The second law expresses the fact that the ratio $\beta(t_1)/\beta(t_2)$, where t_1 and t_2 are arbitrary temperatures, is independent of the gas considered. Using these laws, we can define a scale unit α^* by the expression

$$\alpha^* = \frac{\beta_{100} - \beta_0}{100\beta_0} \tag{1-9}$$

where β_0 is the value of β at the ice point and β_{100} is the value of β at the steam point. Substitution of (1-9) into (1-6) yields

$$t^* = \frac{1}{\alpha^*} \lim_{p\to 0} \frac{V - V_0}{V_0} = \frac{1}{\alpha^*} \frac{\beta - \beta_0}{\beta_0} \tag{1-10}$$

or

$$t^* = \frac{\beta}{\alpha^* \beta_0} - \frac{1}{\alpha^*} \tag{1-11}$$

Absolute Temperature Scale. The absolute temperature scale is simply related to the centigrade ideal gas scale. The absolute temperature T is defined by the equation

$$T = \frac{T_0}{\beta_0} \beta \tag{1-12}$$

where

$$T_0 = \frac{1}{\alpha^*}$$

Using Eqs. (1-11) and (1-12), we obtain

$$T = t^* + T_0 \tag{1-13}$$

The absolute temperature T defined by Eq. (1-12) is of fundamental importance in thermodynamics. It appears again in the discussion of the second law of thermodynamics. The constant T_0 can be determined experimentally from the limiting value of α as p approaches zero. The value $T_0 = 273.16$ degrees centigrade (°C) has been obtained. By international convention the value of T_0 is now arbitrarily fixed. The absolute temperature is measured in degrees absolute or degrees Kelvin (°K). The scale unit is the same as that for the centigrade scale. Thus 0°K corresponds to −273.16°C and 0°C corresponds to 273.16°K.

1-3. THE UNIVERSAL GAS CONSTANT AND MOLECULAR WEIGHTS

It is convenient to introduce the concepts of molecular weight and the universal gas constant at this point. We shall introduce these concepts by making use of Boyle's law and the absolute temperature scale.

At the ice point,

$$\lim_{p \to 0} pV = \beta_0 \tag{1-14}$$

by Boyle's law. It is an experimental fact that the volume of a pure gas is a linear homogeneous function of the mass of the gas at constant T and p, that is,

$$V = nv \tag{1-15}$$

where V = total volume
n = mass of gas, in arbitrary units
v = volume of arbitrary unit of mass, in arbitrary units

Making use of (1-15), Eq. (1-14) may be rewritten in the form

$$\beta_0 = n \lim_{p \to 0} pv = nRT_0 \tag{1-16}$$

where R is defined by (1-16) and may vary from gas to gas. Substituting for T_0 by means of Eq. (1-12), we obtain

$$\beta = nRT \tag{1-17}$$

The definition of β, given by Eq. (1-8), and Eqs. (1-15) and (1-17) may be combined to yield

$$\lim_{p \to 0} \frac{pv}{RT} = 1 \tag{1-18}$$

We shall now demonstrate that the arbitrary mass unit m_i for gas i can be chosen in such a way that R has the same value for all gases. The mass units M_i, which yield a universal gas constant R, are, respectively, the molecular weights of the gases i. We first choose an arbitrary mass unit for oxygen gas in order to determine the value of R. The mass unit for oxygen, M_{O_2}, is arbitrarily set equal to 32 g. By definition,

$$v_{O_2} = \frac{M_{O_2}}{\rho_{O_2}} \tag{1-19}$$

where v_{O_2} is the molar volume of oxygen and ρ_{O_2} is the density of oxygen gas in grams per unit volume. Substitution of (1-19) in (1-18) results in

$$R = \lim_{p \to 0} \frac{pM_{O_2}}{T\rho_{O_2}} \tag{1-20}$$

Equation (1-20) determines the value of R to be

$$R = 0.08206 \text{ liter atm/g mole deg}$$

$$= 8.3149 \times 10^7 \text{ ergs/g mole deg}$$

In order to establish experimental values for the mass units M_i, it is sufficient to measure the limit, as the pressure tends to zero, of the ratio of the density of gas i, ρ_i, to the pressure p at any temperature. The molecular weight M_i can then be determined from the relation

$$M_i = RT \lim_{p \to 0} \frac{\rho_i}{p} \tag{1-21}$$

This argument, then, introduces the molecular weights M_i and the universal gas constant R into thermodynamics.

2 GENERAL THERMODYNAMIC PROPERTIES

In the study of thermodynamics, extensive and intensive properties are constantly employed. In this chapter we discuss the dependence of extensive properties on the mass of the system and demonstrate how to define a set of intensive properties related to a given extensive property. We shall describe experimental methods for the measurement of these sets of intensive properties. Finally, we present a list of a number of commonly used composition variables and show how these may be related to each other.

2-1. EXTENSIVE AND INTENSIVE PROPERTIES

We consider a homogeneous system of r components. No external force may act on this system except for a uniform normal pressure. The system is also assumed to be so large that the configuration of its surface does not affect its bulk properties. Under these conditions, a general extensive property of this system, G, may be considered to be a function of temperature T, pressure p, and the masses $m_1, \ldots, m_r$ of the r components. Thus, we may write

$$G = G(T,p,m_1, \ldots, m_r) \tag{2-1}$$

It is found by experiment that the extensive properties are linear homogeneous functions of the masses $m_1, \ldots, m_r$ at constant T and p. That is,

$$G(T,p,\lambda m_1, \ldots, \lambda m_r) = \lambda G(T,p,m_1, \ldots, m_r) \tag{2-2}$$

Making use of Euler's theorem (Appendix, Sec. A-2), we can write

$$\begin{aligned} G(T,p,m_1, \ldots, m_r) &= \sum_{i=1}^{r} m_i \left(\frac{\partial G}{\partial m_i}\right)_{T,p,m_j} \qquad j = 1, \ldots, r \quad \neq i \\ &= \sum_{i=1}^{r} m_i \bar{g}_i \end{aligned} \tag{2-3}$$

where

$$\bar{g}_i = \left(\frac{\partial G}{\partial m_i}\right)_{T,p,m_j} \tag{2-4}$$

The quantities $\bar{g}_i$, $i = 1, \ldots, r$, are intensive properties, and Eq. (2-3) makes explicit the dependence of the extensive property G on the mass of the system. The operation expressed by Eq. (2-4) is physically equivalent to a change produced in G when one mass unit of component i is added to a system of infinite size.

The expression (2-4) provides the definition of a partial molal quantity if the gram-molecular weight (mole) is the unit of mass and of a partial specific quantity if the gram is the unit of mass. In the future, the symbol $\bar{g}_i$ will denote a partial molal quantity defined by the relation

$$\bar{g}_i = \left(\frac{\partial G}{\partial n_i}\right)_{T,p,n_j} \tag{2-5}$$

where n_i, the number of moles of component i, is given by

$$n_i = \frac{w_i}{M_i} \tag{2-6}$$

where w_i is the mass of component i in grams and M_i is the gram-molecular weight of component i. The relationship between a partial molal and a partial specific property is given by

$$\bar{g}_i = M_i \bar{g}'_i \tag{2-7}$$

where

$$\bar{g}'_i = \left(\frac{\partial G}{\partial w_i}\right)_{T,p,w_j} \tag{2-8}$$

It is sometimes convenient to consider an intensive property g a mean molal property, defined by

$$g = \frac{G}{n} = \sum_{i=1}^{r} x_i \bar{g}_i \tag{2-9}$$

where $n = \sum_{i=1}^{r} n_i$ is the total number of moles in the system and $x_i = n_i/n$ is the mole fraction of component i. Similarly, a mean specific property g' is defined by

$$g' = \frac{G}{w} = \sum_{i=1}^{r} z_i \bar{g}'_i \tag{2-10}$$

where $w = \sum_{i=1}^{r} w_i$ is the total mass of the system and $z_i = w_i/w$ is the weight fraction of component i. For a one-component system, $g = \bar{g}$ and $g' = \bar{g}'$.

We shall now derive a differential equation for the mean molal property g which is of considerable importance. We consider G as a function of $T, p, n_1, \ldots, n_r$ and write its total differential in the form

$$dG = \left(\frac{\partial G}{\partial T}\right)_{\substack{p,n_i \\ i=1,\ldots,r}} dT + \left(\frac{\partial G}{\partial p}\right)_{T,n_i} dp + \sum_{i=1}^{r} \bar{g}_i \, dn_i \tag{2-11}$$

where we have used Eq. (2-5). An alternative expression for the total differential of G can be obtained from Eq. (2-3) in the form

$$dG = \sum_{i=1}^{r} (n_i \, d\bar{g}_i + \bar{g}_i \, dn_i) \tag{2-12}$$

Subtraction of Eq. (2-12) from Eq. (2-11) and division by n result in

$$\left(\frac{\partial g}{\partial T}\right)_{p,n_i} dT + \left(\frac{\partial g}{\partial p}\right)_{T,n_i} dp - \sum_{i=1}^{r} x_i \, d\bar{g}_i = 0 \tag{2-13}$$

For the special case where G is the free energy, Eq. (2-13) is referred to as the Gibbs-Duhem equation. At constant temperature and pressure, Eq. (2-13) reduces to

$$\sum_{i=1}^{r} x_i \, d\bar{g}_i = 0 \tag{2-14}$$

Differentiation of (2-14) with respect to the mole fraction of component k, x_k, leads to

$$\sum_{i=1}^{r} x_i \left(\frac{\partial \bar{g}_i}{\partial x_k}\right)_{T,p,x_l} = 0 \qquad \begin{aligned} l &= 1, \ldots, r-1 \\ &\neq k \\ k &= 1, \ldots, r \end{aligned} \tag{2-15}$$

The relation (2-15) is of great significance, and it shows that the changes of partial molal quantities with composition are not mutually independent at constant temperature and pressure.

2-2. METHODS OF CALCULATING PARTIAL MOLAL QUANTITIES

In this section we describe two methods for determining partial molal quantities for two-component systems from experimental data. In both cases the experimental data necessary are the behavior of the extensive property G or, equivalently, the intensive property g as a function of the mole fraction of one of the components. (More details can be found in the book: Gilbert Newton Lewis and Merle Randall, "Thermodynamics and the Free Energy of Chemical Substances," pp. 36–41, McGraw-Hill Book Company, Inc., New York, 1923.)

The Method of Intercepts. For a two-component system, Eq. (2-9) becomes

$$g = x_1 \bar{g}_1 + x_2 \bar{g}_2 \tag{2-16}$$

Differentiation of (2-16) with respect to x_2, at constant temperature and pressure, results in

$$\left(\frac{\partial g}{\partial x_2}\right)_{T,p} = \bar{g}_2 - \bar{g}_1 \tag{2-17}$$

where we have made use of Eq. (2-15) and the fact that, since

$$x_1 + x_2 = 1 \tag{2-18}$$

we may write

$$\frac{dx_1}{dx_2} = -1 \tag{2-19}$$

The dependence of the generalized mean molal property g on the mole fraction of component 2, x_2, can be determined by experiment. A plot of g versus x_2 yields a curve (Fig. 2-1). The equation of the tangent to this curve at the point $x_2 = a$ is

$$g = [\bar{g}_2(a) - \bar{g}_1(a)]x_2 + \bar{g}_1(a) \tag{2-20}$$

The tangent intercepts the ordinate at the value $g = \bar{g}_1(a)$ when $x_2 = 0$ and at the value $g = \bar{g}_2(a)$ when $x_2 = 1$. We thus obtain the partial molal quantities $\bar{g}_1$ and $\bar{g}_2$ as functions of x_2 by observing the two intercepts of the tangents to the curve of the experimental values of g versus x_2.

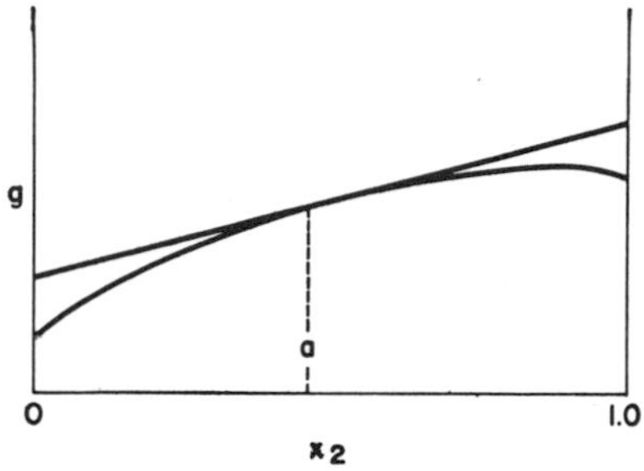

FIG. 2-1. Plot of the mean molal property g versus the mole fraction of component 2, x_2.

The Method of Apparent Molal Properties. We again consider a two-component system and show how the partial molal properties can be related to experimental data on apparent molal properties. The apparent molal property of component 2, $\tilde{G}_2$, is defined by the equation

$$\tilde{G}_2 = \frac{G - n_1 g_1^\circ}{n_2} \tag{2-21}$$

where g_1° is the molal value of G for pure component 1. Equation (2-21) can be rearranged to yield an expression for the extensive property G in the form

$$G = n_1 g_1^\circ + n_2 \tilde{G}_2 \tag{2-22}$$

In the limit, as $x_2 \to 0$, $\bar{g}_1 \to g_1^\circ$ and therefore, comparing Eqs. (2-3) and (2-22), $\tilde{G}_2 \to \bar{g}_2$. If $\bar{g}_2$ is independent of composition, it is a consequence of Eq. (2-15) that $\bar{g}_1$ must be independent of composition. In this case, $\bar{g}_2 = \tilde{G}_2$ for all values of x_2, $0 \leqslant x_2 \leqslant 1$.

Differentiation of Eq. (2-22) with respect to n_2, holding T, p, and n_1 constant, results in

$$\begin{aligned}\bar{g}_2 &= \tilde{G}_2 + n_2\left(\frac{\partial \tilde{G}_2}{\partial n_2}\right)_{T,p,n_1} \\ &= \tilde{G}_2 + \left(\frac{\partial G_2}{\partial \log n_2}\right)_{T,p,n_1}\end{aligned} \tag{2-23}$$

Since an arbitrary function of n_1, T, and p, $f(n_1,T,p)$, is constant when n_1, T, and p are held fixed, we can rewrite Eq. (2-23):

$$\bar{g}_2 = \tilde{G}_2 + \left[\frac{\partial \tilde{G}_2}{\partial \log n_2/f(n_1,T,p)}\right]_{T,p,n_1} \tag{2-24}$$

In the special case, $f(n_1,T,p) = n_1$, Eq. (2-24) becomes

$$\bar{g}_2 = \tilde{G}_2 + \left(\frac{\partial \tilde{G}_2}{\partial \log n_2/n_1}\right)_{T,p,n_1}$$

$$= \tilde{G}_2 + \left(\frac{\partial \tilde{G}_2}{\partial \log x_2/x_1}\right)_{T,p,n_1} \tag{2-25}$$

The value of $\bar{g}_2$ as a function of x_2 can be simply obtained from a plot of experimental values of $\tilde{G}_2$ versus $y = \log x_2/x_1$. The value of $\bar{g}_2$ at $x_2 = a$ is given by the ordinate at $y = 1 + \log [a/(1 - a)]$ of the tangent to the $\tilde{G}_2$ curve at $y = \log [a/(1 - a)]$.

We can also define an apparent specific property

$$\tilde{G}_2' = \frac{G - w_1 g_1^{\circ\prime}}{w_2} \tag{2-26}$$

so that

$$\bar{g}_2' = \tilde{G}_2' + \left(\frac{\partial \tilde{G}_2'}{\partial \log w_2/w_1}\right)_{T,p,w_1} = \tilde{G}_2' + \left(\frac{\partial \tilde{G}_2'}{\partial \log z_2/z_1}\right)_{T,p,w_1} \tag{2-27}$$

As an example of the above, the apparent specific volume is given by

$$\tilde{v}_2' = \frac{V - w_1/\rho_1^\circ}{w_2} = \frac{1/\rho - z_1/\rho_1^\circ}{z_2} \tag{2-28}$$

where ρ is the density of the homogeneous system and ρ_1° is the density of pure component 1 at temperature T and pressure p.

2-3. COMPOSITION VARIABLES

In this section, definitions of a number of composition variables are listed. Useful relations among these variables are given, and the approximate values of some of these variables for systems in which one component predominates are presented.

The most commonly used composition variables are as follows:

Molecular weight of component $i = M_i$

Number of moles of component $i = n_i$

Total number of moles in an r-component system $n = \sum_{i=1}^{r} n_i$

Mole fraction: $x_i = n_i/n$

Mass of component $i = w_i$

Total mass of an r-component system $w = \sum_{i=1}^{r} w_i$
Weight fraction: $z_i = w_i/w$
Molarity concentration: $c_i = 1000n_i/V$
Partial densities: $\rho_i = w_i/V$
Mole ratio with respect to reference component 1: $r_i = n_i/n_1$
Molality with respect to reference component 1: $m_i = (1000/M_1)(n_i/n_1)$
A number of relations between these variables are the following:

$$m_i = \frac{1000n_i}{M_1 n_1} = \frac{1000x_i}{M_1 x_1} \tag{2-29}$$

$$x_i = \frac{n_i}{n_1 + \sum_{k=2}^{r} n_k} = \frac{m_i}{1000/M_1 + \sum_{k=2}^{r} m_k} \tag{2-30}$$

$$x_i = \frac{w_i/M_i}{\sum_{k=1}^{r} w_k/M_k} = \frac{z_i}{\sum_{k=1}^{r} (M_i/M_k) z_k} \tag{2-31}$$

$$x_i = \frac{\Sigma x_k \bar{v}_k c_i}{1000} \qquad x_i = \frac{c_i \Sigma' x_k \bar{v}_k}{1000 - c_i \bar{v}_i} \tag{2-32}$$

where the prime in Eq. (2-32) denotes summation over all components except component i.

In systems in which component 1 predominates, the following approximate relations are valid:

$$x_i \simeq r \tag{2-33}$$

$$m_i \simeq \frac{1000}{M_1} x_i \tag{2-34}$$

$$c_i \simeq \frac{1000x_i}{v_1^\circ} \tag{2-35}$$

3 THE FIRST LAW OF THERMODYNAMICS

The foundations of thermodynamics rest on two laws. The first law of thermodynamics defines a function of state, the energy, and restricts the region of conceivable processes to those in which the energy is conserved. The second law determines the direction in which the possible processes will proceed in a given system. These laws represent the formalization of a large number of experimental observations. No violations of these laws have been observed, and it is clear, from microscopic statistical mechanical considerations, that the occurrence of such violations is so improbable that they may be considered to be impossible.

The energy change that a system undergoes during a given process is related to the work done by the system and to the heat absorbed by the system during this process. Thus a definition of energy requires preliminary discussions of the concepts of work and heat. In this chapter, we present definitions of work and heat and a discussion of the first law of thermodynamics. A number of thermodynamic functions of state are defined, and some examples of calculations utilizing these functions are given. In particular, we describe, in some detail, a number of calculations of the enthalpy for various systems. The chapter closes with an introduction to the subject of thermochemistry.

3-1. WORK

The concept of work is one that is familiar in the discipline of mechanics. We shall, of course, utilize the same concept here but shall consider some aspects not emphasized in mechanics. *Work* is defined as the line integral of a generalized force over a generalized path. Consequently, the differential element of work is

$$đW = \mathbf{F} \cdot d\mathbf{R} \tag{3-1}$$

where $\mathbf{F}$ is the generalized force and $d\mathbf{R}$ is the generalized differential displacement. The symbol $đ$ expresses the fact that $đW$ is an inexact differential (see Sec. A-3). In a system subjected to no external forces except a uniform, normal pressure p, the force exerted by the surroundings on an element of surface area dA is

$$\mathbf{F} = p(dA)\mathbf{n} \tag{3-2}$$

where **n** is the unit normal vector on the surface. By Eq. (3-2), the element of work done in moving the surface element dA through a distance $d\mathbf{R}$ may be written

$$\begin{aligned} đW &= p(dA)(\mathbf{n}\cdot d\mathbf{R}) = p(dn)(dA) \\ &= p\,dV \end{aligned} \tag{3-3}$$

where dn is the projection of $d\mathbf{R}$ on the vector **n**,

$$dn = \mathbf{n}\cdot d\mathbf{R} \tag{3-4}$$

and dV is the element of volume swept out in moving the surface element dA through a distance $d\mathbf{R}$,

$$dV = dn\, dA \tag{3-5}$$

We emphasize the fact that the symbol p which occurs in Eqs. (3-2) and (3-3) refers to the pressure exerted by the surroundings on the system.

In thermodynamics, the quantity W is defined as the work done by the system on its surroundings in a specified change of state along a specified path. The path must be specified, since $đW$ is an inexact differential form. Physically, the line integral depends upon the path because of the inclusion of dissipative forces. Rigorously, the definition of W demands that the initial and the final states of the system be equilibrium states. The work done by the system when the only external force is a uniform normal pressure is given by

$$W = \int_{A\,C}^{B} p\,dV \tag{3-6}$$

where A and B are the initial and final states of the system, respectively, and C is the path followed from A to B. The path C is specified by determining the pressure p exerted by the surroundings on the system as a function of the volume of the system, V. For those processes in which the volume of the system increases, the experimenter may arbitrarily determine the pressure, subject to the condition $p \leqslant p_e$, where p_e is the pressure for the corresponding reversible path. A reversible path is one for which the system passes through a series of equilibrium states. The system must proceed along the reversible path so slowly that it can come to equilibrium at each point. These paths are, therefore, sometimes termed quasi-static. In the case of pV work, a reversible path is executed when the pressure of the surroundings on the system is infinitesimally less than the pressure given by the equation of state of the system (see Sec. 7-1). Thus, in a reversible path, $p = p_e$ is given by the equation of state of the system.

We note that the equilibrium states mentioned are not absolute equilibrium states but states maintained in equilibrium by the restraints imposed on the system. Transitions between them are effected by removal of some of these restraints.

For pV work, W', the work done by the surroundings on the system, is equal to the negative of the work done by the system, W, provided that the pressure is continuous across the boundary. In general, however, $W' \neq W$. For example, if the mass in a system is redistributed, keeping the center of gravity fixed, work is done on the system whereas the system does no work on its surroundings.

3-2. HEAT

In this section we discuss the concepts of heat and heat capacity. Some experimental observations pertinent to the existence of the physical quantity heat are mentioned, and quantitative methods of measurement are given.

It is found by experiment that, at constant pressure or volume, the intermediate temperature at which two systems attain equilibrium on thermal contact is uniquely determined by their initial states. In addition, we find that, to a specified temperature of a suitably selected standard body of given initial temperature, there correspond unique temperature increments in all other systems of given initial states thermally contacted with the standard at constant p or v. These facts allow us to associate temperature changes produced by thermal contact between two systems with the transfer of a physical quantity heat between them and to assign to every system an extensive property called *heat capacity*.

Heat is quantitatively defined by measurement with a calorimeter, that is, by the temperature increment produced in its transfer to a standard body in the course of a change of state of the system. The unit of heat is the calorie; the *mean gram-calorie* is one one-hundredth of the heat absorbed by one gram of liquid water under a pressure of one atmosphere on raising its temperature from 0 to 100°C. The 15° *gram-calorie* is defined as the heat required to raise the temperature of one gram of water from 14.5 to 15.5°C. The ratio of the latter to the former is 1.00024.

Q, the heat absorbed *by* the system in a change of state from A to B, depends on the path C as well as on A and B:

$$Q = \int_{A\,C}^{B} đQ \qquad (3\text{-}7)$$

Thus Q, like W, is an integral of an inexact differential form and is therefore not a function of state.

The heat capacity of a system for a given process is defined as the quantity of heat required to produce a unit temperature increment in that process.

A mean heat capacity $\bar{C}$ for a given process can be defined in the form

$$\bar{C} = \frac{Q}{T_2 - T_1} \tag{3-8}$$

where Q = heat absorbed in process
T_1 = initial temperature of system
T_2 = final temperature

A more precise definition of heat capacity is obtained as the limit of Eq. (3-8) as the temperature interval goes to zero. In this case,

$$C = \frac{đQ}{dT} \tag{3-9}$$

for a specified process.

Thus, for example, the heat absorbed by the system in a quasi-static process involving a temperature change from T_0 to T, at constant pressure, is given by

$$Q = \int_{T_0}^{T} C_p \, dT \tag{3-10}$$

In a similar process at constant volume

$$Q = \int_{T_0}^{T} C_v \, dT \tag{3-11}$$

C_p and C_v are the heat capacities at constant pressure and volume, respectively. The heat capacities at constant pressure and volume are functions of state and are found to be linear homogeneous functions of the masses.

3-3. FIRST LAW OF THERMODYNAMICS

The first law of thermodynamics expresses the fact that work and heat are different aspects of the same physical quantity. It is based on a number of generalizations of the results of a vast number of experiments. It defines a function of state, the internal energy, in terms of the heat absorbed by the system and the work done on the system.

The temperature of a system may be increased not only by the absorption of heat from a body of higher temperature but also by the frictional dissipation of work in its interior. Thus, work may be converted into heat. By suitably constructed heat engines, heat may be converted into work, subject to certain limitations. It is an experimental fact that the ratio W/Q for a quantity of work W converted to a quantity of heat Q is a constant independent of the system or processes by which the conversion is carried out. This constant, the mechanical equivalent of heat, has the value: one 15° calorie = 4.1833 international joules. Because of their mutual convertibility and common characteristics, it is convenient to apply a generic term, *energy*, to both heat and work.

From the macroscopic point of view, heat is energy exchanged between systems in thermal contact by virtue of a temperature difference. Heat exchange may also occur in interactions between open systems in which there is a diffusion of matter from one system to the other. Work is the energy transferred to a system by displacement of its parts under the action of external forces.

The distinctions and similarities between heat and work are more easily seen on the microscopic, molecular level. In the case of pressure-volume work, work is done when the volume of the system undergoes a systematic, macroscopic change. Heat can be regarded as being the energy transferred by the random, microscopic Brownian motion of the surface of the system.

Although Q and W depend upon the path traversed in a given change of state of a system, the first law of thermodynamics states that, in closed systems, the difference $Q - W$ is independent of the path and depends only upon the initial and final states. The difference $Q - W$ defines a function of state E, called the *internal energy* of the system, such that, for a change of state from the equilibrium state A to the equilibrium state B,

$$\Delta E = E_B - E_A = Q - W \tag{3-12}$$

The statement of the first law given in Eq. (3-12) applies, for example, to cases in which only pV work is considered. A more general and precise statement of the first law is

$$\Delta E = Q + W' \tag{3-13}$$

where W' is the work done on the system by the surroundings. We shall use the form of the first law given in Eq. (3-12) unless it is necessary to utilize Eq. (3-13).

For an adiabatic system, Eq. (3-12) reads

$$\Delta E = -W \tag{3-14}$$

Thus, the work done by the system in an adiabatic process is independent of the path. This is an important experimental fact and was quite significant in the history of the formulation of the first law.

For a cyclical path, $A \equiv B$, the first law states that

$$Q - W = \oint (đQ - đW) = 0 \tag{3-15}$$

The fact that the integral of $đQ - đW$ around a closed path is zero is a necessary and sufficient condition that $đQ - đW$ be an exact differential form (Appendix). Thus, a function E can be defined such that

$$dE = đQ - đW \tag{3-16}$$

where dE is an exact differential form. Equation (3-16) is the differential form of the first law.

We shall now derive some relations involving the heat absorbed by the system in a change of state from A to B along a reversible path. We consider a closed, one-component system with no external forces except a uniform normal pressure. Under these conditions, the state of the system may be defined by T and V. Thus, the work done by the system can be written

$$W = \int_{V_A}^{V_B} p\, dV \qquad (3\text{-}17$$

and

$$đW = p\, dV \tag{3-18}$$

where $p = p(T,V)$ is the equilibrium pressure given by the equation of state. The heat absorbed by the system is given by

$$Q = \int_A^B đQ \tag{3-19}$$

where

$$đQ = X(T,V)\, dV + Y(T,V)\, dT \tag{3-20}$$

and X and Y are functions of T and V which are to be determined. The exact differential form, dE, can be expressed as a linear differential form

$$dE = \left(\frac{\partial E}{\partial T}\right)_V dT + \left(\frac{\partial E}{\partial V}\right)_T dV \tag{3-21}$$

Substituting (3-21) and (3-18) in (3-16), we obtain

$$đQ = \left(\frac{\partial E}{\partial T}\right)_V dT + \left[p + \left(\frac{\partial E}{\partial V}\right)_T\right] dV \tag{3-22}$$

so that

$$X(T,V) = p + \left(\frac{\partial E}{\partial V}\right)_T \quad \text{and} \quad Y(T,V) = \left(\frac{\partial E}{\partial T}\right)_V \tag{3-23}$$

Integration of Eq. (3-22) at constant temperature yields

$$Q = \Delta E + \int_{V_A}^{V_B} p\, dV \tag{3-24}$$

where

$$\Delta E = E(T,V_B) - E(T,V_A) \tag{3-25}$$

For a constant-volume process (isometric), integration of (3-22) yields

$$Q = \Delta E = E(T_B,V) - E(T_A,V) \tag{3-26}$$

Thus the heat absorbed in a constant-volume process is equal to the energy change in that process. For a constant-pressure process (isobaric),

$$Q = \Delta E + p\,\Delta V = \Delta H \tag{3-27}$$

where H, the enthalpy, is defined by the relation

$$H = E + pV \tag{3-28}$$

In Eq. (3-28), p is the equilibrium pressure of the system. The enthalpy is a function of state.

For a system performing only pV work, the heat capacities C_v and C_p, defined by Eqs. (3-10) and (3-11), are given by

$$C_v = \left(\frac{\partial E}{\partial T}\right)_v \tag{3-29}$$

$$C_p = \left(\frac{\partial H}{\partial T}\right)_p \tag{3-30}$$

where we have used Eqs. (3-26) and (3-27).

3-4. ENTHALPY CALCULATIONS

In this section, we present calculations of the enthalpy change in one-component systems for various changes of state from an initial equilibrium state to a final equilibrium state. Since enthalpy is a function of state, its change is independent of the path and depends only upon the initial and final states. The equilibrium states of the closed one-component systems under discussion may be considered to be defined by values of T and p. We shall first consider changes of state in which the initial and final states are in the same phase. Later, we consider changes of state in which the initial and final states are in different phases. The examples presented are

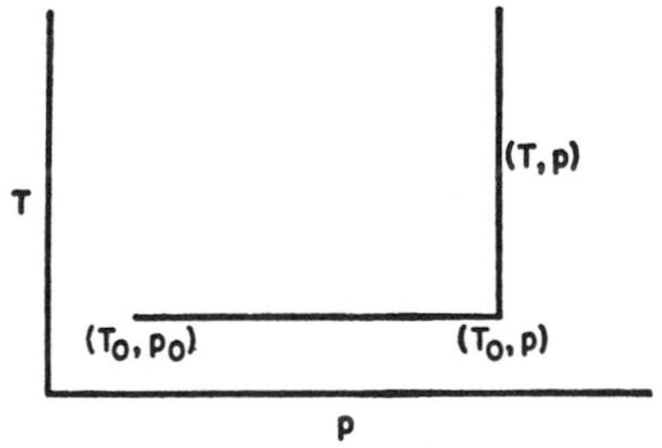

FIG. 3-1. Path of integration in Eq. (3-33).

typical of a large number of thermodynamic calculations carried out for various functions of state.

For a one-component system,

$$h = h(T,p) \tag{3-31}$$

where $h = H/n$ is the molal enthalpy, H is the total enthalpy, and n is the number of moles in the system. Consequently, the total differential of h is given by

$$dh = \left(\frac{\partial h}{\partial T}\right)_p dT + \left(\frac{\partial h}{\partial p}\right)_T dp \tag{3-32}$$

Integration of Eq. (3-32) along the path indicated in Fig. 3-1 yields

$$h(T,p) - h_0 = \int_{p_0}^{p} \left(\frac{\partial h}{\partial p'}\right)_{T_0} dp' + \int_{T_0}^{T} \left(\frac{\partial h}{\partial T'}\right)_p dT' \tag{3-33}$$

where $h_0 = h(T_0,p_0)$ and $(\partial h/\partial p')_{T_0}$ is the partial derivative of h with respect to pressure at constant temperature evaluated at pressure p' and temperature T_0. Integration of Eq. (3-32) along a constant-pressure path and use of Eq. (3-30) yield

$$h(T,p) - h(T_0,p) = \int_{T_0}^{T} \left(\frac{\partial h}{\partial T'}\right)_p dT'$$

$$= \int_{T_0}^{T} C_p(T',p)\, dT' \tag{3-34}$$

From a derivation based on the second law (6-28), we obtain

$$\left(\frac{\partial h}{\partial p}\right)_T = v - T\left(\frac{\partial v}{\partial T}\right)_p = v(1 - T\beta) \tag{3-35}$$

where v is the molal volume and β, the coefficient of thermal expansion, is given by

$$\beta = \frac{1}{v}\left(\frac{\partial v}{\partial T}\right)_p \tag{3-36}$$

By use of Eqs. (3-34) and (3-35), Eq. (3-33) can be rewritten in the form

$$h(T,p) - h_0 = \int_{p_0}^{p} v(1 - T_0\beta)\, dp' + \int_{T_0}^{T} C_p(T',p)\, dT' \tag{3-37}$$

If phase boundaries are traversed along the path (Fig. 3-2), integration of Eq. (3-32) yields

$$h^{(2)}(T,p) - h^{(1)}(T_0,p_0) = \int_{p_0}^{p_{12}} v^{(1)}(1 - T_0\beta^{(1)})\, dp'$$

$$+ \Delta h^{(1\to 2)}(T_0) + \int_{p_{12}}^{p} v^{(2)}(1 - T_0\beta^{(2)})\, dp' + \int_{T_0}^{T} C_p^{(2)}(T',p)\, dT' \tag{3-38}$$

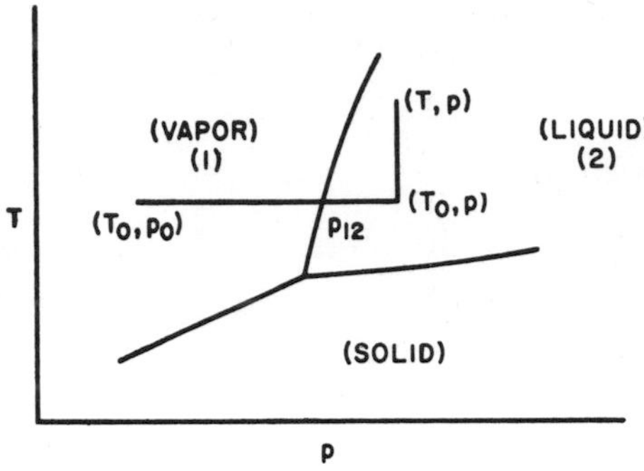

FIG. 3-2. Path of integration in Eq. (3-38).

The superscripts (1) and (2) refer to the phases illustrated in Fig. 3-2 and $\Delta h^{(1\to 2)}(T_0)$ is the enthalpy change at pressure p_{12} and temperature T_0, on going from phase 1 to 2:

$$\Delta h^{(1\to 2)}(T_0) = h^{(2)}(T_0,p_{12}) - h^{(1)}(T_0,p_{12}) \tag{3-39}$$

Integration of Eq. (3-32) along the path indicated in Fig. 3-3 yields

$$h^{(2)}(T,p) - h^{(2)}(T_1,p_1) = \int_{T_1}^{T_{12}} C_p^{(2)}(T',p_1)\,dT' + \Delta h^{(2\to 1)}(p_1) + \int_{T_{12}}^{T} C_p^{(1)}(T',p_1)\,dT' + \int_{p_1}^{p_{12}} v^{(1)}(1 - T\beta^{(1)})\,dp' + \Delta h^{(1\to 2)}(T) + \int_{p_{12}}^{p} v^{(2)}(1 - T\beta^{(2)})\,dp' \tag{3-40}$$

where

$$\Delta h^{(2\to 1)}(p_1) = h^{(1)}(T_{12},p_1) - h^{(2)}(T_{12},p_1) \tag{3-41}$$

Thus we can calculate the enthalpy of a pure chemical component in an arbitrary state from experimental data on calorimetry and the equation

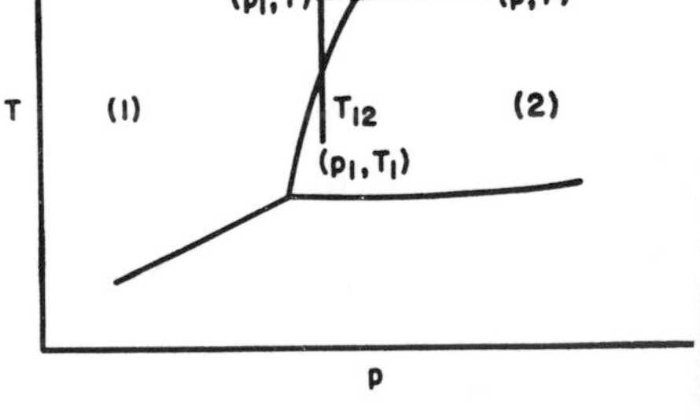

FIG. 3-3. Path of integration in Eq. (3-40).

of state. In all these calculations, there is an arbitrary constant of integration, $h(T_0,p_0)$, which is not determined in thermodynamics.

3-5. THERMOCHEMISTRY

The subject of thermochemistry deals with the heat changes resulting from chemical processes; its laws are direct consequences of the first law of thermodynamics. As most reactions are carried out under constant pressure, our treatment will be restricted to a discussion of enthalpy changes. A corresponding set of equations could easily be obtained for the internal energy. In this section we discuss heat changes in chemical reactions and the thermochemistry of solutions.

3-5a. Chemical Reactions

An arbitrary chemical reaction involving r chemical substances may be written

$$\sum_{i=1}^{r} \nu_i X_i = 0 \tag{3-42}$$

where X_i represents 1 mole of a pure chemical substance in a stable state of aggregation at the temperature T and pressure p at which the reaction takes place, and ν_i is the number of moles of substance i formed in the reaction. Thus, ν_i is positive for the products of the reaction and negative for the reactants. For example, the chemical reaction for the formation of ammonia from hydrogen and nitrogen is usually written in the form

$$\tfrac{3}{2}H_2 + \tfrac{1}{2}N_2 = NH_3 \tag{3-43}$$

When Eq. (3-43) is recast in the form of Eq. (3-42), it reads

$$-\tfrac{1}{2}N_2 - \tfrac{3}{2}H_2 + NH_3 = 0 \tag{3-44}$$

or

$$-\tfrac{1}{2}X_1 - \tfrac{3}{2}X_2 + X_3 = 0 \tag{3-45}$$

where $\nu_1 = -\tfrac{1}{2}$

$\nu_2 = -\tfrac{3}{2}$

$\nu_3 = 1$

If G is any extensive property, g_i the corresponding molal property of pure i, and ΔG the increment of G in the reaction given by Eq. (3-42), then

$$\Delta G = \sum_{i=1}^{r} \nu_i g_i \tag{3-46}$$

We note that the measurement of ΔG, as defined in Eq. (3-46), demands the following idealized experiment:

a. The pure reactants at T and p are mixed.
b. The reaction is allowed to take place.
c. The individual products are isolated from the reaction mixture.

ΔG represents the total change in G for the three steps enumerated above. Many experiments are designed to measure the change in G in step b only:

$$\Delta_2 G = \sum_{i=1}^{r} (n_i \bar{g}_i - n'_i \bar{g}'_i) \qquad (3\text{-}47)$$

where n_i is the number of moles of i in the reaction mixture, $\bar{g}_i$ is the partial molal quantity in the reaction mixture, and n'_i and $\bar{g}'_i$ refer to the same quantities in the reactant mixture, before the reaction takes place. In most gas phase reactions, ΔG is adequately approximated by $\Delta_2 G$. In reactions in solution, however, heats of mixing are of importance.

When the extensive property G is the mass of the system, Eq. (3-46) becomes

$$\Delta M = \sum_{i=1}^{r} \nu_i M_i = 0 \qquad (3\text{-}48)$$

which expresses the conservation of mass.

When the extensive property G is the enthalpy of the system, Eq. (3-46) becomes

$$\Delta H = \sum_{i=1}^{r} \nu_i h_i \qquad (3\text{-}49)$$

By the first law, the heat change of a reaction carried out at constant pressure, in a system subject to $p - V$ work alone, is given by

$$Q = \Delta H = \sum_{i=1}^{r} \nu_i h_i \qquad (3\text{-}50)$$

Hess's law, which relates the heat change of a sum reaction to the heat changes of the contributing reactions, is an immediate consequence of this formulation. We consider a series of s reactions, proceeding at the same fixed temperature T and pressure p,

$$\sum_{k=1}^{r} \nu_k^{(\alpha)} X_k = 0 \qquad \alpha = 1, \ldots, s \qquad (3\text{-}51)$$

with enthalpy increments $\Delta H^{(\alpha)} (\alpha = 1,2, \ldots ,s)$. In addition, we consider an $s + 1$ sum reaction

$$\sum_{i=1}^{r} \nu_i X_i = 0 \qquad (3\text{-}52)$$

which takes place at the same fixed T and p. The coefficients ν_i of the sum reaction are related to the coefficients $\nu_i^{(\alpha)}$ by the relation

$$\nu_i = \sum_{\alpha=1}^{s} \sigma^{(\alpha)} \nu_i^{(\alpha)} \qquad (3\text{-}53)$$

where $\sigma^{(\alpha)}$ denotes the contribution of reaction α to the sum reaction. The heat change of the sum reaction [Eq. (3-52)] is

$$\Delta H = \sum_{i=1}^{r} \nu_i h_i = \sum_{i=1}^{r} \sum_{\alpha=1}^{s} \sigma^{(\alpha)} \nu_i^{(\alpha)} h_i \tag{3-54}$$

Interchange of the summations in Eq. (3-54) gives

$$\Delta H = \sum_{\alpha=1}^{s} \sigma^{(\alpha)} \sum_{i=1}^{r} \nu_i^{(\alpha)} h_i \tag{3-55}$$

However, the heat change of the α reaction is given by

$$\Delta H^{(\alpha)} = \sum_{i=1}^{r} \nu_i^{(\alpha)} h_i \tag{3-56}$$

by Eq. (3-50). Thus,

$$Q = \Delta H = \sum_{\alpha=1}^{s} \sigma^{(\alpha)} \Delta H^{(\alpha)} \qquad \text{(Hess's law)} \tag{3-57}$$

Hess's law states that the heat changes of successive processes are additive if they are carried out at the same temperature and at constant pressure. This property follows from the fact that the enthalpy is a function of state and thus is a function only of the initial and final states of a system. Hess's law is extremely useful in thermochemistry since it permits the calculation of the heat change of a reaction difficult to perform from a series of reactions which are more easily carried out.

We may also use Hess's law to express the heat of a given reaction in terms of the heats of formation of the compounds entering into the reaction. The reaction expressing the formation of 1 mole of compound X_i from its elements is

$$X_i + \sum_k \nu_k^{(i)} \mathscr{E}_k = 0 \tag{3-58}$$

where $\mathscr{E}_k$ represents 1 mole of element k. The summation over k is taken over all the elements composing the compound. Since the elements are reactants, the $\nu_k^{(i)}$ are negative. The enthalpy increment in the reaction of formation is

$$\Delta h_i = h_i + \sum_k \nu_k^{(i)} h_k \tag{3-59}$$

Commonly $-\Delta h_i$ instead of Δh_i is called the heat of formation; this unfortunate practice often leads to confusion.

An expression for an arbitrary chemical reaction, equivalent to Eq. (3-42), may be written

$$\sum_{i=1}^{r} \nu_i \left(X_i + \sum_k \nu_k^{(i)} \mathscr{E}_k \right) = 0 \tag{3-60}$$

since

$$\sum_k \sum_{i=1}^{r} \nu_i \nu_k^{(i)} \mathscr{E}_k = 0 \tag{3-61}$$

in all reactions not involving nuclear transmutations, i.e., for all reactions in which the elements $\mathscr{E}_k$ are conserved. Since $\nu_k^{(i)}$ is a measure of the number of moles of element k in compound i and ν_i is a measure of the number of moles of i in the reaction, $\sum_{i=1}^{r} \nu_i \nu_k^{(i)}$ expresses the net change of element k in the reaction. Thus, the heat of reaction is given by

$$\Delta H = \sum_{i=1}^{r} \nu_i \left(h_i + \sum_k \nu_k^{(i)} h_k \right) \tag{3-62}$$

Comparison of this expression with Eq. (3-59) shows that

$$\Delta H = \sum_{i=1}^{r} \nu_i \, \Delta h_i \tag{3-63}$$

Thus, the evaluation of heats of reaction can be carried out making use of a tabulation of the heats of formation of compounds. In practice, heats of formation are usually not determined directly but are obtained from data on heats of combustion.

The temperature dependence of the enthalpy increment of reaction (3-42) is easily determined. Differentiation of Eq. (3-50) with respect to temperature at constant pressure gives

$$\left(\frac{\partial \Delta H}{\partial T} \right)_p = \sum_{i=1}^{r} \nu_i \left(\frac{\partial h_i}{\partial T} \right)_p = \sum_{i=1}^{r} \nu_i (C_p)_i \tag{3-64}$$

where $(C_p)_i$ is the heat capacity at constant pressure of pure component i.

By defining

$$\Delta C_p = \sum_{i=1}^{r} \nu_i (C_p)_i \tag{3-65}$$

Eq. (3-64) may be rewritten in the form

$$\left(\frac{\partial \Delta H}{\partial T} \right)_p = \Delta C_p \qquad \text{(Kirchhoff's law)} \tag{3-66}$$

Equation (3-66) is the mathematical formulation of Kirchhoff's law. Exact integration of this equation requires a knowledge of ΔC_p as a function of temperature. An expansion of ΔC_p as a power series in T is usually employed.

3-5b. Thermochemistry of Solutions

The heat changes occurring when different molecular species are mixed to form solutions, i.e., homogeneous mixtures, are of interest in the determination of solubility. Consequently, many ways of presenting the data have been developed. The confusion frequently encountered in this subject stems primarily from this multiplicity of definitions.

Heats of solution are usually presented in terms of relative partial enthalpies, which may be defined as

$$\bar{L}_i = \bar{h}_i - \bar{h}_i^\circ \tag{3-67}$$

where $\bar{h}_i$ is the partial molal enthalpy of component i in the system and $\bar{h}_i^\circ(T,p)$ represents a reference enthalpy. For reference value, two conventions are usually employed (for more details see Sec. 10-1). In the first convention, $\bar{h}_i^\circ$ is chosen such that

$$\bar{h}_i^\circ = h_i(T,p) \qquad i = 1, \ldots, r \tag{3-68}$$

where $h_i(T,p)$ is the molal enthalpy of pure liquid i. This convention is used for liquid solutions studied over the entire range of composition. The second convention uses

$$\begin{aligned} \bar{h}_1^\circ &= h_1(T,p) \\ \bar{h}_i^\circ &= \lim_{x_1 \to 1} \bar{h}_i \qquad i = 2, 3, \ldots, r \end{aligned} \tag{3-69}$$

This convention is used when dilute or moderately dilute solutions of components 2, . . . , r in component 1 (solvent) are being considered. We shall restrict ourselves to a discussion of binary solutions and use of the second convention [Eq. (3-69)]; the reader will find no difficulty in extending the treatment to multicomponent solutions. In the following, we define the quantities integral heat of solution, heat of dilution, and heat of concentration. We present three alternative expressions for these quantities in terms of either the relative partial enthalpies, the integral heat of solution per mole of component 2, or the integral heat per mean mole of solution.

1. Integral Heat of Solution. The integral heat of solution is the heat absorbed when n_1 moles of component 1 is mixed with n_2 moles of component 2. The enthalpy change for this process is given by

$$\begin{aligned} \Delta H &= n_1(\bar{h}_1 - h_1) + n_2(\bar{h}_2 - h_2) \\ &= n_1[(\bar{h}_1 - \bar{h}_1^\circ) - (h_1 - \bar{h}_1^\circ)] + n_2[(\bar{h}_2 - \bar{h}_2^\circ) - (h_2 - \bar{h}_2^\circ)] \end{aligned} \tag{3-70}$$

Equation (3-70) can be expressed in terms of relative partial enthalpies in the form

$$\Delta H = n_1\bar{L}_1 + n_2(\bar{L}_2 - L_2) \tag{3-71}$$

since, by definition, $L_1 = h_1 - \bar{h}_1^\circ = h_1 - h_1 = 0$, and $L_2 = h_2 - \bar{h}_2^\circ$.

2. Differential Heat of Solution of Component 1. Since component 1 is the solvent, the differential heat of solution of component 1 is often called the heat of dilution. Consider the enthalpy increment occurring when Δn_1 moles of 1 is added to a solution containing n_1 moles of 1 and n_2 moles of 2. The enthalpy increment is given by

$$\Delta H_d = (n_1 + \Delta n_1)\bar{h}_1' + n_2\bar{h}_2' - (n_1\bar{h}_1 + n_2\bar{h}_2 + \Delta n_1 h_1) \tag{3-72}$$

where $\bar{h}_1'$ and $\bar{h}_2'$ are the molal enthalpies in the final solution and $\bar{h}_1$, $\bar{h}_2$ those in the initial solution. Collecting terms, we may write

$$\Delta H_d = n_1(\bar{h}_1' - \bar{h}_1) + n_2(\bar{h}_2' - \bar{h}_2) + \Delta n_1(\bar{h}_1' - h_1) \tag{3-73}$$

or

$$\Delta H_d = n_1(\bar{L}_1' - \bar{L}_1) + n_2(\bar{L}_2' - \bar{L}_2) + \Delta n_1 \bar{L}_1' \tag{3-74}$$

Division of Eq. (3-74) by Δn_1 results in

$$\frac{\Delta H_d}{\Delta n_1} = n_1 \frac{\Delta \bar{L}_1}{\Delta n_1} + n_2 \frac{\Delta \bar{L}_2}{\Delta n_1} + \bar{L}_1' \tag{3-75}$$

Passing to the limit $\Delta n_1 \to 0$, we obtain the differential heat of solution of component 1 in the form

$$\lim_{\Delta n_1 \to 0} \frac{\Delta H_d}{\Delta n_1} = \bar{L}_1 \tag{3-76}$$

since by Eq. (2-15)

$$n_1\left(\frac{\partial \bar{L}_1}{\partial n_1}\right) + n_2\left(\frac{\partial \bar{L}_2}{\partial n_1}\right) = 0 \tag{3-77}$$

at constant T and p and since

$$\lim_{\Delta n_1 \to 0} \bar{L}_1' = \bar{L}_1 \tag{3-78}$$

The differential heat of solution of component 1 is the heat change resulting from the process of dissolving 1 mole of component 1 in an infinite amount of solution.

3. Differential Heat of Solution of Component 2. The differential heat of solution of component 2 is also called the heat of concentration. Following the same reasoning as that used in the computation of the heat of dilution, we obtain, as a result analogous to Eq. (3-74),

$$\Delta H_c = n_1(\bar{L}_1' - \bar{L}_1) + n_2(\bar{L}_2' - \bar{L}_2) + \Delta n_2(\bar{L}_2' - L_2) \tag{3-79}$$

Thus

$$\lim_{\Delta n_2 \to 0} \frac{\Delta H_c}{\Delta n_2} = \bar{L}_2 - L_2 \tag{3-80}$$

is the expression for the differential heat of solution of component 2.

The various heats of solution (1-3) may also be written in terms of the quantities

$$\mathscr{L} = \frac{\Delta H}{n_2} \tag{3-81}$$

the integral heat of solution per mole of component 2, and

$$r_2 = \frac{n_2}{n_1} \tag{3-82}$$

the mole ratio of component 2 with respect to reference component 1. Since this notation is employed in the "International Critical Tables," we shall rewrite heats 1, 2, and 3 in terms of these quantities.

(1) Integral heat of solution

From the definition of $\mathscr{L}$,

$$\Delta H = \mathscr{L} n_2 \tag{3-83}$$

(2) Heat of dilution

The integral heat of solution of the initial solution is $\mathscr{L}n_2$; that of the final solution, formed by adding Δn_1 moles of 1, is $\mathscr{L}'n_2$. By Hess's law, the heat of dilution is, therefore, given by

$$\Delta H_d = n_2(\mathscr{L}' - \mathscr{L}) \tag{3-84}$$

where $$\mathscr{L}' = \frac{\Delta H'}{n_2}$$

(3) Heat of concentration

If Δn_2 moles of component 2 is added to the solution,

$$\mathscr{L}' = \frac{\Delta H'}{n_2 + \Delta n_2} \tag{3-85}$$

When the argument employed above is used,

$$\Delta H_c = (n_2 + \Delta n_2)\mathscr{L}' - n_2\mathscr{L} \tag{3-86}$$

or $$\Delta H_c = n_1(r_2'\mathscr{L}' - r_2\mathscr{L}) \tag{3-87}$$

where $$r_2' = \frac{n_2 + \Delta n_2}{n_1} \tag{3-88}$$

Corresponding expressions may also be written in terms of ℓ, the integral heat per mean mole of solution.

(1) Integral heat of solution

By definition, $$\Delta H = n\ell \tag{3-89}$$

where $$n = n_1 + n_2 \tag{3-90}$$

(2) Heat of dilution for Δn_1 moles of 1

$$\Delta H_d = n\left(\frac{x_2}{x_2'}\ell' - \ell\right) \tag{3-91}$$

where x_2 is the mole fraction of component 2 in the original solution and x'_2 is the mole fraction of 2 in the final solution. That is,

$$x'_2 = \frac{n_2}{n + \Delta n_1} \tag{3-92}$$

(3) Heat of concentration for Δn_2 moles of 2

$$\Delta H_c = n\left(\frac{x_1}{x'_1}\ell' - \ell\right) \tag{3-93}$$

4 THE SECOND LAW OF THERMODYNAMICS

In the preceding chapter we discussed the formulation of the first law of thermodynamics and some of its consequences. The first law defines a function of state, the energy, and restricts the region of conceivable processes to those in which the energy is conserved. In this chapter we shall formulate the second law of thermodynamics and develop some of its consequences. The second law defines a function of state, the entropy, and determines the direction in which possible processes will proceed in a given system. Those processes which are physically realizable are termed *natural* processes.

The second law of thermodynamics, like the first, represents a generalization of the results of a large number of experiments. In Sec. 4-1 we present two equivalent physical statements of the second law. In Sec. 4-2 we present the mathematical statement of the second law and determine how a criterion for equilibrium can be set up, making use of the mathematical statement. In Sec. 4-3 the mathematical statement of the second law is shown to be equivalent to the physical statements. The argument proceeds by demonstrating that Carathéodory's principle can be derived from the physical statements.

4-1. PHYSICAL STATEMENTS

We consider two equivalent physical expressions of the second law, one based on Kelvin's principle and the other a generalization of Clausius' postulate.

a. The uncompensated conversion of heat into work does not occur in natural processes. An uncompensated conversion is one which is not attended by auxiliary processes, such as the transfer of an additional quantity of heat from a higher to a lower temperature or changes in state of the system or surroundings which cannot be reversed without the expenditure of a quantity of work greater than that produced. Kelvin's principle states: In a cycle of processes, it is impossible to transfer heat from a heat reservoir and convert it all into work, without at the same time transferring a certain amount of heat from a hotter to a colder body.

b. All natural processes are irreversible. An irreversible process is one which cannot be reversed without an expenditure of work by the surroundings greater than the work done by the system. This statement is a generalization of that enunciated by Clausius: It is impossible that, at the end of a cycle of changes, heat has been transferred from a colder to a hotter body without at the same time converting a certain amount of work into heat.

4-2. MATHEMATICAL STATEMENT OF THE SECOND LAW

The mathematical statement of the second law defines a function of state, the entropy, and presents a relationship between the entropy change in a given process and the heat absorbed by the system during that process.

The mathematical statement of the second law is: The heat change $đQ$ on a reversible path, regarded as a linear differential form in V and t, the temperature of the surroundings, possesses an integrating factor $1/T(t)$. $T(t)$ is a function of t alone and is identical for all thermodynamic systems. It is called the thermodynamic temperature and is identical with the absolute temperature. The function S, defined by $dS = đQ/T$, is called the entropy and is a function of state. In all natural processes

$$\Delta S = S_2 - S_1 > \int_1^2 \frac{đQ}{T} \tag{4-1}$$

where T is the thermodynamic temperature of the surroundings.

In particular, for an isolated system, $\Delta S > 0$ in all natural processes. For a reversible process, one in which just sufficient work is produced to return the system and the surroundings to their original state,

$$\Delta S = \int_1^2 \frac{đQ}{T} \tag{4-2}$$

Thus, in order to calculate the entropy change in a transition from state 1 to state 2 from the heat absorbed in that transition, a reversible path connecting the two states must be considered.

The mathematical statement of the second law provides, as a corollary, a criterion for thermodynamic equilibrium. It is clear that a thermodynamic system must be in an equilibrium state if there are no natural processes by which it can proceed from its specified state to another state. Thus, a state of a thermodynamic system is an equilibrium state if all virtual variations in state fail to satisfy the inequality

$$\Delta S > \int \frac{đQ}{T} \tag{4-3}$$

A virtual variation, indicated by δ, is one of the class of all conceivable variations. In terms of this notation, the general criterion for equilibrium is

$$\delta S \leqslant \frac{\delta Q}{T} \tag{4-4}$$

for all virtual variations in state. Thus, for a system in contact with isothermal surroundings, the paths for which

$$\delta S = \frac{\delta Q}{T} \tag{4-5}$$

are in the field of equilibrium states. Systems usually considered are in equilibrium states only by virtue of restraints, such as partitions and insulators, imposed on them. Removal of some of the restraints may permit passage from one equilibrium state to another equilibrium state.

4-3. MATHEMATICAL STATEMENT DERIVED FROM THE PHYSICAL STATEMENTS

In this section, we present two derivations of Carathéodory's principle from the physical statements of the second law; one is based on physical statement *a* and the other is based on physical statement *b*. Then we derive the mathematical statement of the second law from Carathéodory's principle.

The system under consideration is such that all its parts are at the same temperature. We assume that no phase transitions occur during the processes discussed in order that we may make assumptions about the continuity of the heat absorbed or liberated during these processes as a function of the variables of state. This restriction is easily removed.

Proof I. We first consider a system, states of which are functions of the empirical temperature t and one parameter x (e.g., the volume). We assume that the heat absorbed in any process is a continuous function of x along the isotherms.

Consider state 1 at t_1 and x_1 (Fig. 4-1). To it, we connect a series of states 1′, 1″, etc., along the isotherm at temperature t_1, by a reversible process. Through 1′, 1″, etc., we draw paths representing reversible adiabatic processes which intersect

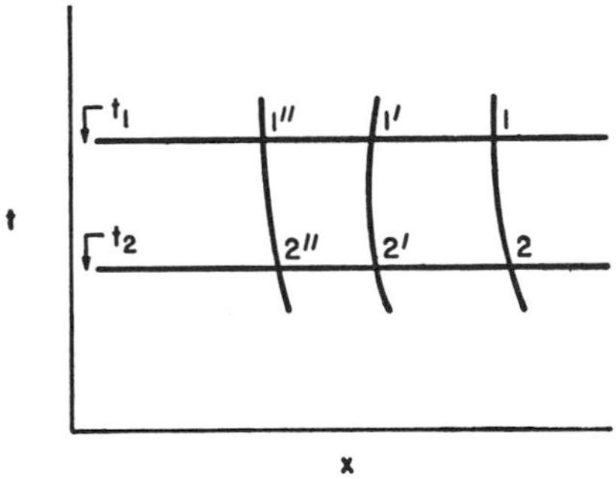

FIG. 4-1. Plot of isotherms t_1 and t_2, and adiabatic paths $1 \rightarrow 2$, $1' \rightarrow 2'$, $1'' \rightarrow 2''$.

the isotherm at arbitrary temperature t_2, at the points 2′, 2″, etc., respectively. Adiabatic processes are those in which no heat is absorbed or liberated by the system. We now make the assertion that no points along these adiabatics are accessible from 1 by an adiabatic path, reversible or irreversible. If such a path existed, we could, for example, go around the cycle $1 \to 2' \to 1' \to 1$. The net heat absorbed by the system in this cycle would be $Q_{1'1} = -Q_{11'}$, which is assumed to be greater than zero. (If $Q_{1'1}$ decreases as x_1 increases, we may choose the points 1′, 1″, etc., to the right of 1 on the isotherm.) The work done by the system in the cycle would be

$$W = Q - \Delta E = Q_{1'1} \tag{4-6}$$

which follows from the first law. Thus, the net result of such a cycle would be the conversion of heat into work without transferring any heat from a higher to a lower temperature. This is contrary to Kelvin's principle.

Thus, no adiabatic paths through 1 can intersect the isotherm, t_2, at the points 2′, 2″, etc. The points 2′, 2″, etc., cannot coincide since we have established by the argument above that reversible adiabatics cannot cross. Because of the continuity properties assumed, all points on the isotherm, t_2, that are to the left of 2 can be reached by reversible adiabatics from points on the isotherm, t_1, which are to the left of 1. Since the temperature t_2 is arbitrary and since the system has the proper continuity properties, similar conclusions hold for all isotherms.

In this manner, we find that all points in the t, x plane lying to the left of the reversible adiabatic through 1 are inaccessible from 1 along an adiabatic from 1. We have also proved that reversible adiabatics cannot cross and must be monotonic as a function of t.

If the states of the system are functions of t and more than one other parameter, we note that the conclusions drawn from Fig. 4-1 hold for any plane in the space of the variables characterizing the system that is parallel to the t axis. Thus the region around 1 that is inaccessible adiabatically from 1 may be rotated about 1, thereby sweeping out a finite volume inaccessible adiabatically from 1. This volume includes points that are arbitrarily close to 1. We note that reversible adiabatic paths through 1 are restricted to lying on a surface through 1.

We have proved Carathéodory's principle. Carathéodory's principle states: From an arbitrary point (state), there is a finite region (set of states of finite measure) which cannot be reached by an adiabatic process, reversible or irreversible. This region may be taken arbitrarily near to the initial point.

Proof II. In this proof we start from a physical postulate which embodies Clausius' statement of the second law. The physical postulate is: A

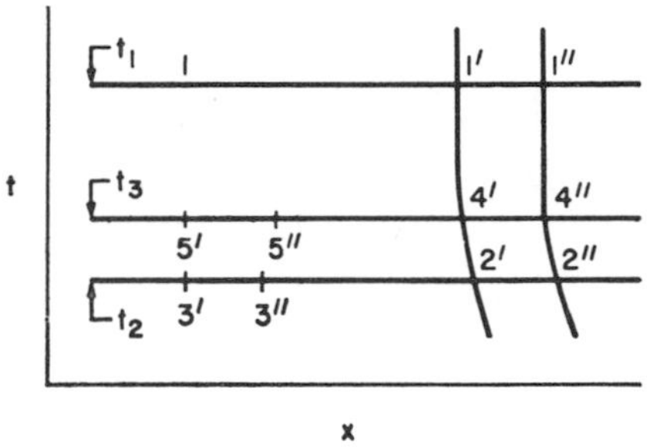

FIG. 4-2. Plot of isotherms t_1, t_2, and t_3, and reversible adiabatic paths $1' \rightarrow 2'$ $1'' \rightarrow 2''$.

process whose net result is the transfer of heat from one body to another can occur only if the temperature of the first exceeds that of the second.

The system considered is identical to that in Proof I. We consider state 1 specified by temperature t_1 and parameter x_1.† (See Fig. 4-2.) To it, we connect a series of states $1', 1'', \ldots$, at the same temperature t_1, differing in parameters x, by a reversible process. We assume that heat is absorbed as x increases (otherwise we could let x decrease). We also assume that Q is a continuous function of x along the isotherm.

Through $1'$ and $1''$ we draw paths representing reversible adiabatic processes which intersect the isotherm at temperature t_2 at the points $2'$ and $2''$, respectively. The temperature t_2 is arbitrary subject to the restriction that $t_2 < t_1$. The heat absorbed by the system proceeding from 1 to $1'$ is $Q_{11'} > 0$. We now connect the points along the isotherm at temperature t_2 by a reversible process and locate state $3'$ on this isotherm, so that $Q_{3'2'} = Q_{11'}$.

We now assert that no adiabatic path, reversible or irreversible, connects states 1 and $3'$. If such a path existed, we could go around the cycle $1 \rightarrow 3' \rightarrow 2' \rightarrow 1' \rightarrow 1$. The net heat absorbed by the system around the cycle would be 0 since $Q_{3'2'} = Q_{11'} = -Q_{1'1}$. The work done by the system around the cycle would also be 0 by the first law. Thus, the net result would be a transfer of heat, in amount $Q_{11'}$, from the reservoir at t_2 to the higher temperature t_1. This is contrary to the physical postulate.

We now locate state $3''$ so that the heat absorbed by the system in the reversible process from $3''$ to $2''$, $Q_{3''2''}$, is equal to the heat absorbed by the system in the reversible process from 1 to $1''$, $Q_{11''}$. We assert that $3''$ does not coincide with $3'$. This follows from the facts that $Q_{1'1''}$ cannot be equal to $Q_{2'2''}$ since the paths $1'$–$2'$ and $1''$–$2''$ are both adiabatic. Thus,

$$
\begin{aligned}
Q_{3''2''} - Q_{3'2''} &= Q_{11''} - Q_{3'2''} \\
&= (Q_{11'} + Q_{1'1''}) - (Q_{3'2'} + Q_{2'2''}) \\
&= Q_{1'1''} - Q_{2'2''} \neq 0 \qquad (4\text{-}7)
\end{aligned}
$$

† The argument presented here is due to H. Grad and B. Crawford (private communication, B. Crawford).

Since the heat absorbed by the system when it proceeds from 3″ to 2″ is not equal to the heat absorbed from 3′ to 2″ along the same path, states 3′ and 3″ do not coincide.

Any points along the line 3′–3″ on the isotherm at temperature t_2 are adiabatically inaccessible from state 1. Since the temperature t_2 is arbitrary, we may carry through the argument presented above for any isotherm at temperature $t < t_1$. We consider, for example, the isotherm at temperature t_3. The points of intersection of the adiabatics through 1′ and 1″ with the isotherm at temperature t_3 are 4′ and 4″, respectively. The points 5′ and 5″ on the isotherm at temperature t_3 are chosen such that $Q_{5'4'} = Q_{11'}$ and $Q_{5''4''} = Q_{11''}$. We consider the region included between the paths along the isotherms between 3′ and 3″ and 5′ and 5″ and the paths which determine the locus of points along the isotherms between t_2 and t_3 which have the property that the heat absorbed in the reversible process from one of the points, along the isotherm, to the intersection of the reversible adiabatic through 1′ and the isotherm is equal to $Q_{11'}$; the heat absorbed in the reversible process from the other point, along the isotherm, to the intersection of the reversible adiabatic through 1″ and the isotherm is equal to $Q_{11''}$. (It is clear that the paths 3′–5′ and 3″–5″ cannot be adiabatic.) The entire area 3′, 3″, 5″, 5′, 3′ is inaccessible by adiabatics from 1. This area can be extended arbitrarily close to 1.

Thus, we have again proved Carathéodory's principle.

The well-known procedure of Carathéodory applies a restricted Carathéodory's principle (there exist a set of states of finite measure neighboring a given one which are inaccessible along reversible adiabatics) to a treatment of the geometry of solutions of Pfaffian expressions

$$dQ = \sum_{i=1}^{r} X_i \, dx_i \tag{4-8}$$

Use is made of Carathéodory's theorem: If a Pfaffian expression has the property that, in every neighborhood of a point P, there are points which cannot be connected to P along curves which satisfy the Pfaffian equation, $dQ = 0$, then the Pfaffian expression must admit an integrating denominator.

We shall present a brief sketch of the argument here. (More details can be found in the book: S. Chandrasekhar, "An Introduction to the Study of Stellar Structure," chap. I, University of Chicago Press, Chicago, 1939.) We have already indicated in Proof I that those states which are accessible from a given point P along reversible adiabatic paths must lie on a surface through P. Thus, we can construct a family of nonintersecting surfaces which fill the $x_1, \ldots, x_r$ space so that only points on any given surface are accessible along reversible adiabatics from points on the surface. This family of surfaces can be described by the one-parametric relation

$$\sigma(x_1, \ . \ . \ . \ , x_r) = \text{cons} \tag{4-9}$$

On each of these surfaces,

$$d\sigma = \sum_{i=1}^{r} \left(\frac{\partial \sigma}{\partial x_i}\right)_{x_{j \neq i}} dx_i = 0 \tag{4-10}$$

implies the Pfaffian equation

$$đQ = \sum_{i=1}^{r} X_i \, dx_i = 0 \tag{4-11}$$

Thus,

$$đQ = \tau(x_1, \ . \ . \ . \ ,x_r) \, d\sigma(x_1, \ . \ . \ . \ ,x_r) \tag{4-12}$$

where τ, the integrating denominator, is given by

$$\tau = \frac{X_1}{(\partial\sigma/\partial x_1)_{x_{j\neq 1}}} = \frac{X_2}{(\partial\sigma/\partial x_2)_{x_{j\neq 2}}} = \cdot \cdot \cdot = \frac{X_r}{(\partial\sigma/\partial x_r)_{x_{j\neq r}}} \tag{4-13}$$

It is clear that, if a Pfaffian expression admits one integrating denominator, it must admit an infinite number of them. Any function of σ, $S(\sigma)$, can be used to describe the family of surfaces, by the relation

$$S(\sigma) = \text{const} \tag{4-14}$$

and we can therefore write

$$đQ = T(x_1, \ . \ . \ . \ ,x_r) \, dS = T \frac{dS}{d\sigma} \, d\sigma \tag{4-15}$$

Thus,

$$T = \tau \frac{d\sigma}{dS} = \frac{X_i}{(\partial S/\partial x_i)_{x_{j\neq i}}} \qquad i = 1, \ . \ . \ . \ , r \tag{4-16}$$

is an integrating denominator. It now remains for us to show that a possible choice of an integrating denominator is the absolute temperature defined by Eq. (1-12).

We consider an arbitrary adiabatically isolated system consisting of two parts in thermal contact. The system is at a uniform temperature t, and we assume that the equilibrium states of each of the parts can be characterized by t and one other parameter. Thus, for a quasi-static process,

$$đQ = đQ_1 + đQ_2 = \tau(\sigma_1,\sigma_2,t) \, d\sigma(\sigma_1,\sigma_2,t) \tag{4-17}$$

where $đQ_1$, the differential heat absorbed by part 1 in the quasi-static process, is given by

$$đQ_1 = \tau_1(\sigma_1,t) \, d\sigma_1 \tag{4-18}$$

and

$$đQ_2 = \tau_2(\sigma_2,t) \, d\sigma_2 \tag{4-19}$$

Comparison of Eqs. (4-17), (4-18), and (4-19) yields

$$\tau\, d\sigma = \tau_1\, d\sigma_1 + \tau_2\, d\sigma_2 \tag{4-20}$$

It is clear from Eq. (4-20) that

$$\left(\frac{\partial \sigma}{\partial t}\right)_{\sigma_1,\sigma_2} = 0 \tag{4-21}$$

and therefore σ, $(\partial\sigma/\partial\sigma_1)_{\sigma_2,t} = \tau_1/\tau$, and $(\partial\sigma/\partial\sigma_2)_{\sigma_1,t} = \tau_2/\tau$ must be independent of t. Therefore

$$\frac{\partial}{\partial t}\left(\frac{\tau_1}{\tau}\right) = 0 = \frac{\partial}{\partial t}\left(\frac{\tau_2}{\tau}\right) \tag{4-22}$$

and thus

$$\frac{\partial \log \tau_1}{\partial t} = \frac{\partial \log \tau_2}{\partial t} = \frac{\partial \log \tau}{\partial t} \tag{4-23}$$

Since $\tau_1 = \tau_1(\sigma_1,t)$ and $\tau_2 = \tau_2(\sigma_2,t)$ and σ_1 and σ_2 are independent, the first equality in Eq. (4-23) can hold only when the terms appearing are functions of t alone. This function of t must be a universal function since it has the same value for the arbitrary system and its arbitrary parts. Thus we can write

$$\tau = f(t)h(\sigma_1,\sigma_2) \qquad \tau_1 = f(t)h_1(\sigma_1) \qquad \tau_2 = f(t)h_2(\sigma_2) \tag{4-24}$$

Substitution of (4-24) in (4-18), (4-19), and (4-17) yields

$$đQ_1 = f(t)h_1(\sigma_1)\, d\sigma_1 = f(t)\, dS_1 \tag{4-25}$$

$$đQ_2 = f(t)h_2(\sigma_2)\, d\sigma_2 = f(t)\, dS_2 \tag{4-26}$$

and

$$\begin{aligned} đQ &= f(t)h(\sigma_1,\sigma_2)\, d\sigma \\ &= f(t)h_1(\sigma_1)\, d\sigma_1 + f(t)h_2(\sigma_2)\, d\sigma_2 \end{aligned} \tag{4-27}$$

The quantities $S_1 = S_1(\sigma_1)$ and $S_2 = S_2(\sigma_2)$ are defined by the relations (4-25) and (4-26) and are constant along reversible adiabatic paths. The function $h(\sigma_1,\sigma_2)$ is only a function of σ, $h = h(\sigma(\sigma_1,\sigma_2))$, and thus we may define $S = S(\sigma)$ by the relation

$$đQ = f(t)\, dS \tag{4-28}$$

Since $f(t)$ is a universal function of the empirical temperature t, we need to determine it only for one special system. We consider a gaseous system of one component. In this case we can write, from Eq. (3-22),

$$\begin{aligned} đQ &= \left(\frac{\partial E}{\partial t}\right)_V dt + \left[p + \left(\frac{\partial E}{\partial V}\right)_T\right] dV \\ &= pV\left\{\frac{1}{pV}\left(\frac{\partial E}{\partial t}\right)_V dt + \left[\frac{1}{pV}\left(\frac{\partial E}{\partial V}\right)_T + \frac{1}{V}\right] dV\right\} \end{aligned} \tag{4-29}$$

We consider this system in the limit as the pressure tends to zero. In this case, Eq. (4-29) becomes

$$đQ = \beta(t)\left[\frac{1}{\beta(t)}\left(\frac{\partial E}{\partial t}\right)_V dt + \frac{1}{V}\,dV\right] \tag{4-30}$$

where we have made use of Eq. (1-8) and the experimental fact that

$$\lim_{p\to 0}\left(\frac{\partial E}{\partial V}\right)_t = 0 \tag{4-31}$$

Equation (4-30) can now be written in the form

$$đQ = T\,dS \tag{4-32}$$

where T, the absolute temperature, is defined by Eq. (1-12) and dS is given by

$$dS = \frac{\beta_0}{T_0}\left[\frac{1}{\beta}\left(\frac{\partial E}{\partial t}\right)_V dt + \frac{1}{V}\,dV\right] \tag{4-33}$$

Thus we have completed the proof of that part of the mathematical statement of the second law that applies to reversible processes. We have shown that the differential $đQ$ for a reversible process becomes a perfect differential when divided by T:

$$dS = \frac{đQ}{T} \tag{4-34}$$

The quantity S is the entropy function and is a function of state. The quantity T, the thermodynamic temperature, is identical to the absolute temperature.

We shall now prove that for a natural adiabatic process

$$\Delta S > 0 \tag{4-35}$$

We consider a system whose states are defined by the variables T, S, and x, where x represents a set of parameters, and assume that reversible paths exist between any two states. We investigate necessary conditions for the existence of an adiabatic process from the state A to the state B.

Equation (4-35) can be proved most directly by using the arguments of Proof I of Carathéodory's principle. In Fig. 4-3 we have drawn a representation of the various processes undergone by the system in the T-S plane. We have drawn a line through the states A and A' representing a reversible

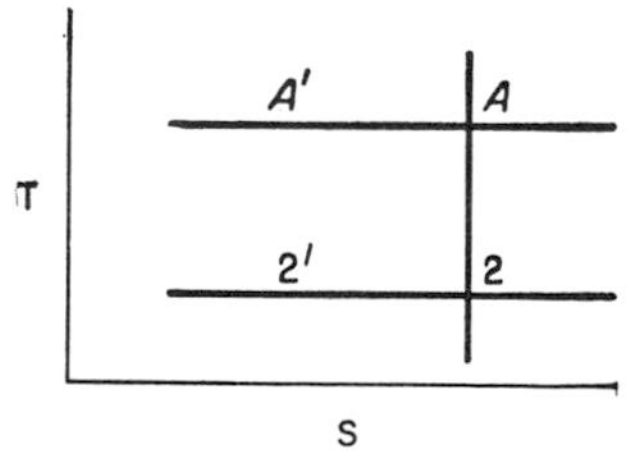

FIG. 4-3. Plot of isotherms $A' \to A$ and $2' \to 2$ and reversible adiabatic path $A \to 2$.

isothermal path between these states. The heat absorbed by the system in a given reversible isothermal process increases from left to right since

$$đQ = T\,dS \tag{4-36}$$

We have also drawn the line through state A representing a reversible adiabatic process. Since

$$đQ = dS = 0 \tag{4-37}$$

in a reversible adiabatic process, this line must be perpendicular to the S axis. We have established in Proof I that the state A cannot be connected by an adiabatic process to any state to the left of the reversible adiabatic through A. Thus, in order for a natural adiabatic process to exist between state A and state B, B must lie to the right of the reversible adiabatic through A. Thus, we have proved that

$$\Delta S = S_B - S_A > 0 \tag{4-38}$$

in a natural adiabatic process.

Equation (4-35) can also be proved using the arguments of Proof II of Carathéodory's principle.† Again we consider various processes represented in the T-S plane. We consider the following cycle represented in Fig. 4-4:

A reversible adiabatic path from state B at T_B, S_B, x to state C at T_C, S_B, x, where $T_C > T_B, T_A$.

A reversible isothermal path from C to D at T_C, S_D, x. The heat absorbed along this path is $Q_C = T_C(S_D - S_B)$.

A reversible adiabatic path from D to E at T_A, S_D, x.

A reversible isothermal path from E to A at T_A, S_A, x. The heat absorbed along this path is $Q_A = T_A(S_A - S_D)$.

We wish to consider a cycle such that, if B is accessible from A along an adiabatic, the net result is a transfer of heat. Thus, we must choose S_D such that

$$Q_C + Q_A = T_C(S_D - S_B) + T_A(S_A - S_D) = 0 \tag{4-39}$$

Solving for S_D, we obtain

$$S_D = \frac{T_C S_B - T_A S_A}{T_C - T_A} \tag{4-40}$$

Now if we go adiabatically from A to B the net result of the cycle will be a transfer of heat Q_C from T_C to T_A. This is permissible if

$$Q_C = T_C(S_D - S_B) > 0 \qquad \text{(Clausius)} \tag{4-41}$$

† This argument is due to B. Crawford (private communication).

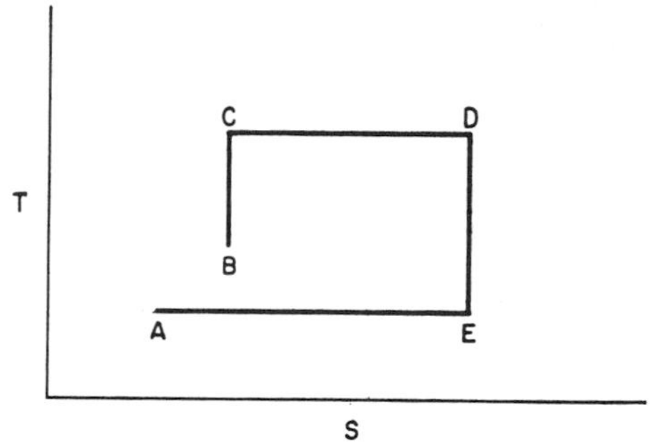

FIG. 4-4. Plot of cycle involving isotherm AE, reversible adiabatic ED, isotherm DC, and reversible adiabatic CB.

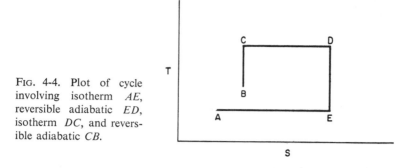

If Q_C were less than zero, the cyclic process would be in contradiction to Clausius' physical statement of the second law. From Eqs. (4-40) and (4-41), we find

$$\frac{T_A}{T_C - T_A}(S_B - S_A) = S_D - S_B > 0 \tag{4-42}$$

Since $T_C > T_A$, we conclude from Eq. (4-42) that

$$S_B > S_A \tag{4-43}$$

Thus, for a natural process to exist, S_B must be larger than S_A. In a natural adiabatic process, then,

$$\Delta S > 0 \tag{4-44}$$

If $S_B = S_A$, a reversible adiabatic could be drawn between A and B.

In order to complete the derivation of the mathematical statement of the second law from the physical statements, we must prove that

$$\Delta S > \int \frac{đQ}{T} \tag{4-45}$$

for any irreversible process. We consider an isolated over-all system consisting of a system (α) and its surroundings (β). We assume that the system (α) undergoes an irreversible change while the surroundings (β) undergo a reversible change. Thus, since the over-all system undergoes an irreversible process,

$$\Delta S = \Delta S^{(\alpha)} + \Delta S^{(\beta)} > 0 \tag{4-46}$$

where

$$\Delta S^{(\beta)} = \int \frac{đQ^{(\beta)}}{T^{(\beta)}} \tag{4-47}$$

Since the over-all system is isolated,

$$đQ^{(\alpha)} = -đQ^{(\beta)} \tag{4-48}$$

and Eq. (4-46) may be rewritten in the form

$$\Delta S^{(\alpha)} > -\int \frac{đQ^{(\beta)}}{T^{(\beta)}} \tag{4-49}$$

or

$$\Delta S^{(\alpha)} > \int \frac{đQ^{(\alpha)}}{T^{(\beta)}} \tag{4-50}$$

We have proved that

$$\Delta S > \int \frac{đQ}{T} \tag{4-51}$$

for an irreversible process, where T is the thermodynamic temperature of the surroundings. This completes the derivation of the mathematical statement of the second law from the physical statements.

It is relatively easy to derive the physical statements of the second law from the mathematical statements and thus complete the verification of their equivalence.

5 THE THIRD LAW OF THERMODYNAMICS

The third law of thermodynamics, like the first and second laws, is a postulate based on a large number of experiments. In this chapter we present the formulation of the third law and discuss the causes of a number of apparent deviations from this law. The foundations of the third law are firmly rooted in molecular theory, and the apparent deviations from this law can be easily explained using statistical mechanical considerations. The third law of thermodynamics is used primarily for the determination of entropy constants which, combined with thermochemical data, permit the calculation of equilibrium constants.

5-1. NERNST HEAT THEOREM AND THE THIRD LAW

In 1902, T. W. Richards found experimentally that the free-energy increment of a reaction approached the enthalpy change asymptotically as the temperature was decreased. From a study of Richards' data, Nernst suggested that at absolute zero the entropy increment of reversible reactions among perfect crystalline solids is zero. This heat theorem was restated by Planck in 1912 in the form: The entropy of all perfect crystalline solids is zero at absolute zero.† This postulate is the third law of thermodynamics. A perfect crystal is one in true thermodynamic equilibrium. Apparent deviations from the third law are attributed to the fact that measurements have been made on non-equilibrium systems.

An equivalent statement of the third law is: It is impossible to reduce the temperature of any system to absolute zero. (A discussion of the equivalence of this formulation with that enunciated by Planck is given in the book: E. A Guggenheim, "Thermodynamics," p. 161, Interscience Publishers, Inc., New York, 1949.)

The third law is used for the calculation of absolute entropies. The differential change in entropy in a reversible process is given by

$$dS = \frac{đQ}{T} \tag{5-1}$$

† It is probably true that the entropy of any state, in true thermodynamic equilibrium, at absolute zero, is zero (e.g., liquid He).

The difference in entropy between a state at temperature T and the perfect crystalline solid at absolute zero is obtained by integrating Eq. (5-1) along any reversible path between the state at T and the state at absolute zero. Thus,

$$S(T) = S_0 + \int_0^T \frac{đQ}{T} \tag{5-2}$$

where S_0, the integration constant, is the entropy of the given perfect crystalline substance at absolute zero. In practice, measurements are made to some low temperature T^*, below which a theoretical extrapolation is made. Hence, Eq. (5-2) becomes

$$S = S_0 + \left(\int_0^{T^*} \frac{đQ}{T}\right)_{extrap} + \left(\int_{T^*}^{T} \frac{đQ}{T}\right)_{exp't} \tag{5-3}$$

The last term is evaluated from experimental measurements of heat capacities and heats of transition (Sec. 6-1). The extrapolated term is usually evaluated with the aid of the Debye equation for the heat capacity of crystals. The Debye equation for the heat capacity of crystals at low temperature is

$$C_v \simeq aT^3 \tag{5-4}$$

where a is an empirical constant, evaluated by fitting the extrapolated curve to the empirical one. The third law states that the integration constant S_0 is zero, and consequently the absolute value of the entropy can be determined from Eq. (5-3).

The statistical mechanical basis for the third law is a simple consequence of the Gibbs or Boltzmann definition of entropy. We consider a system at low temperature which has an energy spectrum of such a form that $(E_i - E_0)/kT \ll 1$ for a group of energy levels and $(E_j - E_0)/kT \gg 1$ for the remaining levels, where E_0 is the energy of the ground level, E_i is a typical energy of the first set of levels, and E_j is a typical energy of the second set of levels. Under these circumstances the entropy of the system is given by

$$S = k \ln W \tag{5-5}$$

where k is Boltzmann's constant and W is the sum of the degeneracies of the energy levels for which $(E_i - E_0)/kT \ll 1$. A crystal in thermodynamic equilibrium at absolute zero has a molal entropy

$$S = k \ln W_0 \tag{5-6}$$

where W_0 is the degree of degeneracy of the lowest energy state, i.e., the number of quantum states available to the system in the lowest energy state. The third law is true for all crystalline solids for which $W_0 = 1$; no exceptions have been found.

5-2. DEVIATIONS FROM THE THIRD LAW

There are many cases in which calculation of the entropy change in a reaction from values of the absolute entropy obtained from thermal data and the third law are in disagreement with values calculated directly from measurements of the enthalpy and free-energy change. Satisfactory explanations of these discrepancies were not possible until the development of quantum statistical mechanics. The apparent deviations from the third law are due to the fact that measurements have been made on nonequilibrium systems. From the quantum statistical mechanics point of view, true thermodynamic equilibrium is that condition in which opportunity is given for the free passage of each of the molecules of a crystal among all the permitted states of energy in accordance with an appropriate distribution law. In this section, we shall discuss some of the numerous causes of nonconformity with the third law.

Crystals of certain linear molecules such as nitric oxide, NO, carbon monoxide, CO, and nitrous oxide, NNO, may exist near absolute zero with a randomness of structure which gives rise to an additional entropy. The state of lowest energy is that in which the molecules are all aligned in one direction. Given similar end atoms, however, many of the molecules will be arranged in both forward and reverse positions at some low temperature. As the crystal is cooled, a point is reached where the molecules are "frozen" in position and can no longer rotate. The molecules will remain frozen down to the lowest temperature, T^*, at which measurements are made and will thus give rise to a residual entropy. The amount of residual entropy can be calculated in some simple cases. If there are p states available for each molecule, then p^N is the total number of configurations that the system can assume, where N is the number of molecules. In this case, $W = p^N$, and the entropy of randomness is

$$S = k \ln W = Nk \ln p \tag{5-6}$$

For linear molecules where $p = 2$, $S = 1.38$ cal/deg mole. This is very close to the observed discrepancy in entropy for the molecules cited above.

Nonconformity with the third law also arises when a substance can exist in more than one state of such low energy that the distribution among these states is not influenced by the falling temperature down to the lowest attainable T^*. These states are frequently due to interactions of electronic or nuclear magnetic dipoles. An extrapolation to zero using the Debye law would reduce the system to a state of zero vibrational entropy, but the rotational entropy due to nuclear spin or the entropy associated with random orientation of magnetic dipoles in paramagnetic substances would still exist. Transitions between the low energy states must not necessarily be "frozen" out in these systems; it is sufficient that at the lowest temperature of measurement, T^*, the system has not reached the lowest energy state with respect to nonvibrational interactions. The amount of heat given out in orienting these interacting particles is very small, but since it is liberated at low temperatures (often $< 1°K$), the amount of residual entropy is considerable.

Another system in which deviations from the third law appear is a mixture of ortho and para hydrogen. In the lowest energy state all the hydrogen molecules would be in the para state. However, since the rate of conversion from ortho to para is quite slow in the absence of catalysts, several units of entropy are retained in hydrogen as it is cooled. However, if an appropriate catalyst is present for ortho-para conversion, the entropy can be calculated correctly by placing $S_0 = 0$.

Another source of residual entropy is the presence of isotopic molecules scattered throughout the crystal. In the lowest energy state, the isotopes separate into the component phases. Since the mixture of isotopes is usually present in both products and reactants, their contribution is usually neglected in chemical calculations.

Some liquids may become glasslike rather than crystalline solids as the temperature is lowered. In this case, the molecules exhibit considerable randomness of arrangement and can be "frozen" in on further cooling so as to yield a positive entropy at 0°K. Both glycerol and ethanol can be cooled to yield positive entropies in this way.

We conclude this brief discussion of deviations from the third law by stating that, although the cases of nonconformity are frequent, we can usually understand their origin with the aid of molecular concepts and quantum statistics. The latter discipline permits calculation of thermodynamic quantities, thereby providing a useful check on experimental data; indeed, it often supplies answers of greater accuracy. In this way, it is possible to use the third law to build up tables of absolute entropies of chemical substances.

6 GENERAL CONDITIONS FOR EQUILIBRIUM

In this chapter we make use of the first and second laws of thermodynamics in the derivation of general conditions for equilibrium. In Sec. 6-1 we present the criteria for equilibrium for closed systems under various restraints. We define two extensive functions of state, the Helmholtz and Gibbs free energies, and write a number of fundamental equations for closed equilibrium systems. We apply some of these equations to the calculation of the entropy change for an arbitrary process in a closed system. In Sec. 6-2 we consider homogeneous open systems and derive the fundamental equations describing the equilibrium states of these systems. In Sec. 6-3 we derive and discuss in some detail some of the results on the criteria for equilibrium for heterogeneous systems. In Sec. 6-4 we discuss conditions for stable equilibrium. A number of interesting results concerning thermodynamic quantities are shown to be necessary and sufficient conditions for stability of thermodynamic systems.

6-1. EQUATIONS FOR CLOSED SYSTEMS IN EQUILIBRIUM

We have demonstrated from the second law of thermodynamics that a system is in a state of equilibrium if

$$\delta S \leqslant \frac{\delta Q}{T} \tag{6-1}$$

[see Eq. (4-4)] for all virtual processes to neighboring states. In Eq. (6-1), T is the uniform temperature of the surroundings of the system. We shall make use of Eq. (6-1) and the first law of thermodynamics to derive criteria of equilibrium for closed systems subject to various restraints.

The first law of thermodynamics for closed systems can be written in the form

$$\delta Q = \delta E + \delta W \tag{6-2}$$

The restriction to a closed system is necessary since, in the first law, energy changes due to transfer of mass between the system and the surroundings are not considered. It is possible to extend the first law to open systems by enlarging the definition of work to include energy increments resulting from the addition of matter. We note that changes in the masses of the various components within a closed system, due to chemical reactions, do not involve work done by the surroundings on the system and thus do not appear in the expression for the first law. Limiting ourselves to systems in which the only external force is a uniform normal pressure, we may rewrite Eq. (6-2) in the form

$$\delta Q = \delta E + p\,\delta V \tag{6-3}$$

where p is the pressure exerted by the surroundings on the system. Substituting Eq. (6-1) into Eq. (6-3), we obtain

$$\delta E + p\,\delta V - T\,\delta S \geqslant 0 \tag{6-4}$$

Equation (6-4) is the general criterion of equilibrium for closed systems. It applies to heterogeneous as well as homogeneous systems. Special forms of this criterion, applicable to a system subject to additional restraints, are of interest.

a. The criterion of equilibrium for a closed system at constant energy E and volume V is

$$(\delta S)_{E,V} \leqslant 0 \tag{6-5}$$

b. The criterion of equilibrium for a closed system at constant entropy S and volume V is

$$(\delta E)_{S,V} \geqslant 0 \tag{6-6}$$

c. The criterion of equilibrium for a closed system at constant volume V and with a uniform, constant temperature T is

$$(\delta E)_{T,V} - T(\delta S)_{T,V} \geqslant 0 \tag{6-7}$$

In order to express Eq. (6-7) in a more concise fashion, it is useful to define an extensive function of state, A, the work function or Helmholtz free energy. The Helmholtz free energy is defined by the relation

$$A = E - TS \tag{6-8}$$

Differentiation of Eq. (6-8) yields

$$dA = dE - T\,dS - S\,dT \tag{6-9}$$

Thus we may write

$$(\delta A)_{T,V} = (\delta E)_{T,V} - T(\delta S)_{T,V} \tag{6-10}$$

and Eq. (6-7) may be rewritten in the form

$$(\delta A)_{T,V} \geqslant 0 \tag{6-11}$$

d. The criterion of equilibrium for a closed system characterized by a uniform, constant temperature T and a uniform, constant pressure p is

$$(\delta E)_{T,p} + p(\delta V)_{T,p} - T(\delta S)_{T,p} \geqslant 0 \tag{6-12}$$

This criterion of equilibrium is an important one and is frequently used, since most experiments are carried out at constant temperature and pressure. In order to express Eq. (6-12) in a more concise fashion, it is useful to define an extensive function of state, F, the Gibbs free energy. The Gibbs free energy is defined by the relation

$$F = E + pV - TS = H - TS \tag{6-13}$$

Differentiation of Eq. (6-13) results in

$$dF = dE + p\,dV + V\,dp - T\,dS - S\,dT \tag{6-14}$$

Thus we may write

$$(\delta F)_{T,p} = (\delta E)_{T,p} + p(\delta V)_{T,p} - T(\delta S)_{T,p} \tag{6-15}$$

and Eq. (6-12) can be rewritten in the form

$$(\delta F)_{T,p} \geqslant 0 \tag{6-16}$$

It should be pointed out that, when Eq. (6-16) is used as the criterion of equilibrium, one is unable to prove anything concerning the temperature and pressure conditions necessary for equilibrium. That temperature and pressure must be uniform throughout the equilibrium system can be proved by use of Eq. (6-5) or Eq. (6-6).

In the field of equilibrium states,

$$dS = \frac{đQ}{T} \tag{6-17}$$

By the use of this equation and the first law, the fundamental equations for closed systems in states of equilibrium may be easily obtained. Substitution of Eq. (6-17) into Eqs. (3-16) and (3-18) results in

$$dE = T\,dS - p\,dV \tag{6-18}$$

Use of Eq. (6-18) and Eq. (3-28), which defines the enthalpy, yields

$$dH = T\,dS + V\,dp \tag{6-19}$$

Substitution of Eq. (6-18) into Eq. (6-9) yields

$$dA = -S\,dT - p\,dV \tag{6-20}$$

Substitution of Eq. (6-18) into Eq. (6-14) results in

$$dF = -S\,dT + V\,dp \tag{6-21}$$

Many important relations may be derived from Eqs. (6-18) to (6-21). A few illustrative examples are obtained here. Differentiation of Eq. (6-18) with respect to T at constant V yields

$$\left(\frac{\partial S}{\partial T}\right)_V = \frac{1}{T}\left(\frac{\partial E}{\partial T}\right)_V = \frac{C_v}{T} \tag{6-22}$$

Correspondingly, differentiation of (6-19) with respect to T at constant p gives

$$\left(\frac{\partial S}{\partial T}\right)_p = \frac{1}{T}\left(\frac{\partial H}{\partial T}\right)_p = \frac{C_p}{T} \tag{6-23}$$

Applying the Euler condition [Eq. (A-32)] to Eqs. (6-20) and (6-21), we obtain

$$\left(\frac{\partial S}{\partial V}\right)_T = \left(\frac{\partial p}{\partial T}\right)_V \tag{6-24}$$

and

$$\left(\frac{\partial S}{\partial p}\right)_T = -\left(\frac{\partial V}{\partial T}\right)_p \tag{6-25}$$

Differentiation of Eq. (6-18) with respect to V at constant T and substitution of Eq. (6-24) result in

$$\left(\frac{\partial E}{\partial V}\right)_T = T\left(\frac{\partial p}{\partial T}\right)_V - p \tag{6-26}$$

Corresponding manipulations with Eqs. (6-19) and (6-25) yield

$$\left(\frac{\partial H}{\partial p}\right)_T = V - T\left(\frac{\partial V}{\partial T}\right)_p \tag{6-27}$$

Equations (6-26) and (6-27) are known as the thermodynamic equations of state.

Differentiating Eq. (6-20) with respect to T at constant V and with respect to V at constant T, we obtain

$$\left(\frac{\partial A}{\partial T}\right)_V = -S \tag{6-28}$$

and

$$\left(\frac{\partial A}{\partial V}\right)_T = -p \tag{6-29}$$

Analogous procedures applied to Eq. (6-21) yield

$$\left(\frac{\partial F}{\partial T}\right)_p = -S \tag{6-30}$$

and

$$\left(\frac{\partial F}{\partial p}\right)_T = V \tag{6-31}$$

We may use some of the formulas derived above to calculate the entropy change in a one-component system for an arbitrary process. The total differential of the molal entropy may be written in the form

$$ds = \frac{c_p}{T}\,dT - \left(\frac{\partial v}{\partial T}\right)_p dp \tag{6-32}$$

where we have made use of Eqs. (6-23) and (6-25).

We consider two processes. In one process no phase transition occurs; in the other process a phase transition does occur. Case I: no discontinuities in phase on the path of integration. Integration of Eq. (6-32) along the path indicated in Fig. 6-1 yields

$$s(T,p) = s(T_0,p_0) + \int_{T_0}^{T} \frac{c_p}{T'}\, dT' - \int_{p_0}^{p} \left(\frac{\partial v}{\partial T}\right)_{p'} dp' \tag{6-33}$$

where $s(T_0,p_0)$ is some reference value of the entropy. Case II: discontinuities in phase on the path of integration. Integration of Eq. (6-32) along the path indicated in Fig. 6-2 yields

$$s^{(\beta)}(T,p) = s^{(\alpha)}(T_0,p_0) + \int_{T_0}^{T_{\alpha\beta}} \frac{c_p^{(\alpha)}}{T'}\, dT' + \Delta s^{(\alpha\beta)}(T_{\alpha\beta},p_0)$$
$$+ \int_{T_{\alpha\beta}}^{T} \frac{c_p^{(\beta)}}{T'}\, dT' - \int_{p_0}^{p} \left(\frac{\partial v^{(\beta)}}{\partial T}\right)_{p'} dp' \tag{6-34}$$

where the superscripts (α) and (β) refer to phases α and β, respectively, and

$$\Delta s^{(\alpha\beta)}(T_{\alpha\beta},p_0) = s^{(\beta)}(T_{\alpha\beta},p_0) - s^{(\alpha)}(T_{\alpha\beta},p_0) \tag{6-35}$$

is the entropy change in going from phase α to phase β at temperature $T_{\alpha\beta}$ and pressure p_0. If the two phases are in equilibrium, the entropy change $\Delta s^{(\alpha\beta)}$ can be related to the enthalpy change $\Delta h^{(\alpha\beta)}$ by the equation

$$\Delta s^{(\alpha\beta)} = \frac{\Delta h^{(\alpha\beta)}}{T_{\alpha\beta}} \tag{6-36}$$

Equation (6-36) is a consequence of the conditions of equilibrium for a heterogeneous system and will be discussed further in Chap. 9.

To carry out these entropy calculations, we make use of experimentally determined heats of transition, equations of state, and heat capacities.

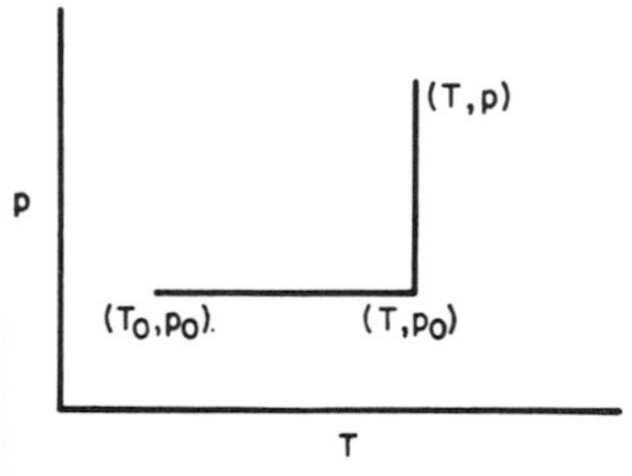

FIG. 6-1. Path of integration in Eq. (6-33).

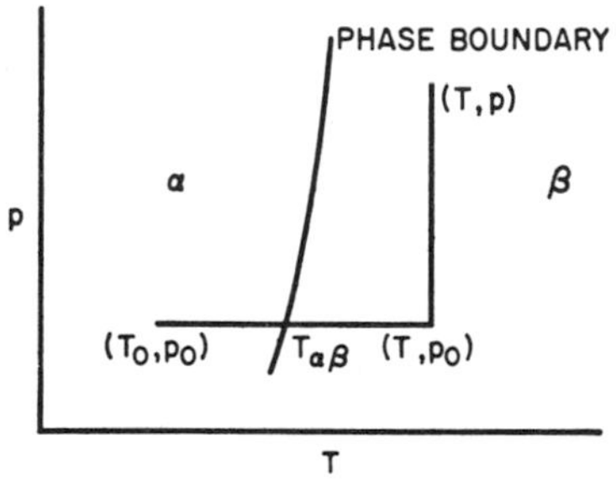

FIG. 6-2. Path of integration in Eq. (6-34).

6-2. FUNDAMENTAL EQUATIONS OF HOMOGENEOUS OPEN SYSTEMS

In this section we shall generalize the equations obtained in Sec. 6-1 to include positive or negative changes in the mass of the system due to a transfer of mass between the system and its surroundings. A criterion for equilibrium for a homogeneous open system in which there are no chemical reactions is immediately obtainable from Eq. (6-6) in the form

$$(\delta E)_{S,V,n_i} \geqslant 0 \tag{6-37}$$

In the field of equilibrium states, the internal energy can be expressed as a function of the volume V, entropy S, and the number of moles of component i, $n_i(i = 1, \ldots ,r)$, in the system, that is,

$$E = E(V,S,n_1, \ldots ,n_r) \tag{6-38}$$

Consequently, the total derivative of the energy is given by

$$dE = \left(\frac{\partial E}{\partial V}\right)_{S,n_i} dV + \left(\frac{\partial E}{\partial S}\right)_{V,n_i} dS + \sum_{i=1}^{r} \left(\frac{\partial E}{\partial n_i}\right)_{\substack{S,Vn_j \\ j=1,\ldots,r,\neq i}} dn_i \qquad i = 1, \ldots, r \tag{6-39}$$

The first two partial derivatives in Eq. (6-39) can be determined from the equations for closed systems, since the composition is held constant. For an infinitesimal reversible process in which no mass is transferred, we obtain from Eq. (6-18)

$$\left(\frac{\partial E}{\partial S}\right)_{V,n_i} = T \tag{6-40}$$

and

$$\left(\frac{\partial E}{\partial V}\right)_{S,n_i} = -p \tag{6-41}$$

Equation (6-39) becomes

$$dE = T\,dS - p\,dV + \sum_{i=1}^{r} \mu_i\,dn_i \tag{6-42}$$

where the quantity μ_i is defined by the relation

$$\mu_i = \left(\frac{\partial E}{\partial n_i}\right)_{S,V,n_j} \tag{6-43}$$

By use of Eq. (6-42) and the relation

$$dH = dE + p\,dV + V\,dP \tag{6-44}$$

we may write the total differential of the enthalpy as

$$dH = T\,dS + V\,dp + \sum_{i=1}^{r} \mu_i\,dn_i \tag{6-45}$$

Since the total differential of the enthalpy is given by

$$dH = T\,dS + V\,dp + \sum_{i=1}^{r} \left(\frac{\partial H}{\partial n_i}\right)_{S,p,n_j} dn_i \tag{6-46}$$

it is evident that

$$\mu_i = \left(\frac{\partial H}{\partial n_i}\right)_{S,p,n_j} \tag{6-47}$$

In a similar manner, using the Helmholtz work function A and the Gibbs free energy F, two additional equations, analogous to Eqs. (6-42) and (6-46), are obtained. The four equations

$$dE = T\,dS - p\,dV + \sum_{i=1}^{r} \mu_i\,dn_i \tag{6-48}$$

$$dH = T\,dS + V\,dp + \sum_{i=1}^{r} \mu_i\,dn_i \tag{6-49}$$

$$dA = -S\,dT - p\,dV + \sum_{i=1}^{r} \mu_i\,dn_i \tag{6-50}$$

$$dF = -S\,dT + V\,dp + \sum_{i=1}^{r} \mu_i\,dn_i \tag{6-51}$$

constitute the fundamental relations for a homogeneous open system in equilibrium. From Eqs. (6-48) to (6-51), it follows that μ_i can be related to E, H, A, and F by the equations

$$\begin{aligned}\mu_i &= \left(\frac{\partial E}{\partial n_i}\right)_{S,V,n_j} = \left(\frac{\partial H}{\partial n_i}\right)_{S,p,n_j} \\ &= \left(\frac{\partial A}{\partial n_i}\right)_{T,V,n_j} = \left(\frac{\partial F}{\partial n_i}\right)_{T,p,n_j}\end{aligned} \tag{6-52}$$

The symbol μ_i was first used by Gibbs and called by him the "chemical potential" of component i. It can be seen from Eq. (6-52) and the definition of partial molal quantities [Eq. (2-5)] that μ_i is the partial molal free energy $\bar{f}_i$ and is an intensive property.

Equations (6-48) to (6-51) can be manipulated to obtain many useful relationships. Application of the Euler condition to Eq. (6-51) yields

$$\left(\frac{\partial \mu_i}{\partial T}\right)_{p,n_i} = -\left(\frac{\partial S}{\partial n_i}\right)_{T,p,n_j} = -\bar{s}_i \tag{6-53}$$

$$\left(\frac{\partial \mu_i}{\partial p}\right)_{T,n_i} = \left(\frac{\partial V}{\partial n_i}\right)_{T,p,n_j} = \bar{v}_i \tag{6-54}$$

$$\left(\frac{\partial \mu_i}{\partial n_k}\right)_{T,p,n_l} = \left(\frac{\partial \mu_k}{\partial n_i}\right)_{T,p,n_j} \qquad l = 1, \ldots, r, \neq k \tag{6-55}$$

Thus, the total differential of the chemical potential of component k can be written

$$d\mu_k = -\bar{s}_k \, dT + \bar{v}_k \, dp + \sum_{i=1}^{r-1} \left(\frac{\partial \mu_k}{\partial x_i}\right)_{T,p,x_j} dx_i \qquad j = 1, \ldots, r-1, \neq i \quad (6\text{-}56)$$

Application of Eq. (2-3), which determines the general relation between an extensive property and the corresponding partial molal properties, to the free energy yields

$$F = \sum_{i=1}^{r} n_i \bar{f}_i = \sum_{i=1}^{r} n_i \mu_i \qquad (6\text{-}57)$$

Differentiation of Eq. (6-57) results in

$$dF = \sum_{i=1}^{r} \mu_i \, dn_i + \sum_{i=1}^{r} n_i \, d\mu_i \qquad (6\text{-}58)$$

Combining Eq. (6-58) and Eq. (6-51), we have

$$\sum_{i=1}^{r} n_i \, d\mu_i + S \, dT - V \, dp = 0 \qquad (6\text{-}59)$$

Division of Eq. (6-59) by $n = \sum_{i=1}^{r} n_i$, the total mass in moles, yields

$$\sum_{i=1}^{r} x_i \, d\mu_i + s \, dT - v \, dp = 0 \qquad (6\text{-}60)$$

where s and v are the mean molal entropy and the mean molal volume, respectively. This equation was deduced independently by Gibbs (1875) and Duhem (1886). At constant T and p, the Gibbs-Duhem equation reduces to

$$\sum_{i=1}^{r} n_i \, d\mu_i = \sum_{i=1}^{r} x_i \, d\mu_i = 0 \qquad (6\text{-}61)$$

6-3. CRITERIA OF HETEROGENEOUS EQUILIBRIUM

In this section, we present a discussion of the equilibrium criteria of an isolated heterogeneous system in which no chemical reactions occur.

A heterogeneous system is one consisting of two or more phases. By definition, these are separated from each other by surfaces of discontinuity in one or more of the intensive properties. We will assume that the phases are originally isolated, with each of them in internal equilibrium, and thus that each phase is homogeneous. The problem is thereby reduced to finding conditions on the intensive properties which are necessary and sufficient to ensure equilibrium after the restraint of isolation is removed. The heterogeneous system considered here is an isolated system in which no chemical reactions occur.

We note that the arguments presented here can be applied to a one-phase system. In this case the conditions on the intensive properties within the phase necessary to ensure internal equilibrium can be derived.

The criterion for equilibrium of a system may be written in the form [see Eq. (6-6)]

$$(\delta E)_{S, V, n_1, \ldots, n_r} \geqslant 0 \tag{6-62}$$

where r is the minimum number of components which must be specified to make up the system.

Since the internal energy is an extensive property, the total internal energy E is, approximately, the sum of the internal energies of the several phases. More accurately, one should also include the energies which are associated with surfaces and interfacial boundaries. These may be included by considering such surfaces as separate phases. Since the entropy and the masses of the components are also extensive properties, a corresponding argument holds for them. However, in the following, we shall assume that the phases are so large, and of such a shape, that the surface contributions may be neglected compared with the bulk-volume effects. Thus, we shall neglect the surface contributions and consider only bulk phases.

In this approximation, we have for a system of v bulk phases

$$\begin{aligned} E &= \sum_{\alpha=1}^{v} E^{(\alpha)} \\ S &= \sum_{\alpha=1}^{v} S^{(\alpha)} \\ V &= \sum_{\alpha=1}^{v} V^{(\alpha)} \\ n_i &= \sum_{\alpha=1}^{v} n_i^{(\alpha)} \qquad i = 1, \ldots, r \end{aligned} \tag{6-63}$$

where $E^{(\alpha)}$, $S^{(\alpha)}$, $V^{(\alpha)}$, and $n_i^{(\alpha)}$ refer to the internal energy, entropy, volume, and mass of the ith component in phase α, respectively. Application of Eq. (6-62) requires that S, V, and n_i be held fixed. In variational form, this may be expressed by the relations

$$\delta S = \sum_{\alpha=1}^{v} \delta S^{(\alpha)} = 0 \tag{6-64}$$

$$\delta V = \sum_{\alpha=1}^{v} \delta V^{(\alpha)} = 0 \tag{6-65}$$

$$\delta n_i = \sum_{\alpha=1}^{v} \delta n_i^{(\alpha)} = 0 \qquad i = 1, \ldots, r \tag{6-66}$$

Equation (6-65) implies that we consider those variations in which the system may be assumed to be enclosed in a rigid container. Equation (6-66) is the condition for conservation of the ith material component. Operationally, then, Eqs. (6-64) to (6-66) imply that we consider an isolated system in which no chemical reactions may occur.

The fundamental equations for open homogeneous systems hold for an arbitrary homogeneous system and will hold, in particular, for the αth phase of the heterogeneous system. Application of Eq. (6-42) to the αth phase, using the symbol δ instead of d, since variations are involved, results in

$$\delta E^{(\alpha)} = T^{(\alpha)}\,\delta S^{(\alpha)} - p^{(\alpha)}\,\delta V^{(\alpha)} + \sum_{i=1}^{r} \mu_i^{(\alpha)}\,\delta n_i^{(\alpha)} \tag{6-67}$$

Thus, the criterion for equilibrium [Eq. (6-62)] may be written

$$\delta E = \sum_{\alpha=1}^{\nu}\left(T^{(\alpha)}\,\delta S^{(\alpha)} - p^{(\alpha)}\,\delta V^{(\alpha)} + \sum_{i=1}^{r} \mu_i^{(\alpha)}\,\delta n_i^{(\alpha)}\right) \geqslant 0 \tag{6-68}$$

where S, V, and n_i are held fixed in accordance with Eqs. (6-64) to (6-66).

We now seek to determine conditions on the set of intensive quantities $T^{(\alpha)}$, $p^{(\alpha)}$, and $\mu_i^{(\alpha)}$, $i = 1, \ldots, r, \alpha = 1, \ldots, \nu$, such that the originally isolated phases will remain in equilibrium when brought into contact with each other. These conditions may be found by considering a number of particular, conceivable variations of the extensive properties $S^{(\alpha)}$, $V^{(\alpha)}$, $n_i^{(\alpha)}$, $i = 1, \ldots, r, \alpha = 1, \ldots, \nu$.

Consider first the set of variations in which

$$\begin{aligned}
&\delta S^{(\alpha)} = 0 && \alpha = 1, \ldots, \nu \\
&\delta n_i^{(\alpha)} = 0 && i = 1, \ldots, r, \quad \alpha = 1, \ldots, \nu \\
&\delta V^{(\alpha)} = 0 && \alpha = 3, \ldots, \nu \\
&\delta V^{(1)} = -\,\delta V^{(2)}
\end{aligned} \tag{6-69}$$

It is clear that these variations satisfy the restrictions of Eqs. (6-64) to (6-66). In this case, the criterion for equilibrium [Eq. (6-68)] becomes

$$(p^{(2)} - p^{(1)})\,\delta V^{(1)} \geqslant 0 \tag{6-70}$$

If the phases 1 and 2 are separated by a deformable surface or membrane, then it is possible for $\delta V^{(1)}$ to be either positive or negative. If the system is in equilibrium, it is necessary that Eq. (6-70) hold for a variation $\delta V^{(1)} < 0$, and thus $p^{(2)} - p^{(1)} \leqslant 0$, and for a variation $\delta V^{(1)} > 0$, and thus $p^{(2)} - p^{(1)} \geqslant 0$. These conditions on $p^{(2)} - p^{(1)}$ are consistent only when

$$p^{(1)} = p^{(2)} \tag{6-71}$$

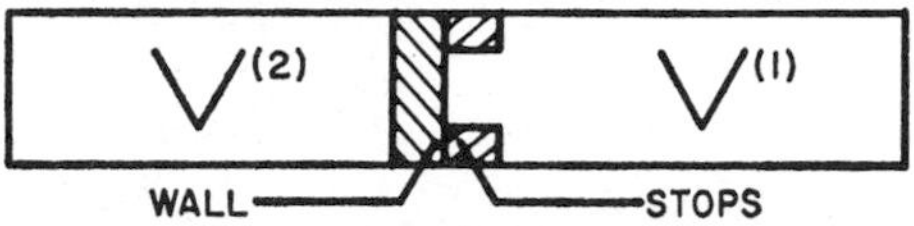

FIG. 6-3. System in which $\delta V^{(1)} \geqslant 0$.

Thus, the pressures of phases separated by a deformable surface must be equal when the phases are in equilibrium.

It may happen that phases 1 and 2 are separated by a membrane which is semideformable; i.e., the membrane may permit an increase of $V^{(1)}$ but not a decrease. The membrane may be, for example, a sliding wall in a cylinder up against stops (see Fig. 6-3). It is clear that, in such a system, only those variations $\delta V^{(1)}$ in which $V^{(1)}$ increases or remains constant need be considered in the criteria for equilibrium. Under these conditions, Eq. (6-70) holds, provided that

$$p^{(2)} \geqslant p^{(1)} \tag{6-72}$$

Thus, a condition for equilibrium between phases 1 and 2, when the volume of 1 cannot decrease, is that the pressure of phase 2 be larger than, or equal to, the pressure of phase 1. This condition is intuitively obvious. If the wall separating 1 and 2 is completely rigid,

$$\delta V^{(1)} = \delta V^{(2)} = 0$$

and Eq. (6-70) is automatically satisfied. Thus, the equilibrium conditions impose no requirements on the relative magnitudes of $p^{(1)}$ and $p^{(2)}$.

The special case where all interphase surfaces are deformable is of particular importance. Here, one has $p^{(1)} = p^{(2)}$, and similarly $p^{(2)} = p^{(3)}$, etc. Thus,

$$p^{(1)} = p^{(2)} = p^{(3)} = \cdots = p^{(\nu)} \tag{6-73}$$

so that the pressure is uniform throughout the equilibrium system. We have also proved here that the pressure of a homogeneous deformable system must be uniform at equilibrium.

We next consider the set of variations

$$\delta V^{(\alpha)} = 0 \qquad \alpha = 1, \ldots, \nu \tag{6-74}$$

$$\delta n_i^{(\alpha)} = 0 \qquad i = 1, \ldots, r, \qquad \alpha = 1, \ldots, \nu \tag{6-75}$$

$$\delta S^{(\alpha)} = 0 \qquad \alpha = 3, \ldots, \nu \tag{6-76}$$

$$\delta S^{(1)} = -\,\delta S^{(2)} \tag{6-77}$$

which satisfy the conditions of Eqs. (6-64) to (6-66). The criterion for equilibrium [Eq. (6-68)] becomes

$$(T^{(1)} - T^{(2)})\,\delta S^{(1)} \geqslant 0 \tag{6-78}$$

If phases 1 and 2 are separated by a heat insulator, then

$$\delta S^{(1)} = \delta S^{(2)} = 0$$

and Eq. (6-78) is satisfied by any temperatures $T^{(1)}$ and $T^{(2)}$. If the wall between the phases were a semiconductor of heat, allowing the variations $\delta S^{(1)} \geqslant 0$, then the condition of equilibrium would be $T^{(1)} \geqslant T^{(2)}$. If all walls are heat-conducting and if all positive and negative variations $\delta S^{(\alpha)}$ are allowed, then

$$T^{(1)} = T^{(2)} = T^{(3)} = \cdots = T^{(\nu)} \tag{6-79}$$

Hence, temperature must be uniform throughout the heterogeneous system at equilibrium. It follows that the temperature of a homogeneous heat-conducting system must be uniform at equilibrium.

Finally, we consider the set of variations

$$\begin{aligned} \delta S^{(\alpha)} &= 0 && \alpha = 1, \ldots, \nu \\ \delta V^{(\alpha)} &= 0 && \alpha = 1, \ldots, \nu \\ \delta n_j^{(\alpha)} &= 0 && j = 1, \ldots, r, \neq i, \quad \alpha = 1, \ldots, \nu \\ \delta n_i^{(\alpha)} &= 0 && \alpha = 3, \ldots, \nu \\ \delta n_i^{(1)} &= -\,\delta n_i^{(2)} \end{aligned} \tag{6-80}$$

which satisfy the conditions of Eqs. (6-64) to (6-66). The criterion for equilibrium [Eq. (6-68)] becomes

$$(\mu_i^{(1)} - \mu_i^{(2)})\, \delta n_i^{(1)} \geqslant 0 \tag{6-81}$$

When phases 1 and 2 are separated by a membrane impermeable to the ith component, or if the ith component is completely absent from phases 1 and 2, then $\delta n_i^{(1)} = 0$, and Eq. (6-81) puts no restriction on $\mu_i^{(1)}$ and $\mu_i^{(2)}$. However, if the ith component appears in phase 2 but not in phase 1, i.e., it is a virtual component of 1, it is possible for $\delta n_i^{(1)}$ to be positive but not negative. Equation (6-81) then requires that

$$\mu_i^{(1)} \geqslant \mu_i^{(2)} \tag{6-82}$$

for equilibrium. When free transport is allowed and i is a real component of all the phases, the equilibrium criterion requires that

$$\mu_i^{(1)} = \mu_i^{(2)} = \mu_i^{(3)} = \cdots = \mu_i^{(\nu)} \tag{6-83}$$

The chemical potential of component i must be uniform throughout all phases. It follows that the chemical potential of component i must be uniform throughout a homogeneous phase in equilibrium.

To summarize, when all interphase surfaces are deformable, permeable to all components, and heat-conducting, a necessary condition for equilibrium is

$$\begin{aligned} p^{(\alpha)} &= p \qquad \text{for all } \alpha \\ T^{(\alpha)} &= T \qquad \text{for all } \alpha \\ \mu_i^{(\alpha)} &= \mu_i \qquad \text{for all } \alpha \text{ and } i \end{aligned} \tag{6-84}$$

Equations (6-84) imply that a homogeneous system that is deformable and heat-conducting, in which all the components may diffuse freely, has uniform pressure, temperature, and chemical potentials of all components at equilibrium.

The conditions expressed in Eqs. (6-84) are necessary conditions for equilibrium. They are also sufficient. This can be demonstrated by substituting Eqs. (6-84) in Eq. (6-68) and making use of Eqs. (6-64) to (6-66) as follows:

$$\begin{aligned} (\delta E)_{S,V,n_i} &= \sum_{\alpha=1}^{\nu} \left(T^{(\alpha)}\,\delta S^{(\alpha)} - p^{(\alpha)}\,\delta V^{(\alpha)} + \sum_{i=1}^{r} \mu_i^{(\alpha)}\,\delta n_i^{(\alpha)}\right) \\ &= T \sum_{\alpha=1}^{\nu} \delta S^{(\alpha)} - p \sum_{\alpha=1}^{\nu} \delta V^{(\alpha)} + \sum_{i=1}^{r} \mu_i \sum_{\alpha=1}^{\nu} \delta n_i^{(\alpha)} \\ &= T\,\delta S - p\,\delta V + \sum_{i=1}^{r} \mu_i\,\delta n_i \\ &= 0 \end{aligned} \tag{6-85}$$

It is clear that, if we had considered only the equality in Eq. (6-68), the above discussion could have been simplified by using the method of Lagrange multipliers.

In a nonequilibrium system in which the temperature is not uniform, heat flow ensues; in a similar manner, nonuniform pressure leads to convective flow; and if, in the system, the chemical potential of component i is not uniform, diffusive transport of this component occurs.

We note that thermodynamics gives no information concerning the existence of phases; it only determines the conditions under which existing phases will be in equilibrium.

6-4. STABILITY

In the previous sections of this chapter we have developed criteria for states of thermodynamic equilibrium in various systems. In this section we shall discuss the stability of equilibrium states and present some conclusions concerning the properties of thermodynamic variables in stable, equilibrium systems.

The criterion of heterogeneous equilibrium for a system of v phases and r real components

$$(\delta E)_{S,V,n_i} = 0 \tag{6-86}$$

implies that, in the consideration of virtual variations for the determination of equilibrium, infinitesimals of higher order than the first are to be neglected. Determination of the stability of the equilibrium, however, requires consideration of higher-order infinitesimals.

In thermodynamic systems, as in mechanical systems, three kinds of equilibrium are distinguished. A thermodynamic system is in stable equilibrium if the condition

$$\Delta E > 0 \tag{6-87}$$

holds for all conceivable variations in state. The quantity ΔE is the change in energy of the system of interest when it passes from the given initial equilibrium state to some neighboring state under the constraints of constant total volume V, entropy S, and number of moles of component i, n_i, $i = 1, \ldots, r$. A thermodynamic system is in neutral equilibrium if the condition

$$\Delta E = 0 \tag{6-88}$$

holds for some variations and the condition $\Delta E > 0$ holds for all other variations. A thermodynamic system is in unstable equilibrium if the condition

$$\Delta E < 0 \tag{6-89}$$

holds for any conceivable variation in state.

Thermodynamic systems may change in either a continuous or a discontinuous fashion. In a continuous change of state all the intensive properties of the system are continuous functions of the independent variables. In a discontinuous change of state, discontinuities appear in some of the intensive properties of the system. Discontinuous changes of state involve the formation of new phases in the system. Equation (6-87) is the necessary and sufficient condition for stable equilibrium with respect to discontinuous changes and continuous changes. Very frequently there are forces within the system which prevent discontinuous changes and the system may be in a metastable state, stable with respect to continuous changes but not with respect to discontinuous changes. (Examples of such metastable states are supercooled or superheated liquids.) Because of microscopic fluctuations, a system in a state of unstable equilibrium, with respect to continuous changes, will remain in equilibrium only for times far shorter than those considered in thermodynamics. In this section we shall be concerned with the conditions for stability with respect to continuous changes. These conditions are necessary, but not sufficient, for absolute stability.

We consider the total energy of a heterogeneous system, E, to be a function of the volumes $V^{(1)}, \ldots, V^{(\nu)}$, the entropies $S^{(1)}, \ldots, S^{(\nu)}$, and the number of moles of component i in the various phases, $n_i^{(1)}, \ldots, n_i^{(\nu)}$, $i = 1, \ldots, r$. Thus we may write

$$E = E(V^{(1)}, \ldots, V^{(\nu)}; S^{(1)}, \ldots, S^{(\nu)}; n_1^{(1)}, \ldots, n_r^{(\nu)})$$

$$= E(y_1, \ldots, y_{(r+2)\nu}) \tag{6-90}$$

The energy of the system is a function of $(r + 2)\nu$ variables that we denote by $y_1, \ldots, y_{(r+2)\nu}$. The difference in energy between states in a continuous change can be expanded in a Taylor's series in the form

$$\Delta E = \delta E + \delta^2 E + \delta^3 E + \cdots \tag{6-91}$$

where

$$\delta E = \sum_{i=1}^{(r+2)\nu} \left(\frac{\partial E}{\partial y_i}\right) \delta y_i \tag{6-92}$$

$$\delta^2 E = \frac{1}{2} \sum_i \sum_k E_{ik}\, \delta y_i\, \delta y_k \tag{6-93}$$

and

$$E_{ik} = \left[\frac{\partial}{\partial y_k}\left(\frac{\partial E}{\partial y_i}\right)_{y_j}\right]_{y_l}$$

where $j = 1, \ldots, (r + 2)\nu, \neq i$ and $l = 1, \ldots, (r + 2)\nu \neq k$. If the system is in stable equilibrium, the quantity ΔE in Eq. (6-91) will satisfy the condition of Eq. (6-87), and the quantity δE in Eq. (6-92) will satisfy the condition expressed in Eq. (6-86). All variations in Eqs. (6-91) are under the restraints

$$\delta S = \sum_{\alpha=1}^{\nu} \delta S^{(\alpha)} = 0$$

$$\delta V = \sum_{\alpha=1}^{\nu} \delta V^{(\alpha)} = 0 \tag{6-94}$$

$$\delta n_i = \sum_{\alpha=1}^{\nu} \delta n_i^{(\alpha)} = 0 \qquad i = 1, \ldots, r$$

In order for the condition $\Delta E > 0$ to be satisfied in a continuous change, the first nonvanishing variation in Eq. (6-91) must be greater than zero. It is easy to show that if

$$\delta E = \delta^2 E = \cdots = \delta^{2n} E = 0 \qquad n = 1, 2, 3, \ldots \tag{6-95}$$

for a given variation, then

$$\delta^{2n+1} E = 0 \tag{6-96}$$

for the same variation from a stable equilibrium state. Conditions (6-87) to (6-89) can be rewritten

Stable equilibrium: $$\delta^2 E > 0 \tag{6-97}$$

Undetermined: $$\delta^2 E = 0 \tag{6-98}$$

Unstable equilibrium: $$\delta^2 E < 0 \tag{6-99}$$

We shall now consider the consequences of Eq. (6-97) and shall later make some remarks about the relation of Eq. (6-98) to critical points.

The quadratic form $\delta^2 E$ is positive for all considerable variations of the parameters, if, and only if, all the roots λ of the equation

$$\begin{vmatrix} E_{11} - \lambda & E_{12} \cdots\cdots & E_{1(r+2)\nu} \\ E_{21} & E_{22} - \lambda \cdots & \cdots\cdots\cdots \\ \cdots\cdots & \cdots\cdots & \cdots\cdots \\ E_{(r+2)\nu 1} & \cdots\cdots & E_{(r+2)\nu(r+2)\nu} - \lambda \end{vmatrix} = 0 \tag{6-100}$$

are greater than zero. The quadratic form is then said to be positive definite.

In order to illustrate the restrictions on the thermodynamic properties of a system that the criterion for stable equilibrium imposes, we shall discuss a homogeneous system of two components. We consider the homogeneous phase to be divided into two portions, 1 and 2. At equilibrium, Eqs. (6-84) demand that

$$\begin{aligned} \mu_i^{(1)} &= \mu_i^{(2)} = \mu_i \qquad i = 1, 2 \\ T^{(1)} &= T^{(2)} = T \\ p^{(1)} &= p^{(2)} = p \end{aligned} \tag{6-101}$$

The total energy of the system, E, is a sum of the energies $E^{(1)}$ and $E^{(2)}$ of the two portions of the system. As in Eq. (6-90), we consider the energy E to be a function of the volumes, entropies, and numbers of moles of the components in the two portions of the system. Thus, we may write

$$\begin{aligned} E &= E(V^{(1)},S^{(1)},n_1{}^{(1)},n_2{}^{(1)};V^{(2)},S^{(2)},n_1{}^{(2)},n_2{}^{(2)}) \\ &= E^{(1)}(V^{(1)},S^{(1)},n_1{}^{(1)},n_2{}^{(1)}) + E^{(2)}(V^{(2)},S^{(2)},n_1{}^{(2)},n_2{}^{(2)}) \\ &= E^{(1)}(y_1{}^{(1)},y_2{}^{(1)},y_3{}^{(1)},y_4{}^{(1)}) + E^{(2)}(y_1{}^{(2)},y_2{}^{(2)},y_3{}^{(2)},y_4{}^{(2)}) \end{aligned} \tag{6-102}$$

The variation $\delta^2 E$ can be written as a sum

$$\delta^2 E = \delta^2 E^{(1)} + \delta^2 E^{(2)} \tag{6-103}$$

where $\delta^2 E^{(1)}$ can be written in the form of Eq. (6-93) as

$$\delta^2 E^{(1)} = \frac{1}{2} \sum_{i=1}^{4} \sum_{k=1}^{4} \left(\frac{\partial^2 E^{(1)}}{\partial y_i^{(1)}\, \partial y_k^{(1)}} \right) \delta y_i^{(1)}\, \delta y_k^{(1)} \tag{6-104}$$

A similar equation holds for $\delta^2 E^{(2)}$, m.m. Remembering that we wish to impose the restraints of Eqs. (6-94), we may write $\delta^2 E$ in the form

$$\delta^2 E = \frac{1}{2} \sum_{i=1}^{4} \sum_{k=1}^{4} \left(\frac{\partial^2 E^{(1)}}{\partial y_i^{(1)}\, \partial y_k^{(1)}} + \frac{\partial^2 E^{(2)}}{\partial y_i^{(2)}\, \partial y_k^{(2)}} \right) \delta y_i^{(1)}\, \delta y_k^{(1)} \tag{6-105}$$

Making use of the relations

$$\begin{aligned} \left(\frac{\partial E^{(1)}}{\partial S^{(1)}} \right)_{V^{(1)}, n_i^{(1)}} &= T \\ \left(\frac{\partial T^{(1)}}{\partial S^{(1)}} \right)_{V^{(1)}, n_i^{(1)}} &= \frac{T^{(1)}}{C_v^{(1)}} \\ \left(\frac{\partial E^{(1)}}{\partial V^{(1)}} \right)_{S^{(1)}, n_i^{(1)}} &= -p^{(1)} \\ \left(\frac{\partial E^{(1)}}{\partial n_1^{(1)}} \right)_{S^{(1)}, V^{(1)}, n_2^{(1)}} &= \mu_1^{(1)} \end{aligned} \tag{6-106}$$

and the conditions (6-101), Eq. (6-105) becomes

$$\begin{aligned} \delta^2 E = \frac{1}{2} \Bigg\{ & T \left(\frac{1}{C_v^{(1)}} + \frac{1}{C_v^{(2)}} \right) (\delta S^{(1)})^2 \\ & + \left[-\left(\frac{\partial p}{\partial V^{(1)}} \right)_{S^{(1)}, n_i^{(1)}} - \left(\frac{\partial p}{\partial V^{(2)}} \right)_{S^{(2)}, n_i^{(2)}} \right] (\delta V^{(1)})^2 \\ & + \left[\left(\frac{\partial \mu_1}{\partial n_1^{(1)}} \right)_{S^{(1)}, V^{(1)}, n_2^{(1)}} + \left(\frac{\partial \mu_1}{\partial n_1^{(2)}} \right)_{S^{(2)}, V^{(2)}, n_2^{(2)}} \right] (\delta n_1^{(1)})^2 \\ & + \cdots \Bigg\} \end{aligned} \tag{6-107}$$

We shall now consider a number of particular variations in order to obtain some necessary conditions for $\delta^2 E$ to be positive definite. First we consider the set of variations for which

$$\begin{aligned} \delta V^{(1)} &= 0 \\ \delta n_1^{(1)} &= 0 \\ \delta n_2^{(1)} &= 0 \end{aligned} \tag{6-108}$$

and $\delta S^{(1)}$ is arbitrary. For these variations, Eq. (6-107) becomes

$$\delta^2 E = T \left(\frac{1}{C_v^{(1)}} + \frac{1}{C_v^{(2)}} \right) (\delta S^{(1)})^2 \tag{6-109}$$

Thus, since $(\delta S^{(1)})^2$ and T must be positive,

$$\frac{1}{C_v^{(1)}} + \frac{1}{C_v^{(2)}} = \frac{1}{n^{(1)}c_v^{(1)}} + \frac{1}{n^{(2)}c_v^{(2)}} > 0 \tag{6-110}$$

is a necessary condition for $\delta^2 E > 0$. In Eq. (6-110), $n^{(1)} = n_1^{(1)} + n_2^{(1)}$ and $c_v^{(1)}$ is the mean molal heat capacity of portion 1. If 1 and 2 are portions of the same homogeneous phase,

$$c_v^{(1)} = c_v^{(2)} = c_v \tag{6-111}$$

and Eq. (6-110) implies that

$$c_v \geqslant 0 \tag{6-112}$$

is a necessary condition for the internal stability of a homogeneous system. We know from experimental results or molecular considerations that c_v is equal to zero only at absolute zero.

We next consider the set of variations for which

$$\delta S^{(1)} = 0 \qquad \delta n_1^{(1)} = 0 \qquad \delta n_2^{(1)} = 0 \tag{6-113}$$

and $\delta V^{(1)}$ is arbitrary. We obtain

$$-\left[\frac{1}{n^{(1)}}\left(\frac{\partial p}{\partial v^{(1)}}\right)_{S^{(1)},n_i^{(1)}} + \frac{1}{n^{(2)}}\left(\frac{\partial p}{\partial v^{(2)}}\right)_{S^{(2)},n_i^{(2)}}\right] > 0 \tag{6-114}$$

as a necessary condition for $\delta^2 E > 0$. Thus

$$\left(\frac{\partial p}{\partial v}\right)_{S,n_i} < 0 \tag{6-115}$$

is a condition for the internal stability of a homogeneous system.

Similarly, for the set of variations

$$\delta S^{(1)} = 0 \qquad \delta V^{(1)} = 0 \qquad \delta n_2^{(1)} = 0 \tag{6-116}$$

$\delta n_1^{(1)}$ arbitrary, we obtain the condition

$$\frac{x_2^{(1)}}{n^{(1)}}\left(\frac{\partial \mu_1^{(1)}}{\partial x_1^{(1)}}\right)_{S^{(1)},V^{(1)},n_2^{(1)}} + \frac{x_2^{(2)}}{n^{(2)}}\left(\frac{\partial \mu_1^{(2)}}{\partial x_1^{(2)}}\right)_{S^{(2)},V^{(2)},n_2^{(2)}} > 0 \tag{6-117}$$

as a necessary condition for $\delta^2 E > 0$. Thus

$$\left(\frac{\partial \mu_1}{\partial x_1}\right)_{S,V,n_2} > 0 \tag{6-118}$$

is a condition for internal stability of a homogeneous system.

Information concerning the restrictions imposed on other thermodynamic functions in stable-equilibrium systems can be obtained by using alternative criteria for stable equilibrium. A sufficient criterion for stable equilibrium that involves the variation of the enthalpy is

$$(\delta H)_{S,p,n_i} = 0 \qquad (\delta^2 H)_{S,p,n_i} > 0 \tag{6-119}$$

Using arguments similar to those above, we can infer that

$$C_p \geqslant 0 \tag{6-120}$$

and

$$\left(\frac{\partial \mu_1}{\partial x_1}\right)_{S,p,n_2} > 0 \tag{6-121}$$

are necessary conditions for Eq. (6-119). A sufficient criterion for stable equilibrium involving the variation of the Helmholtz free energy is

$$(\delta A)_{T,V,n_i} = 0 \qquad (\delta^2 A)_{T,V,n_i} > 0 \tag{6-122}$$

The inequalities

$$\left(\frac{\partial p}{\partial v}\right)_{T,n_i} < 0 \tag{6-123}$$

and

$$\left(\frac{\partial \mu_1}{\partial x_1}\right)_{T,V,n_2} > 0 \tag{6-124}$$

are necessary conditions for Eq. (6-122). A sufficient criterion for stable equilibrium involving the variation of the Gibbs free energy is

$$(\delta F)_{T,p,n_i} = 0 \qquad (\delta^2 F)_{T,p,n_i} > 0 \tag{6-125}$$

The inequality

$$\left(\frac{\partial \mu_1}{\partial x_1}\right)_{T,p,n_2} > 0 \tag{6-126}$$

is a necessary condition for Eq. (6-125). Furthermore, since

$$C_p = C_v + \frac{VT\beta^2}{\kappa} \tag{6-127}$$

where

$$\beta = \frac{1}{V}\left(\frac{\partial V}{\partial T}\right)_p \tag{6-128}$$

and

$$\kappa = -\frac{1}{V}\left(\frac{\partial V}{\partial p}\right)_T > 0 \tag{6-129}$$

the inequality

$$C_p > C_v \tag{6-130}$$

must hold.

We shall now consider the consequences of allowing some of the variations $\delta^2 E$ to be zero. If

$$\left(\frac{\partial p}{\partial v}\right)_{S,n_i} = 0 \tag{6-131}$$

$\delta^2 E = 0$ for the variation (6-113). If $\delta^2 E \geqslant 0$ for the set of variations in which

$$\begin{aligned} \delta n_1{}^{(2)} &= 0 \\ \delta n_2{}^{(2)} &= 0 \end{aligned} \tag{6-132}$$

and $\delta V^{(1)}$ and $\delta S^{(1)}$ are arbitrary, then the relation

$$T\left(\frac{1}{C_v{}^{(1)}} + \frac{1}{C_v{}^{(2)}}\right)(\delta S^{(1)})^2 + \left[\left(\frac{\partial T^{(1)}}{\partial V^{(1)}}\right)_{S^{(1)},n_i{}^{(1)}} + \left(\frac{\partial T^{(2)}}{\partial V^{(2)}}\right)_{S^{(2)},n_i{}^{(2)}}\right]\delta V^{(1)}\,\delta S^{(1)} \geqslant 0 \tag{6-133}$$

must hold. Making use of Eq. (6-100), we find that Eq. (6-133) will be satisfied for arbitrary $\delta V^{(1)}$ and $\delta S^{(1)}$ if, and only if,

$$-\left[\left(\frac{\partial T}{\partial v}\right)_{S,n_i}\right]^2 \geqslant 0 \tag{6-134}$$

Thus, we conclude that

$$\left(\frac{\partial T}{\partial v}\right)_{S,n_i} = 0 \tag{6-135}$$

In a similar manner we find that, if $\delta^2 E \geqslant 0$ for the set of variations in which $\delta S^{(1)} = 0$, $\delta n_2{}^{(1)} = 0$, and $\delta V^{(1)}$ and $\delta n_1{}^{(1)}$ are arbitrary, then

$$\left(\frac{\partial \mu_1}{\partial v}\right)_{S,n_i} = 0 \tag{6-136}$$

Similarly, we find

$$\left(\frac{\partial \mu_2}{\partial v}\right)_{S,n_i} = 0 \tag{6-137}$$

Furthermore, from a consideration of the variation (6-108) for $\delta^3 E$

$$\delta^3 E = \frac{1}{6}\left[\left(\frac{\partial^2 p}{\partial v^{(1)2}}\right)_{S^{(1)},n_i{}^{(1)}} + \left(\frac{\partial^2 p}{\partial v^{(2)2}}\right)_{S^{(2)},n_i{}^{(2)}}\right][\delta(S^{(1)})]^3 \tag{6-138}$$

we conclude that

$$\left(\frac{\partial^2 p}{\partial v^2}\right)_{S,n_i} = 0 \tag{6-139}$$

since $\delta^3 E$ must be equal to zero for all variations for which $\delta^2 E$ is zero. Thus, the conditions for stable equilibrium impose important restrictions on a number of thermodynamic quantities when we allow some of the variations $\delta^2 E$ to be zero. We have demonstrated here that the assumption that

$$\left(\frac{\partial p}{\partial v}\right)_{S,n_i} = 0 \tag{6-140}$$

implies, among other things, that the equations

$$\left(\frac{\partial T}{\partial v}\right)_{S,n_i} = \left(\frac{\partial \mu_1}{\partial v}\right)_{S,n_i} = \left(\frac{\partial \mu_2}{\partial v}\right)_{S,n_i} = \left(\frac{\partial^2 p}{\partial v^2}\right)_{S,n_i} = 0 \qquad (6\text{-}141)$$

must hold.

A condition similar to Eq. (6-140) defines a critical phase. A critical phase is one at which the distinction between two coexistent phases vanishes. It is also at the limit which divides stable from unstable phases. More familiar conditions for a critical phase are the following:

a. For a one-component system,

$$\left(\frac{\partial p}{\partial v}\right)_T = 0 \qquad \left(\frac{\partial^2 p}{\partial v^2}\right)_T = 0 \qquad \left(\frac{\partial^3 p}{\partial v^3}\right)_T \geqslant 0 \qquad (6\text{-}142)$$

defining the vapor-liquid critical point.

b. For a two-component system,

$$\left(\frac{\partial \mu_1}{\partial x_1}\right)_{T,p} = 0 \qquad \left(\frac{\partial^2 \mu_1}{\partial x_1{}^2}\right)_{T,p} = 0 \qquad \left(\frac{\partial^3 \mu_1}{\partial x_1{}^3}\right)_{T,p} \geqslant 0 \qquad (6\text{-}143)$$

It is easy to extend the above discussion to heterogeneous systems. The same conditions, then, govern the internal stability of the homogeneous phases and the stability of the heterogeneous equilibrium.

More detailed treatments of the topics discussed in this section can be found in the following books:

1. Gibbs, J. W.: "Collected Works," pp. 100–135, Longmans, Green & Co., Inc., New York, 1928.
2. Gibbs, J. W.: Commentary on "Collected Works," pp. 146–175, Yale University Press, New Haven, Conn., 1928.
3. Schottky, W.: "Thermodynamik," pp. 447–486, Springer-Verlag, Berlin, Vienna, 1929.
4. Tisza, L.: in "Phase Transformations in Solids," pp. 1–37, John Wiley & Sons, Inc., New York, 1951.

7 THERMODYNAMICS OF GASES

In this chapter we apply many of the general principles enunciated in the previous chapters to a study of the thermodynamic properties of gases. In Sec. 7-1 we discuss the concept of the equation of state and present a number of postulated forms of the equation of state for pure gases. In Sec. 7-2 we make use of the equation of state to calculate the enthalpy and internal energy of a pure gas. In Sec. 7-3 we describe the Joule-Thomson experiment and its use in a process for the liquefaction of gases. Calculations of the entropy and fugacity of pure real gases are presented in Sec. 7-4. In Sec. 7-5 the relation between the heat capacities at constant pressure and at constant volume for pure gases is demonstrated. The calculation of the chemical potential of a pure real gas is given in Sec. 7-6. Finally, in Sec. 7-7, the results of the previous sections are generalized for the treatment of mixtures of real gases.

7-1. THE EQUATION OF STATE

For systems in thermodynamic equilbrium there exists an equation which connects the intensive thermodynamic variables $(T,p,v,x_1, \ldots ,x_{r-1})$. This is called the equation of state. A macroscopic theory like thermodynamics cannot predict this equation, and its form must be determined by experiment or molecular theory. The equation of state may be written in many forms. For a system of r components, it may be implicit

$$\phi(T,p,v,x_1, \ldots ,x_{r-1}) = 0 \tag{7-1}$$

or explicit in any of the variables, such as

$$v = v(T,p,x_1, \ldots ,x_{r-1}) \tag{7-2}$$

or

$$p = p(T,v,x_1, \ldots ,x_{r-1}) \tag{7-3}$$

In a system of one component, Eqs. (7-1) to (7-3) become

$$\phi(T,p,v) = 0 \qquad p = p(T,v) \qquad v = v(p,T) \tag{7-4}$$

Equations (7-4) describe a surface in T-p-v space. This surface in the three-dimensional temperature, pressure, and molar-volume space is a representation of all the experimental or statistical mechanical information concerning the equation of state of the system. It is usually simpler and more useful to present this information in the form of a contour diagram in two dimensions. The projection of the surface on to the plane of two of the three variables T, p, and v gives rise to a number of curves along which the third variable is held fixed. For example, curves of constant temperature (isotherms) are plotted on the p-v plane. In Fig. 7-1, we have plotted a number of isotherms for a typical system. The solid-phase region is not plotted in Fig. 7-1, and we shall omit it from consideration in the subsequent discussion. The curves of Fig. 7-1 describe the equation of state of fluid systems which may exist either as gases or liquids.

Although many of the detailed features of the isotherms appearing in Fig. 7-1 depend on the system under investigation, a number of remarks can be made concerning their general character which apply to all systems so far studied. As was stated in Chap. 1, it is observed experimentally that

$$\lim_{p\to 0} \frac{pv}{RT} = 1 \tag{7-5}$$

for all gases and gas mixtures. Thus, the isotherms in Fig. 7-1 become hyperbolic at low pressures. It is found experimentally that gases undergo a phase transition to a liquid phase along those isotherms with temperature T less than some temperature T_c characteristic of the substance. In the region of the phase transition, p is a continuous function of v but v is a discontinuous function of p at the phase boundary. The dome-shaped region included in the dashed line in Fig. 7-1 is the two-phase region. The temperature T_c is called the critical temperature. Gases cannot be liquefied at temperatures above T_c. The isotherm with temperature T_c exhibits a point of inflection at the critical point.

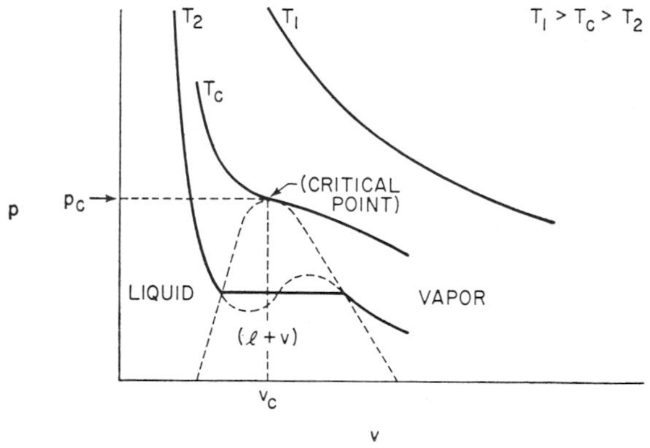

FIG. 7-1. Isotherms in liquid and vapor phases.

The critical point is determined by the relations

$$\left(\frac{\partial p}{\partial v}\right)_{Tc} = 0 \tag{7-6}$$

and

$$\left(\frac{\partial^2 p}{\partial v^2}\right)_{Tc} = 0 \tag{7-7}$$

A brief discussion of the critical point appears in Sec. 6-4.

The distinction between gas and liquid phases is easy to observe along isotherms with $T < T_c$. A discontinuous decrease in molar volume occurs at the transition from gas to liquid. Thus, a common crude distinction can be made by the statement that gases fill whatever container they are in while liquids do not. The distinction between the gas and liquid phase is harder to observe in the following process: The gaseous system is compressed along the isotherm at temperature $T_1 > T_c$ until the pressure p is greater than p_c, the critical pressure; the system is cooled, at constant pressure p, to the temperature $T_2 < T_c$; the system is then allowed to expand along the isotherm at temperature T_2 until the pressure is less than p_c and the system is definitely liquid. No phase transitions occur along this path, and thus there are no singularities in any of the thermodynamic variables.

No analytical expression for the equation of state of real systems, in terms of known functions, has been found. Hence, many approximations have been employed. Many of these apply to the vapor phase but none of them is completely satisfactory. We shall now present some of the approximate equations of state for gases.

Ideal-gas Equation. The simplest form that we can assume for the equation of state of a real gas is

$$p = \frac{RT}{v} \tag{7-8}$$

Equation (7-8) assumes that the low-pressure limit [Eq. (7-5)] applies over the entire range of p and v. No real gas is adequately described by Eq. (7-8) except at low pressures. The system whose equation of state is given by Eq. (7-8) is termed an *ideal gas*. On the molecular level, an ideal gas is one in which there are no interactions between molecules.

Van der Waals Equation. One of the earliest and most famous attempts to describe gaseous behavior was that of van der Waals. The van der Waals equation can be written in the form

$$p = \frac{RT}{v - b_0} - \frac{a_0}{v^2} \tag{7-9}$$

where a_0 and b_0 are constants for each substance. This equation describes condensation in a qualitative manner. In Fig. 7-1, the dashed curve (*a*) is a plot of the van der Waals equation in the liquid-vapor region. E. A. Guggenheim ("Thermodynamics," pp. 129ff., Interscience Publishers, Inc., New York, 1949) has a discussion of the behavior of the van der Waals equation in the two-phase region.

An important feature of the van der Waals equation is that it permits a prediction of a critical point. By applying conditions (7-6) and (7-7) to Eq. (7-9), we obtain the following expressions for the values of v, T, and p, at the critical point:

$$v_c = 3b_0$$
$$T_c = \frac{8a_0}{27Rb_0} \tag{7-10}$$
$$p_c = \frac{a_0}{27{b_0}^2}$$

where the subscript c denotes the critical value of the variable.

There are many modifications of the van der Waals equation such as, for example, those put forth by Dieterici and Berthelot. (Discussions of some of these equations can be found in the text: F. H. MacDougall, "Thermodynamics and Chemistry," 3d ed., chap. 2, John Wiley & Sons, Inc., New York.)

Law of Corresponding States. It is possible to use critical constants as the units of temperature, pressure, and volume. The system may then be described in terms of the reduced variables

$$\tau = \frac{T}{T_c} \qquad \phi = \frac{v}{v_c} \qquad \pi = \frac{p}{p_c} \tag{7-11}$$

where π = reduced pressure
ϕ = reduced volume
τ = reduced temperature

Substituting Eqs. (7-10) and (7-11) into the van der Waals equation, we obtain the reduced van der Waals equation

$$\pi = \frac{8\tau}{3\phi - 1} - \frac{3}{\phi^2} \tag{7-12}$$

which contains no constants characteristic of a particular substance.

Equation (7-12) is a special case of the law of corresponding states which predicts that equations of state of all "normal" substances are the same, if the volume, pressure, and temperature are expressed in terms of their respective values for some unique point in the equation, such as the critical point. Any equation of state which contains two constants characteristic of the gas can be cast into such a form that the law of corresponding states applies.

The law of corresponding states can be deduced by statistical mechanics from certain assumptions concerning the mutual potential of pairs of molecules. It must be remarked, however, that, although the law is approximately valid for chemically saturated nonpolar real gases, it breaks down for polar molecules.

Beattie-Bridgeman Equation. One of the most exact empirical equations of state, useful at high pressures, is that proposed by Beattie and Bridgeman (1928):

$$p = \frac{RT(1 - \mathscr{E})}{v^2}(v + B) - \frac{A}{v^2} \tag{7-13}$$

where $A = A_0(1 - a/v)$
$B = B_0(1 - b/v)$
$\mathscr{E} = c/vT^3$

The five constants, A_0, B_0, a, b, and c, must be evaluated for each gas from experimental data.

Virial Expansion of the Equation of State. The virial expansion of the equation of state of real gases can be derived from molecular theory. From the macroscopic point of view, we assume $\lim_{p \to 0} pv/RT = 1$ and further that pv/RT is an analytic function of p and $1/v$ and therefore can be expanded in power series in these variables. The virial expansion in $1/v$ is

$$\frac{pv}{RT} = 1 + \frac{B}{v} + \frac{C}{v^2} + \cdots \tag{7-14}$$

where the coefficients B, C, . . . , are functions of temperature T and $r - 1$ mole fractions, x_1, . . . , x_{r-1}. The quantity pv is sometimes called the "virial" and the coefficients 1, B, C, . . . , are the virial coefficients; $B(T,x_1, \ldots, x_{r-1})$ is called the second virial coefficient, C the third, etc. The experimental results for equations of state of imperfect gases are sometimes stated by giving tables of values of these coefficients.

Another form of the virial expansion is

$$pv = RT + Bp + C'p^2 + \cdots \tag{7-15}$$

It can be shown by substitution that the second virial coefficient $B(T, x_1, \ldots, x_{r-1})$ is the same in Eqs. (7-14) and (7-15).

The virial expansion converges in the gas phase. Thus, the equation of state of gases can be adequately represented by the virial expansion over the entire range of density and pressure. However, in practice the virial expansion is used only when the first few terms need be kept. At low pressures or densities, the equation of state can be accurately approximated by the two-term virial expansion

$$\frac{pv}{RT} = 1 + \frac{B}{v} \tag{7-16}$$

or

$$pv = RT + Bp \tag{7-17}$$

Any empirical equation of state can be expressed in virial form if desired. The van der Waals equation [Eq. (7-9)] can be expanded in the form

$$\frac{pv}{RT} = 1 + \left(b_0 - \frac{a_0}{RT}\right)\frac{1}{v} + \frac{{b_0}^2}{v^2} + \cdots \tag{7-18}$$

It is clear from Eq. (7-18) that the second virial coefficient for a gas obeying the van der Waals equation is given by

$$B = b_0 - \frac{a_0}{RT} \tag{7-19}$$

This temperature dependence for B, however, is not quite correct.

The Beattie-Bridgeman equation [Eq. (7-13)], on neglecting terms involving a, b, and c, reduces to

$$\frac{pv}{RT} = 1 + \left(B_0 - \frac{A_0}{RT}\right)\frac{1}{v} + \cdots \tag{7-20}$$

which has the same form as the van der Waals equation through the second virial coefficient. The complete Beattie-Bridgeman equation yields a second virial coefficient of the form

$$B = B_0 - \frac{A_0}{RT} - \frac{c}{T^3} \tag{7-21}$$

Equation (7-21) is in closer agreement with experiment than the van der Waals second virial coefficient.

If B is plotted as a function of $1/T$, curves such as those drawn in Fig. 7-2 are obtained. The dashed van der Waals curve is linear, in accordance with Eq. (7-19). A typical experimental curve is also plotted. The form of the experimental curve can be understood on the basis of molecular theory. The initial rise as the temperature decreases is due to the decreasing interpenetration of the molecules. The virial coefficient decreases with decreasing temperature, at lower temperatures, because of the increasing importance of the attractive part of the intermolecular potential. It is possible to apply a linear van der Waals extrapolation to any experimental curve in order to obtain the temperature T_B at which the second virial coefficient is zero. The temperature T_B can also

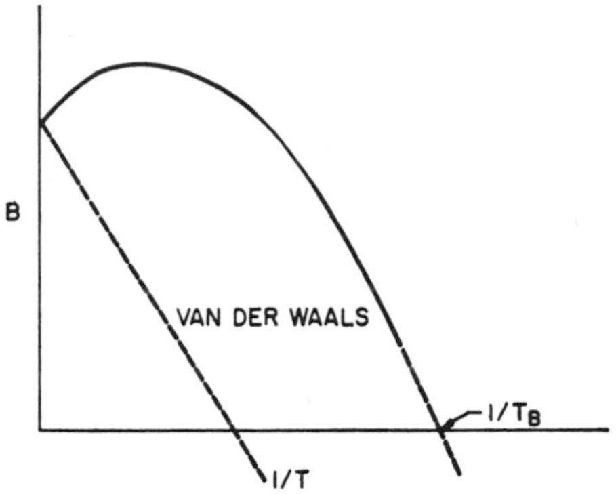

FIG. 7-2. Plot of second virial coefficient B versus $1/T$.

be determined from experimental data on the equation of state. Differentiation of Eq. (7-15) with respect to pressure, at constant T, and taking the limit as the pressure goes to zero yield

$$\lim_{p \to 0} \left(\frac{\partial pv}{\partial p}\right)_T = B(T) \tag{7-22}$$

The temperature T_B at which Eq. (7-22) is zero is called the Boyle point. The term "Boyle point" is used because, at temperatures near T_B, Boyle's law is obeyed over a wider than usual range of values of the pressure.

The Boyle-point temperature for a van der Waals gas is given by

$$T_B = \frac{a_0}{Rb_0} \tag{7-23}$$

from Eq. (7-19). Values of a_0 for hydrogen and helium are low, and the Boyle point for these gases is relatively low in contrast to other gases. In hydrogen, $a_0 = 0.245$ (liter/mole)^2 atm and $b_0 = 2.67 \times 10^{-2}$ liters/mole. Equation (7-23) then predicts a value of 112°K for T_B, which is in good agreement with the experimental value of 106°K. On the other hand, for oxygen, where a_0 and b_0 are 1.32 and 3.12×10^{-2}, respectively, Eq. (7-23) yields the value $T_B = 529$°K which is not in good agreement with the observed value of 423°K.

7-2. ENTHALPY OF A PURE REAL GAS

In this section we make use of the virial expansion of the equation of state in the calculation of the molal enthalpy, $h(T,p)$, of a pure real gas at temperature T and pressure p.

The difference in molal enthalpy between a state at temperature T_1 and pressure p_1 and a state at temperature T_2 and pressure p_2 is given by

$$h(T_2,p_2) - h(T_1,p_1) = \int_{T_1}^{T_2} \left(\frac{\partial h}{\partial T}\right)_{p_1} dT + \int_{p_1}^{p_2} \left(\frac{\partial h}{\partial p}\right)_{T_2} dp \tag{7-24}$$

if the path of integration involves no discontinuities. Thus, the molal enthalpy of a gas can be written in the form

$$h(T,p) = \int^{T} \left(\frac{\partial h}{\partial T'}\right)_0 dT' + \int_0^{p} \left(\frac{\partial h}{\partial p'}\right)_T dp' + h_0 \qquad (7\text{-}25)$$

where

$$\left(\frac{\partial h}{\partial T'}\right)_0 = \lim_{p\to 0} \left(\frac{\partial h}{\partial T'}\right)_p \qquad (7\text{-}26)$$

and h_0, the constant of integration, is a function of the arbitrary lower limit of the temperature integration. In order to evaluate the integrals in Eq. (7-25) it is necessary to establish the existence and the value of $\lim_{p\to 0} (\partial h/\partial T)_p$ and to demonstrate the convergence of the integral over pressure.

Since the heat capacity at constant pressure is given by

$$c_p = \left(\frac{\partial h}{\partial T}\right)_p \qquad (7\text{-}27)$$

we can write

$$\lim_{p\to 0} \left(\frac{\partial h}{\partial T}\right)_p = \lim_{p\to 0} c_p(T,p) = c_p^*(T) \qquad (7\text{-}28)$$

where c_p^* is a function of temperature alone. It can be shown from statistical mechanical considerations that c_p^* can be expressed as a power series in temperature in the form

$$c_p^* = \sum_{j=0}^{\infty} \Gamma_j^* T^j \qquad (7\text{-}92)$$

The coefficients Γ_j^* are determined empirically. Making use of Eqs. (7-25) and (7-28), we find

$$h^*(T) = \lim_{p\to 0} h(T,p) = \int^{T} c_p^* \, dT + h_0 \qquad (7\text{-}30)$$

In order to establish the existence of the quantity $\lim_{p\to 0} (\partial h/\partial p)_T$ and in order to express the integrand in the integral over pressure in Eq. (7-25) in terms of quantities determined by the equation of state of the gas, we make use of the relation (6-27):

$$\left(\frac{\partial h}{\partial p}\right)_T = v - T\left(\frac{\partial v}{\partial T}\right)_p \qquad (7\text{-}31)$$

The virial expansion in powers of the pressure [Eq. (7-15)] can be manipulated to yield

$$v = \frac{RT}{p} + B + O(p) \qquad (7\text{-}32)$$

where the symbol $O(p)$ means terms of order p or higher; i.e.,

$$\lim_{p \to 0} \frac{O(p)}{p} = \text{const} \tag{7-33}$$

Differentiation of Eq. (7-32) with respect to T at constant p yields

$$\left(\frac{\partial v}{\partial T}\right)_p = \frac{R}{p} + \frac{dB}{dT} + O(p) \tag{7-34}$$

since B is a function of T alone for a pure real gas. Substitution of Eqs. (7-32) and (7-34) into Eq. (7-31) results in

$$\left(\frac{\partial h}{\partial p}\right)_T = B - T\frac{dB}{dT} + O(p) \tag{7-35}$$

and

$$\lim_{p \to 0} \left(\frac{\partial h}{\partial p}\right)_T = B - T\frac{dB}{dT} \tag{7-36}$$

Making use of Eqs. (7-25), (7-30), and (7-31), we can write

$$h(T,p) = h^*(T) + \int_0^p \left[v - T\left(\frac{\partial v}{\partial T}\right)_{p'}\right] dp' \tag{7-37}$$

Substitution of Eq. (7-35) in Eq. (7-37) results in

$$\begin{aligned} h(T,p) &= h^*(T) + \int_0^p \left[B - T\frac{dB}{dT} + O(p')\right] dp' \\ &= h^*(T) + \left(B - T\frac{dB}{dT}\right)p + O(p^2) \end{aligned} \tag{7-38}$$

Equation (7-38) is an expression for the enthalpy of a pure real gas that has been evaluated explicitly up to terms proportional to p. Evaluation of the enthalpy thus demands information concerning the dependence of the second virial coefficient on temperature and thermal data on the behavior of the heat capacity at constant pressure in the limit of zero pressure. In addition, there is an undetermined constant of integration. We note that the enthalpy of an ideal gas at T and p is given by $h^*(T)$. Thus the zero-pressure limit of the enthalpy of a pure real gas is the same as the enthalpy of a corresponding ideal gas.

Differentiation of Eq. (7-38) with respect to temperature, at constant p, and use of Eqs. (7-27) and (7-28) and the assumption that the limiting process and the partial differentiation in Eq. (7-28) can be interchanged yield

$$c_p = c_p^* - T\frac{d^2B}{dT^2}p + O(p^2) \tag{7-39}$$

The molal internal energy of the gas can be computed using methods similar to those above. In this case we consider the temperature and molal volume to be the independent variables and write

$$e(T,v) = \int^{T} \left(\frac{\partial e}{\partial T'}\right)_{\infty} dT' - \int_{v}^{\infty} \left(\frac{\partial e}{\partial v'}\right)_{T} dv' + e_0 \tag{7-40}$$

where

$$\left(\frac{\partial e}{\partial T}\right)_{\infty} = \lim_{v \to \infty} \left(\frac{\partial e}{\partial T}\right)_{v} \tag{7-41}$$

Making use of the definitions

$$c_v = \left(\frac{\partial e}{\partial T}\right)_{v} \tag{7-42}$$

$$c_v^* = \lim_{v \to \infty} c_v \tag{7-43}$$

$$e^*(T) = \lim_{v \to \infty} e(T,v) = \int^{T} c_v^* \, dT' + e_0 \tag{7-44}$$

and the relation [Eq. (6-26)]

$$\left(\frac{\partial e}{\partial v}\right)_{T} = T\left(\frac{\partial p}{\partial T}\right)_{v} - p \tag{7-45}$$

we can rewrite Eq. (7-40) in the form

$$e(T,v) = e^*(T) - \int_{v}^{\infty} \left[T\left(\frac{\partial p}{\partial T}\right)_{v'} - p\right] dv' \tag{7-46}$$

The virial expansion in inverse powers of the volume can be manipulated to yield

$$p = \frac{RT}{v} + \frac{RTB}{v^2} + O\left(\frac{1}{v^3}\right) \tag{7-47}$$

Differentiation of Eq. (7-47) with respect to T at constant v results in

$$\left(\frac{\partial p}{\partial T}\right)_{v} = \frac{R}{v} + \frac{RB + RT(dB/dT)}{v^2} + O\left(\frac{1}{v^3}\right) \tag{7-48}$$

Thus, Eq. (7-45) can be written

$$\left(\frac{\partial e}{\partial v}\right)_{T} = \frac{RT^2(dB/dT)}{v^2} + O\left(\frac{1}{v^3}\right) \tag{7-49}$$

and Eq. (7-46) becomes

$$e(T,v) = e^*(T) - \frac{RT^2(dB/dT)}{v} + O\left(\frac{1}{v^2}\right) \tag{7-50}$$

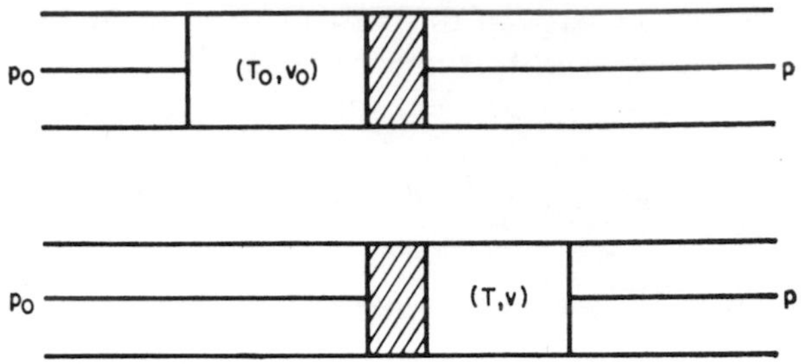

FIG. 7-3. Joule-Thomson experiment.

Equation (7-50) could have been derived directly from Eq. (7-38), making use of the relations

$$e = h + pv \tag{7-51}$$

$$e^* = h^* + RT \tag{7-52}$$

and Eq. (7-47).

7-3. JOULE-THOMSON EXPERIMENT

In this section we discuss an experiment first performed by Joule and Thomson (1853) to measure the quantity

$$\mu_J = \left(\frac{\partial T}{\partial p}\right)_h \tag{7-53}$$

which is called the Joule-Thomson coefficient. This experiment is of particular importance since a common method for the liquefaction of gases is based on its results.

The experiment performed by Joule and Thomson was a "throttling" experiment. One mole of gas is forced through a porous plug by a piston exerting a pressure p_0 against a piston exerting a pressure p, $p_0 > p$, adiabatically and reversibly (Fig. 7-3). Irreversible processes resulting from the existence of a finite pressure difference $p_0 - p$ are assumed to be restricted to the plug. By the first law, the heat absorbed by the gas in this process is given by

$$Q = \Delta E + \int p\, dV = \Delta E + pv - p_0 v_0 \tag{7-54}$$

where

$$\Delta E = e(T,v) - e(T_0,v_0) = e - e_0 \tag{7-55}$$

v is the molal volume in the final state, and v_0 is the molal volume in the initial state. Since the process is adiabatic, the heat absorbed by the system is zero, and Eq. (7-54) becomes

$$e + pv - (e_0 + p_0 v_0) = 0 \tag{7-56}$$

The quantity $e + pv$ is the enthalpy of the gas, and Eq. (7-56) can be rewritten

$$h(T,p) = h(T_0,p_0) \tag{7-57}$$

Thus, the process occurs at constant enthalpy.

Measurements of the temperature change in this process as a function of p, keeping T_0 and p_0 fixed, yield a curve whose slope is the Joule-Thomson coefficient

$$\mu_J = \left(\frac{\partial T}{\partial p}\right)_{h(T_0,p_0)} \tag{7-58}$$

In Fig. 7-4 we have drawn a number of typical experimental curves of T versus p in the throttling experiment. The enthalpy is constant along each of the curves; each of the curves represents a different enthalpy value. The dashed line in Fig. 7-4 is a plot of the inversion temperature T_i; the inversion temperature is the temperature at which

$$\mu_J(T_i,p) = 0 \tag{7-59}$$

For throttling experiments in region a, $\mu_J > 0$ and $T < T_0$; in region b, $\mu_J < 0$, and $T > T_0$.

Defining T_i^* as the inversion temperature at zero pressure, we have

$$\lim_{p\to 0} \mu_J(T_i^*,p) = \mu_J^*(T_i^*) = 0 \tag{7-60}$$

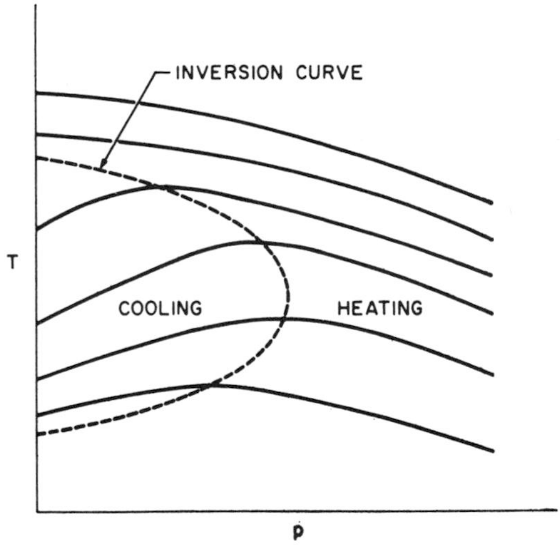

FIG. 7-4. Plot of T versus p along curves at constant enthalpy.

The Joule-Thomson coefficient μ_J can be related to other thermodynamic derivatives by application of the formula of implicit differentiation [Eq. (A-10)]. Thus we may write

$$\mu_J = -\left(\frac{\partial h}{\partial p}\right)_T \left(\frac{\partial T}{\partial h}\right)_p = -\left(\frac{\partial h}{\partial p}\right)_T \frac{1}{c_p} \tag{7-61}$$

Use of Eqs. (7-35) and (7-28) in the zero-pressure limit of Eq. (7-61) yields

$$\mu_J^*(T) = \lim_{p \to 0} \mu_J(T,p) = \frac{T(dB/dT) - B}{c_p^*} \tag{7-62}$$

Thus, T_i^* is determined by the equation

$$T_i^* \left(\frac{dB}{dT}\right)_{T_i*} - B = 0 \tag{7-63}$$

The second virial coefficient of a van der Waals gas is given by

$$B = b_0 - \frac{a_0}{RT} \tag{7-64}$$

and T_i^* becomes

$$T_i^* = \frac{2a_0}{Rb_0} \tag{7-65}$$

Comparison of Eqs. (7-65) and (7-23) yields the conclusion that a van der Waals gas has an inversion temperature equal to two times its Boyle point. It is generally true that $T_i^* > T_B$; however, the ratio T_i^*/T_B varies from gas to gas.

A qualitative molecular interpretation of the inversion temperature may be of interest. For any given temperature, at a high pressure, squeezing molecules together increases their potential energy (repulsive forces are dominant); this means that $(\partial h/\partial p)_T > 0$ and thus, by Eq. (7-61), that $\mu_J < 0$ since $C_p > 0$. At a low pressure, squeezing molecules together decreases their potential energy (attractive forces are important), making $(\partial h/\partial p)_T < 0$ and $\mu_J > 0$.

A method for the liquefaction of gases (see Fig. 7-5) is based on the results of the Joule-Thomson experiment. Gas is fed into the system at (1), expands through the throttle valve, and is allowed to escape through the interchanger in which it comes into thermal contact with entering gas. If the system is set up to provide efficient heat exchange, the unexpanded gas will be in thermal equilibrium with the cooled expanded gas. The gas is sent repeatedly through the system until its temperature is lowered sufficiently for throttling to result in partial liquefaction. A steady state is then reached; each mole of gas entering

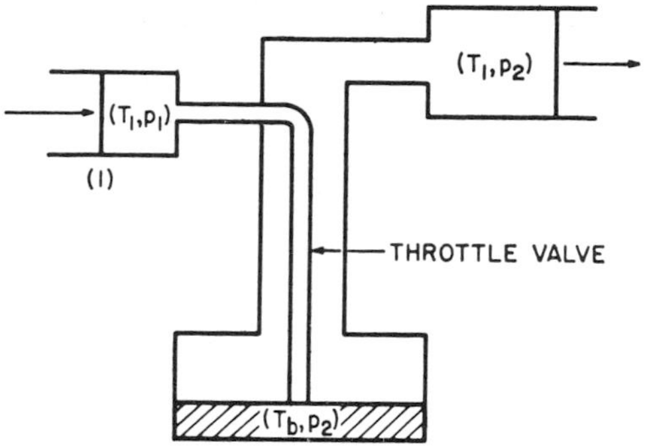

FIG. 7-5. Apparatus for liquefaction of gases.

at T_1, p_1 yields α moles of liquid at T_b, p_2 and $1 - \alpha$ moles of gas at T_1, p_2 (T_b is the boiling-point temperature and $p_2 < p_1$). We wish to determine the efficiency α of the process. In this calculation, we neglect the kinetic energy of flow of the components; i.e., we assume the process to be carried out slowly. Since the Joule-Thomson experiment is carried out adiabatically, $Q = 0$, and the first law becomes

$$\Delta E + W = 0 \tag{7-66}$$

The energy of the system in its initial state e_1 is

$$e_1 = e^g(T_1,p_1) \tag{7-67}$$

where the superscript g refers to the gas phase. The energy of the system after a cycle, e_2, is

$$e_2 = \alpha e^l(T_b,p_2) + (1 - \alpha)e^g(T_1,p_2) \tag{7-68}$$

where the superscript l refers to the liquid phase. The work done by the system W is

$$W = p_1[-v^g(T_1,p_1)] + p_2[\alpha v^l(T_b,p_2) + (1 - \alpha)v^g(T_1,p_2)] \tag{7-69}$$

Substituting Eqs. (7-67), (7-68), and (7-69) into Eq. (7-66) results in

$$\begin{aligned} e_2 - e_1 + W = 0 = e^g(T_1,p_2) - e^g(T_1,p_1) \\ + \alpha[e^l(T_b,p_2) - e^g(T_1,p_2)] + p_2v^g(T_1,p_2) - p_1v^g(T_1,p_1) \\ + \alpha[p_2v^l(T_b,p_2) - p_2v^g(T_1,p_2)] \end{aligned} \tag{7-70}$$

or

$$h^g(T_1,p_2) - h^g(T_1,p_1) + \alpha[h^l(T_b,p_2) - h^g(T_1,p_2)] = 0 \tag{7-71}$$

Equation (7-71) demonstrates that this process is one in which the enthalpy of the system remains constant. Solving Eq. (7-71) for α, we have

$$\alpha = \frac{h^g(T_1,p_2) - h^g(T_1,p_1)}{h^g(T_1,p_2) - h^l(T_b,p_2)} \tag{7-72}$$

The denominator of Eq. (7-72) can be rewritten in the form

$$h^g(T_1,p_2) - h^l(T_b,p_2) = \int_{T_b}^{T_1} c_p^g(T,p_2)\, dT + L_v(T_b,p_2) \tag{7-73}$$

where

$$\int_{T_b}^{T_1} c_p^g\, dT = h^g(T_1,p_2) - h^g(T_b,p_2) \tag{7-74}$$

and

$$L_v(T_b,p_2) = h^g(T_b,p_2) - h^l(T_b,p_2) \tag{7-75}$$

is the molal heat of vaporization at temperature T_b and pressure p_2. Application of Eqs. (7-61) and (7-31) to the numerator of Eq. (7-72) results in

$$\begin{aligned} h^g(T_1,p_2) - h^g(T_1,p_1) &= \int_{p_2}^{p_1} c_p^g(T_1,p)\, \mu_J(T_1,p)\, dp \\ &= \int_{p_2}^{p_1} \left[T_1 \left(\frac{\partial v}{\partial T} \right)_p^g - v^g \right] dp \end{aligned} \tag{7-76}$$

Substitution of Eqs. (7-73) and (7-76) into Eq. (7-72) yields

$$\alpha = \frac{\int_{p_2}^{p_1} \mu_J(T_1,p) c_p^g(T_1,p)\, dp}{L_v(T_b,p_2) + \int_{T_b}^{T_1} c_p^g(T,p_2)\, dT} = \frac{\int_{p_2}^{p_1} [T_1(\partial v/\partial T)_p^g - v^g]\, dp}{L_v + \int_{T_b}^{T_1} c_p^g\, dT} \tag{7-77}$$

If we assume that the pressure p_1 is low and make use of Eq. (7-35), we obtain

$$\alpha = \frac{[T_1(dB/dT) - B(T_1)](p_1 - p_2)}{L_v(T_b,p_2) + \int_{T_b}^{T_1} c_p^g(T,p_2)\, dT} \tag{7-78}$$

which is correct to $O(p_1^2)$. For a van der Waals gas, Eq. (7-78) becomes

$$\alpha = \frac{[(2a_0/RT_1) - b_0](p_1 - p_2)}{L_v + \int_{T_b}^{T_1} c_p^g\, dT} \tag{7-79}$$

The integrals appearing in Eq. (7-77) can be evaluated graphically by use of experimental data and, thus, the efficiency of a liquefaction process can be determined. In order to obtain liquefaction, α must be greater than zero; this means that the integral $\int_{p_2}^{p_1} \mu_J(T_1,p) c_p^g(T_1,p)\, dp$ must be positive since $L_v + \int_{T_b}^{T_1} c_p^g\, dT$ is always greater than zero. Consequently, in order for the Joule-Thomson method to function as a liquefaction process, one must operate at a temperature below T_i^* and at such a pressure that $\mu_J \geqslant 0$. For most substances these requirements do not impose a severe limitation since the inversion temperatures are above room temperature:

Table 7-1

T_i^* *in* °K

CO_2	1500	Air	603
A	723	H_2	195
N_2	621	He	23.6

Helium, however, has $T_i^* = 23.6$°K; thus, its liquefaction by throttling requires precooling with the aid of liquid hydrogen.

Maximum efficiency is attained if p_1 is the pressure corresponding to T_1 along the dashed curve in Fig. 7-4, i.e., if

$$\mu_J(T_1,p_1) = 0 \tag{7-80}$$

This can be seen by differentiating $\alpha(p_1)$ [Eq. (7-77)] with respect to p_1:

$$\left(\frac{\partial \alpha}{\partial p_1}\right)_{T_1} = \frac{c_p{}^g(T_1,p_1)\mu_J(T_1,p_1)}{L_v + \int_{T_b}^{T_1} c_p{}^g\, dT} \tag{7-81}$$

Thus, α is a maximum when

$$\mu_J(T_1,p_1) = 0 \tag{7-82}$$

7-4. ENTROPY AND FUGACITY OF PURE REAL GASES

The difference in entropy per mole between two states characterized by different temperatures and pressures can be written in the form

$$s(T_2,p_2) - s(T_1,p_1) = \int_{p_1}^{p_2} \left(\frac{\partial s}{\partial p}\right)_{T_2} dp + \int_{T_1}^{T_2} \left(\frac{\partial s}{\partial T}\right)_{p_1} dT \tag{7-83}$$

if there are no discontinuities along the path of integration. The integral along the path at constant temperature is evaluated, making use of Eq. (6-25) which states that

$$\left(\frac{\partial s}{\partial p}\right)_T = -\left(\frac{\partial v}{\partial T}\right)_p \tag{7-84}$$

Making use of the virial expansion in powers of p [Eq. (7-15)] we may write

$$\left(\frac{\partial v}{\partial T}\right)_p = \frac{R}{p} + \frac{dB}{dT} + O(p) \tag{7-85}$$

We wish to relate the molal entropy of the gas at temperature T and pressure p to a reference value at zero pressure. It is clear from Eq. (7-85) that $\lim_{p\to 0} (\partial s/\partial p)_T$ diverges. Subtraction of R/p from both sides of Eq. (7-85) yields a quantity which is finite as the pressure tends to zero. Thus,

$$\left(\frac{\partial v}{\partial T}\right)_p - \frac{R}{p} = \frac{dB}{dT} + O(p) \tag{7-86}$$

and

$$\lim_{p\to 0}\left[\left(\frac{\partial v}{\partial T}\right)_p - \frac{R}{p}\right] = \frac{dB}{dT} \tag{7-87}$$

Equations (7-84) and (7-87) demonstrate that the zero-pressure limit of

$$\left(\frac{\partial s}{\partial p}\right)_T + \frac{R}{p} = \left[\frac{\partial(s + R\log p)}{\partial p}\right]_T \tag{7-88}$$

is finite. Integration of Eq. (7-88) along a constant-temperature path yields

$$s(T,p) + R\log p = \int_0^p \left[\frac{R}{p'} - \left(\frac{\partial v}{\partial T}\right)_{p'}\right] dp' + s^*(T) \tag{7-89}$$

where $s^*(T)$, the constant of integration, is given by

$$s^*(T) = \lim_{p\to 0}\,[s(T,p) + R\log p] \tag{7-90}$$

The entropy of a real gas at T and p is thus

$$s(T,p) = s^*(T) + \int_0^p \left[\frac{R}{p'} - \left(\frac{\partial v}{\partial T}\right)_{p'}\right] dp' - R\log p \tag{7-91}$$

We note that equations of the form of Eq. (7-91) must be treated with care since the value of $s^*(T)$ depends on the units chosen for the pressure. Thus, if $s_1^*(T)$ is the value of $s^*(T)$ when p is expressed in atmospheres, $s_2^*(T) = s_1^*(T) + R\log 760$ is the value of $s^*(T)$ when p is expressed in millimeters of Hg.

The mathematical properties of the entropy function are such that we can exchange the differentiation and the limit operation in the equation

$$\frac{ds^*(T)}{dT} = \frac{d}{dT}\lim_{p\to 0}(s + R\log p)$$

$$= \lim_{p\to 0}\left(\frac{\partial s}{\partial T}\right)_p \tag{7-92}$$

It follows from Eqs. (7-92), (6-23), and (7-28) that

$$\frac{ds^*(T)}{dT} = \frac{c_p^*}{T} \tag{7-93}$$

Equation (7-93) can be integrated to yield

$$s^*(T) = \int^T \frac{c_p^*}{T'}\, dT' + s_0 = s_0 + \Gamma_0^* \log T + \Gamma_1^* T + \frac{\Gamma_2^* T^2}{2} + \cdots \tag{7-94}$$

where we have used Eq. (7-29). The quantity s_0 is an entropy constant chosen for some reference temperature; its choice determines the lower limit of the indefinite integral in Eq. (7-94). It can be determined by substituting numerical values from thermochemical data or directly from statistical mechanics.

Substitution of Eq. (7-94) into Eq. (7-91) results in

$$s(T,p) = -R \log p + \int_0^p \left[\frac{R}{p'} - \left(\frac{\partial v}{\partial T}\right)_{p'}\right] dp' + \int^T \frac{c_p^*}{T'}\, dT' + s_0 \tag{7-95}$$

Substitution of the expansion [Eq. (7-86)] into Eq. (7-95) results in

$$s(T,p) = -R \log p + s^*(T) - \frac{dB}{dT}\, p + O(p^2) \tag{7-96}$$

In the zeroth approximation which is valid for very low pressures, Eq. (7-96) becomes

$$s(T,p) = -R \log p + s^*(T) \tag{7-97}$$

Equation (7-97) is the expression for the entropy of an ideal gas for which the equation of state is $v = RT/p$. In the first approximation, terms of order p in the virial expansion of the volume are neglected, and Eq. (7-96) becomes

$$s(T,p) = -R \log p + s^*(T) - \frac{dB}{dT}\, p \tag{7-98}$$

An expression for the molal free energy of a gas at temperature T and pressure p can be simply obtained by making use of the definition

$$f = h - Ts \tag{7-99}$$

and Eqs. (7-30), (7-37), and (7-95). Thus, we may write

$$f(T,p) = RT \log p + \int_0^p \left(v - \frac{RT}{p'}\right) dp' + \int^T \left(1 - \frac{T}{T'}\right) c_p^*(T')\, dT' + h_0 - Ts_0 \tag{7-100}$$

Many formulas for the thermodynamic properties of real gases can be simplified by introducing the concept of fugacity. This quantity was introduced by G. N. Lewis and is defined by the relation

$$p^*(T,p) = p \exp\left[\int_0^p \left(v - \frac{RT}{p'}\right)\frac{dp'}{RT}\right] \tag{7-101}$$

where p^* is the fugacity. Introduction of Eq. (7-101) into Eq. (7-100) results in the simplified expression

$$f = RT \log p^* + \int^T \left(1 - \frac{T}{T'}\right) c_p^*(T')\, dT' + h_0 - Ts_0 \tag{7-102}$$

The fugacity can be determined from the results of equation-of-state measurements of gases. At low pressures its form is particularly simple. It is clear that p^* approaches p as p approaches zero. For an ideal gas, $v = RT/p$ and $p^* = p$. If we retain the term in the virial expansion of v which contains the second virial coefficient, Eq. (7-101) becomes

$$p^* = p \exp\left(\frac{Bp}{RT}\right) \tag{7-103}$$

Expansion of the exponential in Eq. (7-103), retention of terms of order p in the expansion, and comparison with Eq. (7-15) yield

$$\frac{p^*}{p} = 1 + \frac{Bp}{RT} + O(p^2) = \frac{pv}{RT} + O(p^2) \tag{7-104}$$

The pressure of an ideal gas at T and v is

$$p_i = \frac{RT}{v} \tag{7-105}$$

Substitution of Eq. (7-105) into Eq. (7-104) results in

$$p^* = \frac{p^2}{p_i} \tag{7-106}$$

Equation (7-106) is the Lewis and Randall rule for computing the fugacity of a pure real gas. (Further methods of calculation are discussed in Gilbert Newton Lewis and Merle Randall, "Thermodynamics and the Free Energy of Chemical Substances," chap. 17, McGraw-Hill Book Company, Inc., New York, 1923.)

7-5. RELATIONS BETWEEN HEAT CAPACITIES IN PURE REAL GASES

The heat capacities most frequently measured are those at constant pressure and at constant volume. In this section we obtain expressions for the difference and the ratio of these two heat capacities.

The heat capacity at constant pressure is defined by the relation

$$C_p = \left(\frac{đQ}{dT}\right)_p = \left(\frac{\partial E}{\partial T}\right)_p + p\left(\frac{\partial V}{\partial T}\right)_p \tag{7-107}$$

The heat capacity at constant volume is given by

$$C_v = \left(\frac{đQ}{dT}\right)_V = \left(\frac{\partial E}{\partial T}\right)_V \tag{7-108}$$

The total differential of the internal energy in a closed system can be written

$$dE = \left(\frac{\partial E}{\partial T}\right)_V dT + \left(\frac{\partial E}{\partial V}\right)_T dV \tag{7-109}$$

and thus we obtain

$$\left(\frac{\partial E}{\partial T}\right)_p = \left(\frac{\partial E}{\partial T}\right)_V + \left(\frac{\partial E}{\partial V}\right)_T\left(\frac{\partial V}{\partial T}\right)_p \tag{7-110}$$

Subtraction of Eq. (7-108) from Eq. (7-107) and use of Eq. (7-110) result in

$$C_p - C_v = \left[p + \left(\frac{\partial E}{\partial V}\right)_T\right]\left(\frac{\partial V}{\partial T}\right)_p \tag{7-111}$$

Use of Eqs. (6-18) and (6-24) yields

$$p + \left(\frac{\partial E}{\partial V}\right)_T = T\left(\frac{\partial S}{\partial V}\right)_T = T\left(\frac{\partial p}{\partial T}\right)_V \tag{7-112}$$

Equation (7-112) can be rewritten, using the formula for implicit differentiation [Eq. (A-10)], in the form

$$T\left(\frac{\partial p}{\partial T}\right)_V = -T\,\frac{(\partial V/\partial T)_p}{(\partial V/\partial p)_T} \tag{7-113}$$

Finally, in order to express $C_p - C_v$ in terms of frequently measured experimental quantities, we define the coefficient of thermal expansion, β, to be

$$\beta = \frac{1}{V}\left(\frac{\partial V}{\partial T}\right)_p \tag{7-114}$$

and the coefficient of isothermal compressibility, κ_T, to be

$$\kappa_T = -\frac{1}{V}\left(\frac{\partial V}{\partial p}\right)_T \tag{7-115}$$

Substitution of Eqs. (7-112) to (7-115) into Eq. (7-111) results in

$$C_p - C_v = \frac{\beta^2 VT}{\kappa_T} \tag{7-116}$$

As we have shown in Sec. 6-4, κ_T is positive for a system in stable equilibrium and thus $C_p > C_v$ for $T > 0$. In an ideal gas,

$$\beta = \frac{1}{T} \tag{7-117}$$

$$\kappa_T = \frac{1}{p} \tag{7-118}$$

and Eq. (7-116) becomes

$$c_p - c_v = R \tag{7-119}$$

An expression for the ratio c_v/c_p can be easily obtained. We define the coefficient of adiabatic compressibility, κ_s, to be

$$\kappa_s = -\frac{1}{V}\left(\frac{\partial V}{\partial p}\right)_s \tag{7-120}$$

We consider the ratio κ_s/κ_T and make use of Eq. (A-10) to obtain

$$\begin{aligned}\frac{\kappa_s}{\kappa_T} &= \frac{(\partial V/\partial p)_s}{(\partial V/\partial p)_T} \\ &= -\frac{(\partial s/\partial p)_v(\partial V/\partial s)_p}{(\partial V/\partial p)_T} \\ &= \left(\frac{\partial s}{\partial T}\right)_v\left(\frac{\partial T}{\partial s}\right)_p \\ &= \frac{c_v}{c_p}\end{aligned} \tag{7-121}$$

In an ideal gas,

$$\left(\frac{\partial V}{\partial p}\right)_T = -\frac{V}{p} \tag{7-122}$$

and Eq. (7-121) becomes

$$\left(\frac{\partial \log V}{\partial \log p}\right)_s = -\frac{c_v}{c_p} \tag{7-123}$$

Equation (7-123) can be integrated to yield

$$\log p = -\int^V \gamma \, d \log V' + \text{const} \tag{7-124}$$

where

$$\gamma = \frac{c_p}{c_v} \tag{7-125}$$

and the integral is along a constant-entropy path, corresponding to a reversible, adiabatic process. In order to perform the integration in Eq. (7-124) it is necessary to determine the behavior of γ along the isentropic path.

The ideal-gas heat capacities c_p and c_v can be shown to be constant along isothermal paths. This result follows from Eq. (7-45) which yields for an ideal gas

$$\left(\frac{\partial e}{\partial v}\right)_T = \frac{RT}{v} - p = 0 \tag{7-126}$$

Thus, the energy and the enthalpy of an ideal gas

$$h = e + pv = e + RT \tag{7-127}$$

are functions of temperature alone, and the heat capacities c_p and c_v must also be functions of temperature alone. However, c_p and c_v need not be constant along isentropic paths.

It is found by experiment or from statistical mechanics that c_p and c_v will also be independent of temperature for monatomic gases and for other gases at sufficiently high temperatures. Under these conditions, γ is a constant, and Eq. (7-124) can be integrated explicitly to yield

$$pV^{\gamma} = \text{const} \tag{7-128}$$

along an isentropic path. The quantity γ is usually determined experimentally by measuring the speed of sound waves in a gas. The velocity of sound c is related to γ by the expression

$$c^2 = -v^2\left(\frac{\partial p}{\partial v}\right)_s = -v^2\left(\frac{\partial p}{\partial v}\right)_t \gamma$$

7-6. CHEMICAL POTENTIAL OF PURE REAL GASES

In this section we derive an expression for the chemical potential of a pure real gas at temperature T and pressure p. The difference in chemical potentials between states characterized by temperature T_1 and pressure p_1 and by temperature T_2 and pressure p_2 can be written in the form

$$\mu(T_2,p_2) - \mu(T_1,p_1) = \int_{p_1}^{p_2}\left(\frac{\partial \mu}{\partial p}\right)_{T_2} dp + \int_{T_1}^{T_2}\left(\frac{\partial \mu}{\partial T}\right)_{p_1} dT \tag{7-129}$$

We wish to obtain an expression for $\mu(T,p)$ in terms of a properly selected zero-pressure quantity. In order to do this we must investigate the behavior of $(\partial\mu/\partial p)_T$ in the zero-pressure limit. The zero-pressure quantities here, as well as in the preceding sections, are independent of the forces between the gas molecules. In particular, they can be computed from molecular considerations of ideal-gas systems; they may vary from gas to gas since they do depend upon the internal degrees of freedom of the molecules.

Making use of Eq. (6-54), we may write

$$\left(\frac{\partial \mu}{\partial p}\right)_T = v \tag{7-130}$$

Substitution of the virial expansion [Eq. (7-15)] into Eq. (7-130) results in

$$\left(\frac{\partial \mu}{\partial p}\right)_T = \frac{RT}{p} + B(T) + O(p) \tag{7-131}$$

It is clear that Eq. (7-131) diverges in the zero-pressure limit. In order to obtain a convergent quantity, we subtract RT/p from both sides of Eq. (7-131). Since

$$\left(\frac{\partial RT \log p}{\partial p}\right)_T = \frac{RT}{p} \tag{7-132}$$

we can rewrite Eq. (7-130) in the form

$$\left[\frac{\partial(\mu - RT \log p)}{\partial p}\right]_T = v - \frac{RT}{p} \tag{7-133}$$

Integration of Eq. (7-133) along a constant-temperature path yields

$$\mu(T,p) = RT \log p + \int_0^p \left(v - \frac{RT}{p'}\right) dp' + \mu^*(T) \tag{7-134}$$

where
$$\mu^*(T) = \lim_{p \to 0} (\mu - RT \log p) \tag{7-135}$$

As in the expression for the free energy of a pure gas, we make a purely notational change and write

$$\mu(T,p) = \mu^*(T) + RT \log p^* \tag{7-136}$$

for Eq. (7-134), where p^*, the fugacity of the gas at T and p, is defined by Eq. (7-101). It is clear from Eq. (7-136) that $\mu^*(T)$ is the chemical potential of the gas at unit fugacity.

We now investigate approximations to Eq. (7-136) which retain successively higher powers of the pressure. For an ideal gas, $p = p^*$, and Eq. (7-136) reduces to

$$\mu = RT \log p + \mu^*(T) \tag{7-137}$$

Equation (7-137) is often accurate for real gases at low pressures. In the next approximation, terms $O(p)$ or higher in the virial expansion are neglected,

$$v = \frac{RT}{p} + B(T)$$

$$p^* = pe^{Bp/RT} \tag{7-138}$$

and Eq. (7-136) becomes

$$\mu = RT \log p + Bp + \mu^*(T) \tag{7-139}$$

Above the Boyle point (Sec. 7-1), B is positive and $p^*/p > 1$; below the Boyle point, B is negative and $p^*/p < 1$. As an example of the magnitude of this ratio, nitrogen gas near 300°K has $B \simeq 50$ cc/mole, so that $e^{Bp/RT} \simeq e^{p/500}$, where p is expressed in atmospheres. This correction becomes important only at relatively high pressures.

It may be remarked that the law of mass action as it is usually formulated depends upon the validity of the approximation of Eq. (7-137).

We next turn our attention to a study of the relations between the constants of integration occurring in Eqs. (7-37), (7-89), and (7-134). By comparing Eqs. (7-100) and (7-134) and noting that, in a one-component system, $\mu = f$, we see that

$$\mu^*(T) = \int^T \left(1 - \frac{T}{T'}\right) c_p^*(T')\, dT' + h_0 - Ts_0 \tag{7-140}$$

Making use of the expressions for s^* [Eq. (7-94)] and h^* [Eq. (7-30)], Eq. (7-140) can be rewritten

$$\mu^*(T) = h^*(T) - Ts^*(T) \tag{7-141}$$

An alternative expression for $\mu^*(T)$ can be obtained by noting that

$$\left(\frac{\partial \mu}{\partial T}\right)_p = -s \tag{6-53}$$

$$\mu = h - Ts \tag{7-99}$$

and thus

$$\left(\frac{\partial \mu/T}{\partial T}\right)_p = -\frac{1}{T}\left(\frac{\mu}{T} + s\right) = -\frac{h}{T^2} \tag{7-142}$$

Therefore

$$\lim_{p\to 0} \left\{\frac{\partial[(\mu - RT \log p)/T]}{\partial T}\right\}_p = -\frac{h^*}{T^2} \tag{7-143}$$

Taking the limit under the derivative sign and making use of Eq. (7-135), we find

$$\left[\frac{\partial(\mu^*/T)}{\partial T}\right]_p = -\frac{h^*}{T^2} \tag{7-144}$$

and

$$\frac{\mu^*}{T} = -\int^T \frac{h^*(T)}{T^2}\, dT - I \tag{7-145}$$

where I is a constant of integration which depends on the lower limit of integration. The value of the integration constant I can be simply determined. Substitution of Eq. (7-29) into Eq. (7-30) results in

$$h^*(T) = h_0 + \Gamma_0^* T + \cdots + \frac{\Gamma_n^* T^{n+1}}{n+1} + \cdots \tag{7-146}$$

Insertion of Eq. (7-146) into Eq. (7-145) yields

$$\mu^*(T) = h_0 - IT - T\Gamma_0^* \log T - \cdots - \frac{\Gamma_n^* T^{n+1}}{(n+1)n} - \cdots \tag{7-147}$$

Making use of Eqs. (7-94), (7-146), (7-147), and (7-141), we find

$$\begin{aligned} \mu^* - h^* + Ts^* &= 0 \\ &= T(-I - \Gamma_0^* + s_0) \end{aligned} \tag{7-148}$$

Thus, the integration constant I is given by

$$I = s_0 - \Gamma_0^* \tag{7-149}$$

The quantity $\mu^*(T)$ can be determined from thermochemical data which determine the value of the Γ_i, $i = 0, 1, 2, \ldots$, from the third law which determines s_0 and therefore I, and finally from the arbitrary constant h_0. Nernst called I the "thermochemical constant."

7-7. MIXTURES OF REAL GASES

In this section we shall extend some of the results of the previous section to mixtures of real gases.

We shall consider a homogeneous gas phase of r components and $r + 1$ degrees of freedom $(x_1, \ldots, x_{r-1}, p, T)$. In order to compute the chemical potential of component i in the mixture, the notion of the partial pressure of component i will be introduced. The partial pressure of component i in the mixture, p_i, is defined as the pressure exerted by pure i in equilibrium with the mixture through a membrane permeable to i alone.

The conditions for equilibrium between phase A which is the gas mixture under consideration and phase B which consists of pure gas i are

$$\mu_i{}^A = \mu_i{}^B = \mu_i \tag{7-150}$$

$$T^A = T^B = T \tag{7-151}$$

Equations (7-150) and (7-151) are special cases of the conditions of heterogeneous equilibrium, discussed in Sec. 6-3, for phases which are connected by walls that are heat-conducting, permeable to component

, and nondeformable. Therefore, p_i is the pressure that pure i would exert when its chemical potential is the same as the chemical potential of i in the gas mixture. The chemical potential of component i in phase B can be written, using Eqs. (7-136) and (7-101), in the form

$$\mu_i^B(T,p_i) = \mu_i^*(T) + RT \log p_i^{\circ *} \tag{7-152}$$

where $p_i^{\circ *}$, the fugacity of pure i, is

$$p_i^{\circ *}(T,p_i) = p_i \exp \left[\int_0^{p_i} \frac{(v_i - RT/p')\,dp'}{RT} \right] \tag{7-153}$$

and

$$\lim_{p_i \to 0} \frac{p_i^{\circ *}}{p_i} = 1 \tag{7-154}$$

The quantity $v_i(p')$ is the molar volume of pure component i at temperature T and pressure p'.

We now define the fugacity of component i in the mixture by the equation

$$\mu_i^A = \mu_i = \mu_i^*(T) + RT \log p_i^* \tag{7-155}$$

Thus

$$p_i^* = p_i^{\circ *} = p_i \exp \left[\int_0^{p_i} \frac{(v_i - RT/p')\,dp'}{RT} \right] \tag{7-156}$$

and

$$\lim_{p_i \to 0} \frac{p_i^*}{p_i} = 1 \tag{7-157}$$

Equations (7-156) and (7-155) are explicit expressions for p_i^* and μ_i, respectively, as functions of p_i, T, and $v_i(p_i,T)$. We shall now derive an expression for p_i^* giving its explicit dependence on the experimentally measured quantities p, T, x_i, and $\bar{v}_i(x_1, \ldots, x_{r-1}, p, T)$.

Making use of Eqs. (6-54) and (7-155), we may write

$$\left(\frac{\partial \mu_i}{\partial p}\right)_{T,x_i} = \bar{v}_i = RT \left(\frac{\partial \log p_i^*}{\partial p}\right)_{T,x_i} \tag{7-158}$$

where the subscript x_i implies that the mole fractions of all the components reman fiixed. Since

$$RT \left[\frac{\partial \log (px_i)}{\partial p}\right]_{T,x_i} = \frac{RT}{p} \tag{7-159}$$

Eq. (7-158) can be rewritten as

$$RT \left[\frac{\partial \log (p_i^*/px_i)}{\partial p}\right]_{T,x_i} = \bar{v}_i - \frac{RT}{p} \tag{7-160}$$

Integration of Eq. (7-160) along a path of constant temperature and composition yields

$$\log \frac{p_i^*}{px_i} = \frac{1}{RT}\int_0^p \left(\bar{v}_i - \frac{RT}{p'}\right) dp' + \lim_{p\to 0} \log \frac{p_i^*}{px_i} \tag{7-161}$$

The integral in Eq. (7-161) exists because at low enough pressures all real-gas systems behave as ideal gases; that is $\lim_{p\to 0} p\bar{v}_i/RT = 1$.

In order to evaluate the limit in Eq. (7-161) we must use the Gibbs-Dalton law which states that

$$\lim_{p\to 0} \frac{p_i}{px_i} = 1 \tag{7-162}$$

Equation (7-162) implies that p_i approaches zero as p approaches zero and thus the limits in Eqs. (7-154) and (7-157) may be taken as p approaches zero. The Gibbs-Dalton law is an empirical law that cannot be obtained from the general formalism of thermodynamics; it is an additional piece of information. Equation (7-162) follows from Dalton's law and the fact that real-gas mixtures behave like ideal-gas mixtures in the zero-pressure limit. Dalton's law states that, for an ideal-gas mixture, the following equations hold:

$$p = \sum_{i=1}^{r} p_i \tag{7-163}$$

and

$$p_i = \frac{n_i RT}{V} = x_i p \tag{7-164}$$

Making use of Eqs. (7-162) and (7-157), we can write

$$\lim_{p\to 0} \frac{p_i^*}{px_i} = \lim_{p\to 0} \frac{p_i}{px_i} \lim_{p\to 0} \frac{p_i^*}{p_i} = 1 \tag{7-165}$$

Equations (7-161) and (7-155) may now be written

$$p_i^* = px_i \exp\left[\int_0^p \frac{(\bar{v}_i - RT/p')\,dp'}{RT}\right] \tag{7-166}$$

and

$$\mu_i = \mu_i^*(T) + RT\log(px_i) + \int_0^p \left(\bar{v}_i - \frac{RT}{p'}\right) dp' \tag{7-167}$$

Hence, $\mu_i^*(T)$ may be written in the form

$$\mu_i^*(T) = \lim_{p\to 0} [\mu_i - RT\log(px_i)] \tag{7-168}$$

where the limit is taken at constant composition and temperature.

In the zeroth approximation which corresponds to an ideal-gas mixture,

$$\bar{v}_i = \frac{RT}{p} \tag{7-169}$$

and Eq. (7-167) becomes

$$\mu_i(T,p,x_i) = \mu_i^*(T) + RT \log (px_i) \tag{7-170}$$

Comparison of Eqs. (7-170) and Eq. (7-152) yields the result

$$p_i = px_i \tag{7-171}$$

which is an expression of Dalton's law [Eq. (7-164)].

More generally, the mean molal volume of the gas mixture can be expanded in a power series in the pressure p. The virial expansion for v, the mean molal volume of a mixture, is given by

$$v = \frac{RT}{p} + B(x_1, \ . \ . \ . \ ,x_{r-1},T) + O(p) \tag{7-172}$$

where the second virial coefficient $B(x,T)$ is determined by statistical mechanics to be a quadratic function of the mole fractions in the form

$$B(x,T) = \sum_{l,m=1}^{r} B_{lm}(T)x_l x_m \tag{7-173}$$

The quantity $B_{lm}(T)$ is a function of temperature alone and has the property

$$B_{lm}(T) = B_{ml}(T) \tag{7-174}$$

The total volume of the system can be written

$$V = \sum_{k=1}^{r} n_k v = \sum_{k=1}^{r} n_k \frac{RT}{p} + \frac{\sum_{l,m=1}^{r} n_l n_m B_{lm}(T)}{\sum_{k=1}^{r} n_k} + O(p) \tag{7-175}$$

The partial molal volume of component i has the form

$$\bar{v}_i = \left(\frac{\partial V}{\partial n_i}\right)_{T,p,n_{j\neq i}} = \frac{RT}{p} - \frac{\sum_{l,m=1}^{r} n_l n_m B_{lm}(T)}{\left(\sum_{k=1}^{r} n_k\right)^2} + \frac{2\sum_{l=1}^{r} n_l B_{il}(T)}{\sum_k n_k} + O(p) \tag{7-176}$$

where we have used Eq. (7-174). Equation (7-176) can be rewritten to yield

$$\begin{aligned} \bar{v}_i &= \frac{RT}{p} + 2\sum_{l=1}^{r} x_l B_{il} - \sum_{l,m=1}^{r} x_l x_m B_{lm} + O(p) \\ &= \frac{RT}{p} + \sum_{l,m=1}^{r} x_l x_m (2B_{il} - B_{lm}) + O(p) \end{aligned} \tag{7-177}$$

Substituting this expression for $\bar{v}_i$ in Eqs. (7-166) and (7-167), we obtain

$$p_i^* = px_i \exp\left[\frac{\sum_{l,m=1}^{r} x_l x_m (2B_{il} - B_{lm})p}{RT} + O(p^2)\right] \tag{7-178}$$

and

$$\mu_i = \mu_i^*(T) + RT\log(px_i) + \sum_{l,m}^{r} x_l x_m (2B_{il} - B_{lm})p + O(p^2) \tag{7-179}$$

The coefficients $B_{il}(T)$ are functions of temperature and depend on the type of molecular interaction between species i and l. They can be determined from molecular theory or by experiments on gas mixtures. If only pure-gas data are available, we may assume B_{lm} to be of the form

$$B_{lm} = \frac{B_{ll} + B_{mm}}{2} \tag{7-180}$$

where B_{ll} is the second virial coefficient of pure gas l. A better approximation for the second virial coefficient may be obtained by use of the van der Waals expression

$$B_{lm} = b_{lm} - \frac{a_{lm}}{RT} \tag{7-181}$$

and the assumptions that

$$b_{lm} = \frac{b_{ll} + b_{mm}}{2} \tag{7-182}$$

and

$$a_{lm} = (a_{ll}a_{mm})^{\frac{1}{2}} \tag{7-183}$$

Lewis and Randall have proposed an approximate empirical rule for computing the fugacity of component i in a mixture in the form

$$p_i^* = x_i p_i^{\circ *}(T,p) \tag{7-184}$$

where $p_i^{\circ *}$ is the fugacity of pure component i at the same T and p as that of the mixture. This rule is a direct consequence of the assumption that B_{lm} can be represented by Eq. (7-180). Making use of Eq. (7-180), we can write

$$2B_{il} - B_{lm} = B_{ii} + \tfrac{1}{2}B_{ll} - \tfrac{1}{2}B_{mm} \tag{7-185}$$

and

$$\sum_{l,m=1}^{r} x_l x_m (B_{ii} + \tfrac{1}{2}B_{ll} - \tfrac{1}{2}B_{mm}) = B_{ii} \tag{7-186}$$

Substitution of Eq. (7-186) into Eq. (7-178) results in

$$p_i^* = px_i \exp\left[\frac{B_{ii}p}{RT} + O(p^2)\right] \tag{7-187}$$

Comparison of Eq. (7-187) with Eq. (7-103),

$$p_i^{\circ *} = p \exp \left[\frac{B_{ii} p}{RT} + O(p^2) \right] \tag{7-188}$$

yields

$$p_i^*(T,p,x_i) = x_i p_i^{\circ *}(T,p) \tag{7-189}$$

The Lewis and Randall rule is found to be applicable outside the range for which Eq. (7-180) is valid.

The entropy of a mixture of real gases is readily determined by making use of Eq. (7-167) and the relation

$$\bar{s}_i = -\left(\frac{\partial \mu_i}{\partial T}\right)_{p,x_i} \tag{7-190}$$

where the subscript x_i implies that the mole fractions of all components are held fixed. The partial molal entropy of component i can be written

$$\bar{s}_i = s_i^*(T) - R \log x_i - R \log p - \int_0^p \left[\left(\frac{\partial \bar{v}_i}{\partial T}\right)_{p',x_i} - \frac{R}{p'} \right] dp' \tag{7-191}$$

where

$$s_i^*(T) = \lim_{p \to 0} \left[\bar{s}_i + R \log (p x_i) \right] = -\frac{d\mu_i^*(T)}{dT} \tag{7-192}$$

The molal entropy of pure real gas i is given by Eq. (7-91) in the form

$$s_i = s_i^*(T) - R \log p - \int_0^p \left[\left(\frac{\partial v_i}{\partial T}\right)_{p'} - \frac{R}{p'} \right] dp' \tag{7-193}$$

Thus, the molal entropy of mixing of component i is

$$\bar{s}_i - s_i = -R \log x_i + \int_0^p \left[\left(\frac{\partial v_i}{\partial T}\right)_{p'} - \left(\frac{\partial \bar{v}_i}{\partial T}\right)_{p',x_i} \right] dp' \tag{7-194}$$

and the entropy of mixing of real gases at constant T, p is

$$\Delta S = \sum_{i=1}^{r} n_i(\bar{s}_i - s_i) = -R \sum_{i=1}^{r} n_i \log x_i + \sum_i n_i \int_0^p \left[\left(\frac{\partial v_i}{\partial T}\right)_{p'} - \left(\frac{\partial \bar{v}_i}{\partial T}\right)_{p',x_i} \right] dp' \tag{7-195}$$

where n_i is the number of moles of component i in the real-gas mixture.

In the ideal-gas approximation,

$$\left(\frac{\partial v_i}{\partial T}\right)_p = \left(\frac{\partial \bar{v}_i}{\partial T}\right)_{p,x_i} \tag{7-196}$$

and Eq. (7-195) reduces to

$$\Delta S = -R \sum_{i=1}^{r} n_i \log x_i \tag{7-197}$$

There has been a great deal of discussion concerning the physical significance of Eqs. (7-195) and (7-197). The physical basis for these equations, although hinted at, was not properly understood until the advent of quantum mechanics. Consider two pure gases 1 and 2, both at temperature T and pressure p. Equation (7-195) provides an expression for the entropy change associated with mixing these gases. Assume that the gases are so similar that no experimental distinction can be drawn between them. In this case, Eq. (7-196) applies, and Eq. (7-195) reduces to Eq. (7-197). Now assume that the gases 1 and 2 are, in fact, identical. In this case, $x_1 = 1$, and Eq. (7-197) yields the expected result that the entropy of mixing is zero. Before the advent of quantum mechanics, it was difficult to understand why the entropy of mixing should exhibit a discontinuous change between the situation in which identical gases are mixed, $\Delta S = 0$, and the situation in which gases, which are so similar that no experimental distinction between the thermodynamic properties of the pure gases can be made, are mixed, $\Delta S = -R[n_1 \log x_1 + n_2 \log (1 - x_1)]$. The difference in these situations arises from the fact that molecules of the same species are indistinguishable; molecules of different species, even though extremely similar, differ from each other by having different numbers of neutrons or protons and electrons and are therefore distinguishable in principle.

The enthalpy change associated with the process of mixing systems of pure gases of species i at the same temperature T and pressure p to form a mixture at T and p can be computed, using the expression

$$\bar{h}_i = \mu_i + T\bar{s}_i \tag{7-198}$$

for the partial molal enthalpy of component i in the mixture and Eqs. (7-167) and (7-191). The quantity $\bar{h}_i$ can be written in the form

$$\bar{h}_i = h_i^*(T) + \int_0^p \left[\bar{v}_i - T\left(\frac{\partial \bar{v}_i}{\partial T}\right)_{p',x_i}\right] dp' \tag{7-199}$$

where

$$h_i^*(T) = \mu_i^* + Ts_i^* \tag{7-200}$$

The enthalpy of pure real gas i is given by Eq. (7-37) in the form

$$h_i = h_i^*(T) + \int_0^p \left[v_i - T\left(\frac{\partial v_i}{\partial T}\right)_{p'}\right] dp' \tag{7-201}$$

Combination of Eqs. (7-201) and (7-199) results in

$$\bar{h}_i = h_i + \int_0^p \left[\Delta\bar{v}_i - T\left(\frac{\partial\, \Delta\bar{v}_i}{\partial T}\right)_{p',x_i}\right] dp' \tag{7-202}$$

where

$$\Delta\bar{v}_i = \bar{v}_i - v_i \tag{7-203}$$

The heat of solution is defined as

$$\Delta H = \sum_{i=1}^{r} n_i(\bar{h}_i - h_i) \tag{7-204}$$

and thus is given by

$$\begin{aligned} \Delta H &= \sum_{i=1}^{r} n_i \int_0^p \left[\Delta \bar{v}_i - T\left(\frac{\partial\, \Delta \bar{v}_i}{\partial T}\right)_{p',x_i}\right] dp' \\ &= \int_0^p \left[\Delta V - T\left(\frac{\partial\, \Delta V}{\partial T}\right)_{p',x_i}\right] dp' \end{aligned} \tag{7-205}$$

where
$$\Delta V = \sum_{i=1}^{r} n_i\, \Delta \bar{v}_i \tag{7-206}$$

is the volume change on mixing. In the ideal-gas case, $\Delta V = 0$ and $\Delta H = 0$.

This completes our discussion of the thermodynamic properties of real-gas mixtures.

8 CHEMICAL EQUILIBRIUM

In this chapter we apply the general criteria for equilibrium developed in Chap. 6 to systems in which chemical reactions may occur. In Sec. 8-1, we present a general discussion of chemical equilibrium in homogeneous and heterogeneous systems. The concept of a progress variable is introduced, and the conditions for chemical equilibrium are derived. The equilibrium constant is defined, and some of its properties are developed. A discussion of the Le Châtelier-Braun principle applied to chemical reactions is presented. In Sec. 8-2, the results of Sec. 8-1 are applied to chemical reactions in mixtures of real gases.

8-1. GENERAL DISCUSSION

The application of the general criteria for equilibrium to systems in which chemical reactions may occur involves the ability to freeze the chemical reactions at any desired point. Thus, a system containing r substances which may undergo a chemical reaction must be considered to be made up of r independent components. At equilibrium, of course, the number of moles of any component is determined by specifying the numbers of moles of the $r-1$ other components and the values of the other pertinent thermodynamic parameters.

We shall first consider a closed, homogeneous system in which a single chemical reaction occurs. Using the notation of Sec. 3-5, we may write the expression of a general chemical reaction involving r chemical substances in the form

$$\sum_{i=1}^{r} \nu_i X_i = 0 \tag{8-1}$$

The differential increments dn_i in the number of moles of component i, n_i, $i = 1, \ldots, r$, produced by the reaction of Eq. (8-1) are related to each other and to the increment in the progress variable by the relation

$$\frac{dn_1}{\nu_1} = \frac{dn_2}{\nu_2} = \cdots = \frac{dn_r}{\nu_r} = d\lambda \tag{8-2}$$

where λ is the progress variable of the reaction. It is assumed that $d\lambda$ is uniform throughout the one-phase system. If this were not so, gradients of composition and therefore diffusion currents would result.

A criterion of equilibrium under the restraint of closure is

$$(\delta E)_{S,V} \geqslant 0 \tag{8-3}$$

In a closed system in which the masses of the components are changed,

$$dE = T\,dS - p\,dV + \sum_{i=1}^{r} \mu_i\,dn_i \tag{8-4}$$

Thus the variation in the internal energy at constant entropy and volume is given by

$$(\delta E)_{S,V} = \sum_{i=1}^{r} \mu_i\,\delta n_i = \sum_{i=1}^{r} \nu_i \mu_i\,\delta\lambda \tag{8-5}$$

since

$$\delta n_i = \nu_i\,\delta\lambda \tag{8-6}$$

by Eq. (8-2). The equilibrium criterion [Eq. (8-3)] can be written in the form

$$(\delta E)_{S,V} = \Big(\sum_{i=1}^{r} \nu_i \mu_i\Big)\,\delta\lambda \geqslant 0 \tag{8-7}$$

Equation (8-7) must hold for all conceivable variations of the progress variable. If $\delta\lambda > 0$, Eq. (8-7) demands that

$$\sum_{i=1}^{r} \nu_i \mu_i \geqslant 0 \tag{8-8}$$

for equilibrium. If $\delta\lambda < 0$, Eq. (8-7) demands that

$$\sum_{i=1}^{r} \nu_i \mu_i \leqslant 0 \tag{8-9}$$

for equilibrium. Since we have assumed that we can freeze the reaction at any stage, we can vary the progress variable at will and thus $\delta\lambda$ can be either positive or negative when all r substances are present in the reaction mixture. Equations (8-8) and (8-9) must be simultaneously valid, which can only be true if

$$\sum_{i=1}^{r} \nu_i \mu_i = 0 \tag{8-10}$$

Equation (8-10) is the criterion for equilibrium in the system containing r chemically reacting substances. If no products of the reaction are present, $\delta\lambda \geqslant 0$ only and the criterion for equilibrium becomes

$$\sum_{i} \nu_i \mu_i \geqslant 0 \tag{8-11}$$

If no reactants are present, $\delta\lambda \leqslant 0$, and the criterion for equilibrium becomes

$$\sum_{i} \nu_i \mu_i \leqslant 0 \tag{8-12}$$

We now consider a closed homogeneous system in which several reactions may occur. We consider a set of s reactions

$$\sum_{i=1}^{r} \nu_i^{\sigma} X_i = 0 \qquad \sigma = 1, \ldots, s \tag{8-13}$$

Each of the reactions is characterized by a progress variable λ_σ, $\sigma = 1, \ldots, s$. The total change in the number of moles of component i due to the s reactions can be written in the form

$$dn_i = \sum_{\sigma=1}^{s} \nu_i^{\sigma}\, d\lambda_\sigma \tag{8-14}$$

Substitution of Eq. (8-14) into Eq. (8-5) yields

$$\sum_{\sigma=1}^{s} \left(\sum_{i=1}^{r} \nu_i^{\sigma}\mu_i\right) d\lambda_\sigma \geqslant 0 \tag{8-15}$$

as the criterion for equilibrium. We assume that we can freeze the progress of each reaction at any point. For example, we can choose the set of variations for which $\delta\lambda_\sigma = 0$, $\sigma = 2, \ldots, s$, and $\delta\lambda_1$ is arbitrary. The criterion for equilibrium for this set of variations is

$$\sum_{i=1}^{r} \nu_i^{1}\mu_i = 0 \tag{8-16}$$

Thus, the equilibrium criterion for all conceivable variations of the λ_σ is

$$\sum_{i=1}^{r} \nu_i^{\sigma}\mu_i = 0 \qquad \sigma = 1, \ldots, s \tag{8-17}$$

We next consider a closed heterogeneous system of ν phases and r components in which one chemical reaction is in progress. In a heterogeneous system, the reaction may have progressed to a different degree in the several phases so that there may be a different progress variable $\lambda^{(\alpha)}$ for each phase. For a closed system the change in mass of component i is due to the chemical reaction, and we may write

$$dn_i = \sum_{\alpha=1}^{\nu} dn_i^{(\alpha)} = \sum_{\alpha=1}^{\nu} \nu_i\, d\lambda^{(\alpha)} \qquad i = 1, \ldots, r \tag{8-18}$$

We have shown in Sec. 6-3 that the conditions for equilibrium in a heterogeneous system with respect to heat flow, mechanical change, and diffusion are

$$\begin{aligned} T^{(\alpha)} &= T \qquad \alpha = 1, \ldots, \nu \\ p^{(\alpha)} &= p \qquad \alpha = 1, \ldots, \nu \\ \mu_i^{(\alpha)} &= \mu_i \qquad \alpha = 1, \ldots, \nu \qquad i = 1, \ldots, r \end{aligned} \tag{8-19}$$

Thus the variation in internal energy of the system can be written

$$\delta E = T\,\delta S - p\,\delta V + \sum_{i=1}^{r} \mu_i\,\delta n_i \tag{8-20}$$

where

$$\delta S = \sum_{\alpha=1}^{\nu} \delta S^{(\alpha)}$$

$$\delta V = \sum_{\alpha=1}^{\nu} \delta V^{(\alpha)} \tag{8-21}$$

$$\delta n_i = \sum_{\alpha=1}^{\nu} \delta n_i^{(\alpha)}$$

The criterion for equilibrium [Eq. (8-3)] becomes

$$\sum_{i=1}^{r} \mu_i\,\delta n_i = \Big(\sum_{i=1}^{r} \nu_i\mu_i\Big)\,\delta\lambda \geqslant 0 \tag{8-22}$$

where

$$\delta\lambda = \sum_{\alpha=1}^{\nu} \delta\lambda^{(\alpha)} \tag{8-23}$$

and we have used Eq. (8-18). If reactants and products occur in at least one of the phases, then $\delta\lambda$ may be positive or negative and the equilibrium condition with respect to the chemical reaction becomes

$$\sum_{i=1}^{r} \nu_i\mu_i = 0 \tag{8-24}$$

This completes our derivation of the general criteria for chemical equilibrium in various systems.

We now turn our attention to a discussion of a variety of topics involved in the thermodynamic treatment of chemical reactions.

The Progress Variable. It is possible to determine the concentrations of the various components in a reaction mixture at any time during the reaction in terms of the progress variable λ. If $n_1^\circ, \ldots, n_r^\circ$ are the numbers of moles of the various components initially when $\lambda = 0$, Eq. (8-2) can be integrated to yield

$$n_i - n_i^\circ = \nu_i\lambda \qquad i = 1, \ldots, r \tag{8-25}$$

Division of Eq. (8-25) by the total number of moles,

$$n = \sum_{i=1}^{r} n_i \tag{8-26}$$

yields

$$x_i - \frac{n_i^\circ}{n} = \frac{\nu_i\lambda}{n} \tag{8-27}$$

where x_i is the mole fraction of component i. The total number of moles can be expressed in terms of λ and the initial total number of moles n° by use of Eq. (8-25). Thus

$$n = \sum_{i=1}^{r} n_i = \sum_{i=1}^{r} (n_i^\circ + \lambda \nu_i) = n^\circ + \lambda\,\Delta\nu \tag{8-28}$$

where $\Delta\nu = \sum_{i=1}^{r} \nu_i$ and $n^\circ = \sum_{i=1}^{r} n_i^\circ$. Substitution of Eq. (8-28) into Eq. (8-27) and rearrangement yields

$$x_i = \frac{x_i^\circ}{1 + (\lambda\,\Delta\nu/n^\circ)} + \frac{\nu_i\lambda}{n_0 + \lambda\,\Delta\nu} \tag{8-29}$$

where $x_i^\circ = n_i^\circ/n^\circ$ is the mole fraction of component i when $\lambda = 0$.

Unless the progress variable λ can be controlled, the thermodynamic functions cannot be determined at all possible compositions. This is necessary in order for the general discussion of equilibrium criteria to be operationally meaningful. The rigorous thermodynamic theory of chemical equilibrium does not apply to reactions of the type $N_2O_4 \rightleftharpoons 2NO_2$ since neither component can be isolated.

Chemical Potentials and Activity Coefficients. In general, the chemical potential of component i can be written in the form

$$\mu_i(T,p,x_1, \ldots, x_{r-1}) = \mu_i^\circ(T,p) + RT \log (f_i x_i) \tag{8-30}$$

where $\mu_i^\circ(T,p)$ is some arbitrarily selected reference value of the chemical potential and f_i, the activity coefficient of component i, is defined by Eq. (8-30). The activity coefficient of component i is a function of T, p, and $x_1, \ldots, x_{r-1}$. A more detailed discussion of the usefulness of writing the chemical potential in the form of Eq. (8-30) is presented in Sec. 11-1.

Various conventions are used in the determination of the standard state that fixes the reference value of the chemical potential μ_i°. In the case of gases, as mentioned in Sec. 7-7, the standard state is usually chosen to be the zero-pressure limit; $\mu_i^\circ(T,p)$ is a function of T alone and is given by the expression

$$\mu_i^\circ(T,p) = \mu_i^*(T) = \lim_{p\to 0} [\mu_i - RT \log (px_i)] \tag{8-31}$$

In the case of liquids, there are two commonly used conventions: (*a*) μ_i° is a function of T and p only, if the standard state is chosen such that

$$\mu_i^\circ(T,p) = \mu_i^{(l)}(T,p) \qquad i = 1, \ldots, r \tag{8-32}$$

where $\mu_i^{(l)}$ is the chemical potential of pure liquid i; (b) if the standard state is chosen such that

$$\mu_1^\circ(T,p) = \mu_1^{(l)}(T,p)$$

$$\mu_i^\circ(T,p) = \lim_{x_1 \to 1} (\mu_i - RT \log x_i) \qquad i = 2, \ldots, r \tag{8-33}$$

$\mu_i^\circ, i = 2, \ldots, r$, will be a function of T, p, and the solvent, component 1.

Substitution of Eq. (8-30) into the equilibrium condition [Eq. (8-10) or (8-24)] yields

$$\sum_{i=1}^{r} [\nu_i \mu_i^\circ + \nu_i RT \log (f_i x_i)] = \Delta F^\circ + \sum_{i=1}^{r} \nu_i RT \log (f_i x_i) = 0 \tag{8-34}$$

where

$$\Delta F^\circ = \sum_{i=1}^{r} \nu_i \mu_i^\circ \tag{8-35}$$

is the standard free-energy increment of the reaction. Thus, an equilibrium λ and the concentrations of the various components can be determined from a knowledge of the standard chemical potentials and the activity coefficients.

The condition for chemical equilibrium can be formulated in an entirely equivalent way in terms of activities. We define the activity of component i by the relation

$$a_i = \exp\left(\frac{\mu_i - \mu_i^\circ}{RT}\right) \tag{8-36}$$

Since

$$\mu_i = \mu_i^\circ + RT \log a_i \tag{8-37}$$

the condition for chemical equilibrium in a closed system becomes

$$\Delta F^\circ + \sum_{i=1}^{r} \nu_i RT \log a_i = 0 \tag{8-38}$$

The standard free-energy increment of the reaction can be expressed in terms of the standard free energies of formation of the various compounds in the reaction mixture.

The reaction representing the formation of X_i from its elements can be written, using Eq. (3-58), in the form

$$X_i - \sum_k \nu_k^{(i)} \mathscr{E}_k = 0 \tag{8-39}$$

We may write the standard free energy of formation of 1 mole of compound X_i as

$$\Delta F_i^\circ = \mu_i^\circ - \sum_k \nu_k{}^i \mu_k^\circ \tag{8-40}$$

where μ_k° is the chemical potential of pure element $\mathscr{E}_k$ in its stable state of aggregation at T, p. Substitution of Eq. (8-40) into Eq. (8-35) yields

$$\Delta F^\circ = \sum_{i=1}^{r} \nu_i \, \Delta F_i^\circ + \sum_k \left(\sum_{i=1}^{r} \nu_k{}^{(i)} \nu_i \right) \mu_k^\circ \tag{8-41}$$

If nuclear reactions are excluded,

$$\sum_{i=1}^{r} \nu_k{}^{(i)} \nu_i = 0 \tag{8-42}$$

and Eq. (8-41) becomes

$$\Delta F^\circ = \sum_{i=1}^{r} \nu_i \, \Delta F_i^\circ \tag{8-43}$$

Thus the standard free-energy increment of an arbitrary reaction can be computed using tables of the standard free energies of formation of the compounds entering into the reaction. The ΔF_i° are usually tabulated in free-energy tables at 25°C and 1 atm pressure.

The Equilibrium Constant. Experimental results concerning equilibrium compositions of reaction mixtures are conveniently summarized by presenting tables of equilibrium constants. The equilibrium constant of a reaction K is defined by the relation

$$K = \exp\left(\frac{-\Delta F^\circ}{RT}\right) \tag{8-44}$$

The equilibrium constant is a function only of temperature for gases, $K = K(T)$, and a function of temperature and pressure, $K = K(T,p)$, for liquids when convention a is used. The equilibrium constant is a function of T, p and the solvent in liquids when convention b is used. The equilibrium constant can also be expressed in terms of the equilibrium activities by substituting Eq. (8-38) into Eq. (8-44) to yield

$$K = \prod_{i=1}^{r} a_i{}^{\nu_i} \tag{8-45}$$

In general, activities are difficult to measure experimentally. Various ideal approximations to the equilibrium constant involving the use of concentrations and partial pressures in place of activities are in more prevalent use than the exact expression. In ideal gaseous systems,

$$K = \prod_{i=1}^{r} p_i{}^{\nu_i} = p^{\Delta\nu} \prod_{i=1}^{r} x_i{}^{\nu_i} \tag{8-46}$$

and in ideal liquid systems

$$K = \prod_{i=1}^{r} x_i{}^{\nu_i} \tag{8-47}$$

In order to investigate the dependence of K on T and p, it is convenient to reexpress Eq. (8-44) in the form

$$\log K = -\frac{\Delta F^\circ}{RT} = -\sum_{i=1}^{r} \frac{\nu_i \mu_i^\circ}{RT} \tag{8-48}$$

Taking the derivative of Eq. (8-48) with respect to temperature at constant pressure yields

$$\left(\frac{\partial \log K}{\partial T}\right)_p = -\sum_{i=1}^{r} \frac{\nu_i}{R}\left(\frac{\partial \mu_i^\circ/T}{\partial T}\right)_p \tag{8-49}$$

Making use of Eq. (7-142), we may write

$$\left(\frac{\partial \mu_i^\circ/T}{\partial T}\right)_p = -\frac{h_i^\circ}{T^2} \tag{8-50}$$

where h_i° is the standard partial molal enthalpy of component i at temperature T and pressure p. Substitution of Eq. (8-50) into Eq. (8-49) results in

$$\left(\frac{\partial \log K}{\partial T}\right)_p = \sum_{i=1}^{r} \frac{\nu_i h_i^\circ}{RT^2} = \frac{\Delta H^\circ}{RT^2} \tag{8-51}$$

where
$$\Delta H^\circ = \sum_{i=1}^{r} \nu_i h_i^\circ \tag{8-52}$$

is the standard enthalpy increment of the reaction. In a gaseous reaction, ΔH° is the heat absorbed in the forward reaction when all the participants are in their ideal dilute state. In a liquid reaction: Convention (*a*): ΔH° is the heat absorbed in the forward reaction when all the participants are in the pure state; convention (*b*): ΔH° is the heat absorbed in the forward reaction when the solvent is pure and the other components are in the hypothetical infinitely dilute state.

Equation (8-51) is the van't Hoff equation.

Taking the derivative of Eq. (8-48) with respect to pressure at constant temperature and making use of Eq. (6-54) result in

$$\begin{aligned}\left(\frac{\partial \ln K}{\partial p}\right)_T &= -\sum_{i=1}^{r} \frac{\nu_i(\partial \mu_i^\circ/\partial p)_T}{RT} \\ &= -\sum_{i=1}^{r} \frac{\nu_i v_i^\circ}{RT} \\ &= -\frac{\Delta V^\circ}{RT}\end{aligned} \tag{8-53}$$

where v_i° is the standard partial molal volume of component i at T and p and

$$\Delta V^\circ = \sum_{i=1}^{r} \nu_i v_i^\circ \tag{8-54}$$

is the standard volume increment of the reaction. In the case of gases, $\mu_i^\circ = \mu_i^\circ(T)$, and Eq. (8-53) becomes

$$\left(\frac{\partial \ln K}{\partial p}\right)_T = 0 \tag{8-55}$$

The Le Châtelier-Braun Principle. The Le Châtelier-Braun principle states that a thermodynamic system tends to balance the effects of any stress inflicted upon it. We shall present an elementary proof of this principle as applied to chemical reactions. (More complete discussions may be found in W. Schottky, "Thermodynamik," sec. 28, Springer-Verlag, Berlin, Vienna, 1929.)

The change in the free energy of a closed homogeneous system in which a chemical reaction is taking place may be written in the form

$$dF = -S\,dT + V\,dp + \left(\sum_{i=1}^{r} \nu_i \mu_i\right) d\lambda \tag{8-56}$$

where we have made use of Eq. (8-2). The partial derivative of F with respect to λ at constant T and p is given by

$$\begin{aligned}\left(\frac{\partial F}{\partial \lambda}\right)_{T,p} &= \sum_{i=1}^{r} \nu_i \mu_i \\ &= 0 \qquad \text{(at equilibrium)}\end{aligned} \tag{8-57}$$

The total differential of $(\partial F/\partial \lambda)_{T,p}$ can be derived from Eq. (8-56) to be

$$d\left(\frac{\partial F}{\partial \lambda}\right)_{T,p} = -\left(\frac{\partial S}{\partial \lambda}\right)_{T,p} dT + \left(\frac{\partial V}{\partial \lambda}\right)_{T,p} dp + \left(\frac{\partial^2 F}{\partial \lambda^2}\right)_{T,p} d\lambda \tag{8-58}$$

In the field of equilibrium states,

$$d\left(\frac{\partial F}{\partial \lambda}\right)_{T,p} = 0 \tag{8-59}$$

and we obtain from Eq. (8-58)

$$\left(\frac{\partial \lambda_e}{\partial T}\right)_p = \frac{(\partial S/\partial \lambda)_{T,p}}{(\partial^2 F/\partial \lambda^2)_{T,p}} = \frac{T(đQ/d\lambda)_{T,p}}{(\partial^2 F/\partial \lambda^2)_{T,p}} \tag{8-60}$$

and

$$\left(\frac{\partial \lambda_e}{\partial p}\right)_T = -\frac{(\partial V/\partial \lambda)_{T,p}}{(\partial^2 F/\partial \lambda^2)_{T,p}} \tag{8-61}$$

where λ_e is the equilibrium value of the progress variable. Remembering that $(\partial^2 F/\partial \lambda^2)_{T,p} > 0$ for stable systems (Sec. 6-4), we may interpret Eqs. (8-60) and (8-61) in the following manner: An increase in T at constant p causes the reaction to proceed in the direction in which heat is absorbed at constant T and p. An increase in p, at constant T, causes the reaction to proceed in the direction in which the volume of the system is decreased at constant T and p.

8-2. CHEMICAL EQUILIBRIUM IN REAL-GAS REACTIONS

In this section, the general theory of chemical equilibrium is applied to a closed, homogeneous system comprising a real-gas mixture of r components. The approximations inherent in the law of mass action are also indicated.

The chemical potential of component i in a real-gas mixture is given by Eq. (7-155) in the form

$$\mu_i = \mu_i^*(T) + RT \log p_i^* \tag{8-62}$$

where the reference value of the chemical potential is determined by Eq. (7-168) to be

$$\mu_i^*(T) = \lim_{p \to 0} [\mu_i - RT \log (px_i)] \tag{8-63}$$

and the fugacity is given by Eq. (7-166) in the form

$$p_i^* = px_i \exp \left[\frac{\int_0^p (\bar{v}_i - RT/p')\, dp'}{RT} \right] \tag{8-64}$$

The integral in Eq. (8-64) is along a path of constant temperature and composition; its evaluation requires a knowledge of the equation of state of the gas mixture for arbitrary composition.

Substitution of Eq. (8-62) into the general criterion for chemical equilibrium of a homogeneous closed system [Eq. (8-10)] results in

$$\sum_{i=1}^{r} \nu_i \mu_i^*(T) + RT \sum_{i=1}^{r} \nu_i \log p_i^* = \Delta F^* + RT \sum_{i=1}^{r} \nu_i \log p_i^* = 0 \tag{8-65}$$

where

$$\Delta F^* = \sum_{i=1}^{r} \nu_i \mu_i^*(T) \tag{8-66}$$

is the standard free-energy increment of the reaction. The equilibrium constant is defined by Eq. (8-44) to be

$$K(T) = \exp \left(-\frac{\Delta F^*}{RT} \right) \tag{8-67}$$

and thus

$$K(T) = \prod_{i=1}^{r} p_i^{*\nu_i} \tag{8-68}$$

where we have used Eq. (8-65). It is evident from Eqs. (8-66) and (8-67) that the equilibrium constant of a gaseous reaction is a function of temperature alone.

Equation (8-68) can be used to determine the equilibrium composition of the system as a function of T and p. However, since the fugacities p_i^* may be complicated functions of $T, p, x_1, \ldots, x_{r-1}$, in an arbitrary system, it might be difficult to obtain explicit expressions for the mole fractions from Eq. (8-68). To make the theory of chemical equilibrium useful in practice, it is convenient to define a quantity $K_p(T,p,x_1, \ldots, x_{r-1})$ which is easy to measure experimentally. The quantity K_p is defined by the relation

$$K_p = \prod_{i=1}^{r} (px_i)^{\nu_i} \tag{8-69}$$

Combination of Eqs. (8-64), (8-68), and (8-69) results in

$$\log \frac{K_p}{K} = -\sum_{i=1}^{r} \frac{\nu_i}{RT} \int_0^p \left(\bar{v}_i - \frac{RT}{p'}\right) dp' \tag{8-70}$$

Approximations to Eq. (8-70) can be obtained by using successively higher terms in the virial expansion of the equation of state. In the ideal-gas or zero approximation, $\bar{v}_i = RT/p$ and $K_p/K = 1$. Thus, in this approximation,

$$K(T) = \prod_{i=1}^{r} (px_i)^{\nu_i} \tag{8-71}$$

It is only in this approximation that the law of mass action is predicted by thermodynamic theory. Equation (8-71) is an expression of the law of mass action.

In the next approximation, the partial molal volume of component i is given by Eq. (7-177) in the form

$$\bar{v}_i - \frac{RT}{p} = \sum_{k,l=1}^{r} x_k x_l (2B_{ik} - B_{kl}) + O(p) \tag{8-72}$$

where the coefficients B_{ik} are functions of temperature alone. Substitution of Eq. (8-72) into Eq. (8-70) yields

$$\log \frac{K_p}{K} = -\left[\sum_{i=1}^{r} \nu_i \sum_{k,l=1}^{r} x_k x_l (2B_{ik} - B_{kl})\right] \frac{p}{RT} \tag{8-73}$$

The quantity K_p is a function of $T, p, x_1, \ldots, x_{r-1}$ and is not a true equilibrium constant. In this approximation,

$$\prod_{i=1}^{r} (px_i)^{\nu_i} = K(T) \exp\left\{-\frac{p}{RT}\left[\sum_{i=1}^{r} \nu_i \sum_{k,l=1}^{r} x_k x_l (2B_{ik} - B_{kl})\right]\right\} \tag{8-74}$$

By using Eq. (8-74) and the conservation-of-mass equations, the mole fractions of the various components at equilibrium can be calculated. In practice, the mole fractions obtained using the zero approximation [Eq. (8-71)] are substituted in the exponential term of Eq. (8-74). The next iteration is obtained by solving Eq. (8-74), treating the right-hand side as a constant. An iterative procedure is then used to determine the equilibrium mole fractions as accurately as desired.

If the additional approximation suggested by Eq. (7-180) is made,

$$B_{ik} = \frac{B_{ii} + B_{kk}}{2} \tag{8-75}$$

and

$$\sum_{k,l=1}^{r} x_k x_l (2B_{ik} - B_{kl}) = B_{ii} \tag{8-76}$$

Substitution of Eq. (8-76) into Eq. (8-73) results in the relation

$$\log \frac{K_p}{K} = -\frac{p\,\Delta B}{RT} \tag{8-77}$$

where

$$\Delta B = \sum_{i=1}^{r} \nu_i B_{ii}(T) \tag{8-78}$$

In the approximation of Eq. (8-77), K_p is a true equilibrium constant, depending on T and p alone.

It is sometimes more convenient to define a quantity K_x which is, in general, a function of $T, p, x_1, \ldots, x_{r-1}$. By definition,

$$\begin{aligned} K_x &= \prod_{i=1}^{r} x_i^{\nu_i} \\ &= p^{-\Delta\nu} K(T) \exp\left[-\sum_{i=1}^{r} \frac{\nu_i}{RT} \int_0^p \left(\bar{v}_i - \frac{RT}{p'}\right) dp'\right] \end{aligned} \tag{8-79}$$

where $\Delta\nu = \sum_{i=1}^{r} \nu_i$ and we have used Eqs. (8-64) and (8-68). It is clear from the definitions of K_x and K_p that

$$K_x = K_p p^{-\Delta\nu} \tag{8-80}$$

In the zero approximation [Eq. (8-71)], K_x becomes

$$K_x(T,p) = K(T) p^{-\Delta\nu} \tag{8-81}$$

Using the first approximation, Eq. (8-72), and Eq. (8-75), K_x becomes

$$K_x(T,p) = p^{-\Delta\nu} K(T) e^{-p\,\Delta B/RT} \tag{8-82}$$

An alternative expression for K_x can be obtained by utilizing the Lewis and Randall rule [Eq. (7-184)]. By use of this rule, Eq. (8-79) reduces to

$$K_x(T,p) = \frac{K(T)}{\prod_{i=1}^{r} p_i^{\circ *}} \tag{8-83}$$

where $p_i^{\circ *}$ is the fugacity of pure component i at the same T and p as the mixture. Equation (8-83) is derivable from Eqs. (8-72) and (8-75) but seems to have a wider range of validity than expected.

In order to facilitate the calculation of the composition of the reaction mixture at equilibrium, it is convenient to introduce an intensive progress variable ξ defined by the relation

$$dn_i = \nu_i n^\circ \, d\xi \qquad i = 1, \ldots, r \tag{8-84}$$

It is clear from Eqs. (8-2) and (8-84) that

$$\lambda = n^\circ \xi \tag{8-85}$$

Substitution of Eq. (8-85) into Eq. (8-29) yields the expression

$$x_i = \frac{x_i^\circ + \nu_i \xi}{1 + \Delta\nu\xi} \qquad i = 1, \ldots, r \tag{8-86}$$

where x_i is the mole fraction of component i when the reaction has proceeded to the point where its intensive progress variable is ξ. It is clear from the definition that ξ must lie between the limits

$$0 \leqslant \xi \leqslant \text{minimum}\left(-\frac{x_j^\circ}{\nu_j}\right)$$

where X_j is a reactant. The $r + 1$ equations [Eqs. (8-86) and (8-79)] are sufficient to determine the equilibrium values of the $r + 1$ variables, $x_1, \ldots, x_r$ and ξ. Substitution of Eq. (8-86) into Eq. (8-79) yields an implicit equation for ξ as a function of T, p, $x_1^\circ, \ldots, x_{r-1}^\circ$ in the form

$$\prod_{i=1}^{r} \left(\frac{x_i^\circ + \nu_i \xi}{1 + \Delta\nu\xi}\right)^{\nu_i} = p^{-\Delta\nu} K(T) \exp\left[-\sum_{i=1}^{r} \frac{\nu_i}{RT} \int_0^p \left(\bar{v}_i - \frac{RT}{p'}\right) dp'\right] \tag{8-87}$$

As an example of the use of this general formalism, we discuss the gas phase reactions

$$\tfrac{1}{2}N_2 + \tfrac{3}{2}H_2 = NH_3 \tag{8-88}$$

Equation (8-88) can be cast into the form of Eq. (8-1) by making use of the associations

$$X_1 = NH_3 \qquad X_2 = N_2 \qquad X_3 = H_2 \qquad \nu_1 = 1 \qquad \nu_2 = -\tfrac{1}{2} \qquad \nu_3 = -\tfrac{3}{2}$$

Equation (8-88) becomes

$$X_1 - \tfrac{1}{2}X_2 - \tfrac{3}{2}X_3 = 0 \tag{8-89}$$

Making use of Eq. (8-86) and the fact that $\Delta\nu = -1$, we can write

$$\begin{aligned} x_1 &= x_{NH_3} = \frac{x_1^\circ + \xi}{1 - \xi} \\ x_2 &= x_{N_2} = \frac{x_2^\circ - (\xi/2)}{1 - \xi} \\ x_3 &= x_{H_2} = \frac{x_3^\circ - (3\xi/2)}{1 - \xi} \end{aligned} \tag{8-90}$$

Substitution of Eq. (8-90) into Eq. (8-87) yields

$$\frac{(x_1^\circ + \xi)(1 - \xi)}{(x_2^\circ - \xi/2)^{\frac{1}{2}}(x_3^\circ - 3\xi/2)^{\frac{3}{2}}} = pK(T)\exp\left[-\sum_{i=1}^{3}\frac{\nu_i}{RT}\int_0^p\left(\bar{v}_i - \frac{RT}{p'}\right)dp'\right] \tag{8-91}$$

In the zero approximation, Eq. (8-91) reduces to

$$pK(T) = \frac{(x_1^\circ + \xi)(1 - \xi)}{(x_2^\circ - \xi/2)^{\frac{1}{2}}(x_3^\circ - 3\xi/2)^{\frac{3}{2}}} \tag{8-92}$$

In the first approximation of Eq. (8-82), Eq. (8-91) becomes

$$\frac{(x_1^\circ + \xi)(1 - \xi)}{(x_2^\circ - \xi/2)^{\frac{1}{2}}(x_3^\circ - 3\xi/2)^{\frac{3}{2}}} = pK(T)\exp\left[-\frac{p}{RT}\left(B_1 - \frac{B_2}{2} - \frac{3B_3}{2}\right)\right] \tag{8-93}$$

In general, if $\Delta\nu < 0$, $\Delta B < 0$ and a larger increase in yield than predicted by ideal-gas theory is obtained by increasing the pressure. It follows that, in the approximations of Eqs. (8-92) and (8-93), the maximum degree of reaction in the synthesis of NH_3 is obtained when the initial mole fractions are $x_1^\circ = 0$, $x_2^\circ = \frac{1}{4}$, $x_3^\circ = \frac{3}{4}$.

For further illustration, the general formalism can be applied to the gaseous reaction involving the dissociation of HCl. The reaction

$$HCl = \tfrac{1}{2}Cl_2 + \tfrac{1}{2}H_2 \tag{8-94}$$

can be rewritten in the form

$$\tfrac{1}{2}X_1 + \tfrac{1}{2}X_2 - X_3 = 0 \tag{8-95}$$

where $X_1 = Cl_2$, $X_2 = H_2$, $X_3 = HCl$, $\nu_1 = \frac{1}{2}$, $\nu_2 = \frac{1}{2}$, and $\nu_3 = -1$. We use the degree of dissociation of HCl as a special form of the progress variable. Thus, by definition,

$$\begin{aligned} x_1 &= x_2 = \tfrac{1}{2}\alpha \\ x_3 &= 1 - \alpha \end{aligned} \tag{8-96}$$

Substitution of Eq. (8-96) into Eq. (8-79) yields

$$K_x = \frac{\alpha}{2(1-\alpha)}$$
$$= K(T) \exp\left[-\frac{1}{RT}\int_0^p \left(\frac{\bar{v}_{Cl_2}}{2} + \frac{\bar{v}_{H_2}}{2} - \bar{v}_{HCl}\right) dp'\right] \tag{8-97}$$

In the zero approximation, Eq. (8-97) becomes

$$\frac{\alpha}{2(1-\alpha)} = K(T) \tag{8-98}$$

In the approximation of Eq. (8-82), Eq. (8-97) becomes

$$\frac{\alpha}{2(1-\alpha)} = K(T) \exp\left[-\frac{p}{RT}\left(\frac{B_{Cl_2}}{2} + \frac{B_{H_2}}{2} - B_{HCl}\right)\right] \tag{8-99}$$

We may write the general expression [Eq. (8-87)] in terms of the standard free-energy increment of the reaction in the form

$$\prod_{i=1}^{r}\left(\frac{x_i^\circ + \nu_i\xi}{1 + \Delta\nu\xi}\right)^{\nu_i} = \exp -\left(\frac{\Delta F^*}{RT}\right)p^{-\Delta\nu} \exp\left[-\frac{\sum_{i=1}^{r}\nu_i}{RT}\int_0^p\left(\bar{v}_i - \frac{RT}{p'}\right) dp'\right] \tag{8-100}$$

In practice, the most important term on the right-hand side of Eq. (8-100) is usually $e^{-(\Delta F^*/RT)}$. Because of the properties of the equation, ξ is large if the right-hand side is large and small if the right-hand side is small. Thus, if $\Delta F^*/RT \gg 0$, ξ is small and the reaction does not proceed far in the forward direction; if $\Delta F^*/RT \ll 0$, ξ is large and the reaction does proceed.

We conclude this section with a discussion of the temperature dependence of the equilibrium constant. The temperature derivative of $K(T)$ is given by Eq. (8-51) in the form

$$\frac{d \log K}{dT} = -\frac{d(\Delta F^*/T)}{R\,dT} = \frac{\Delta H^*}{RT^2} \tag{8-101}$$

Since K depends on T alone, total derivatives may be used. The temperature dependence of $K(T)$ and its value at any temperature can be determined from thermochemical data. Making use of Eqs. (7-146) and (8-52), we can rewrite Eq. (8-101) in the form

$$R\frac{d \log K}{dT} = \frac{\Delta H_0}{T^2} + \frac{\Delta\Gamma_0^*}{T} + \cdots + \frac{\Delta\Gamma_n^* T^{n-1}}{n+1} + \cdots \tag{8-102}$$

where
$$\Delta H_0 = \sum_{i=1}^{r} \nu_i h_{0i} \tag{8-103}$$

and
$$\Delta\Gamma_n^* = \sum_{i=1}^{r} \nu_i \Gamma_{ni}^* = \sum_{i=1}^{r} \nu_i \lim_{p\to 0} \Gamma_{ni} \tag{8-104}$$

The quantity h_{0i} is an arbitrary constant of integration that appears in the calculation of the molal enthalpy of pure component i and Γ_{ni} is the coefficient of T^n in the expansion of the heat capacity of pure component i in powers of the temperature. Integration of Eq. (8-102), making use of Eq. (7-147), results in

$$R \log K = -\frac{\Delta H_0}{T} + \Delta S_0 - \Delta\Gamma_0^* + \Delta\Gamma_0^* \log T + \cdots + \frac{\Delta\Gamma_n^* T^n}{n(n+1)} + \cdots \tag{8-105}$$

Thus the equilibrium constant at temperature T can be computed from thermochemical data which determine the coefficients $\Delta\Gamma_n^*$ and which, with the aid of the third law, determine ΔS_0. The quantity ΔH_0 is evaluated by use of an experimentally determined value of ΔH^* or K at a given temperature. We note that, at low temperatures, the coefficients of the temperature expansion of the heat capacity at constant pressure of pure component i at 1 atm pressure, rather than the zero-pressure limit, are usually used in the calculation of the equilibrium constant.

9 HETEROGENEOUS EQUILIBRIUM

In this chapter the criteria for heterogeneous equilibrium derived in Sec. 6-3 will be utilized in the description of some of the general properties of heterogeneous systems in equilibrium. In Sec. 9-1, we discuss the phase rule which fixes the number of independent intensive variables that determine the thermodynamic state of the heterogeneous system. In Sec. 9-2, we consider systems that have one degree of freedom and derive the generalized Clapeyron equation. In Sec. 9-3, we develop the theory of phase diagrams by deriving equations that enable us to predict states of coexistence of pairs of phases. In Sec. 9-4, we specialize the general theory developed in Sec. 9-3 to two-component, two-phase systems. Sections 9-5 to 9-10 deal with the application of the theory of Sec. 9-4 to specific systems. In Sec. 9-11, liquid-vapor equilibrium is discussed and the Duhem-Margules equation is derived and applied to the determination of vapor fugacities. Section 9-12 is devoted to a study of the dependence of vapor fugacity on temperature, pressure, and composition in two-component liquid-vapor systems.

9-1. PHASE RULE

As we have seen in Sec. 6-3, a heterogeneous system in equilibrium has certain restraints imposed upon it. In Sec. 6-3, we assumed that surface contributions were negligible and therefore that the extensive properties E, S, and V could be considered to be sums of contributions from the bulk phases. In this approximation and under the assumptions that the only external force acting on the system is a uniform normal pressure and that the interphase surfaces are deformable, permeable to all components, and heat-conducting, the equilibrium restraints imposed upon a system of v phases and r independent components are

$$
\begin{array}{rllll}
 & & \quad 1 & \quad 2 & \quad v-1 \\
1. & p^{(1)} & = p^{(2)} & = \cdots & = p^{(v)} \\
2. & T^{(1)} & = T^{(2)} & = \cdots & = T^{(v)} \\
 & \mu_1{}^{(1)} & = \mu_1{}^{(2)} & = \cdots & = \mu_1{}^{(v)} \\
r+2. & \mu_r{}^{(1)} & = \mu_r{}^{(2)} & = \cdots & = \mu_r{}^{(v)}
\end{array}
\tag{9-1}
$$

There are thus $(r + 2)(v - 1)$ conditions on this system.

The intensive properties of phase α are determined by $T^{(\alpha)}$, $p^{(\alpha)}$, $x_1^{(\alpha)}, \ldots, x_{r-1}^{(\alpha)}$ if we assume that the only external force is a uniform normal pressure. The number of variables determining the equilibrium states of the ν isolated phases is thus $\nu(r + 1)$. The number of variables, f, of the set $T^{(\alpha)}, p^{(\alpha)}, x_1^{(\alpha)}, \ldots, x_{r-1}^{(\alpha)}$ ($\alpha = 1, \ldots, \nu$) which can be specified within the field of heterogeneous equilibrium states is therefore

$$f = \nu(r + 1) - (r + 2)(\nu - 1) = r + 2 - \nu \tag{9-2}$$

under the condition that the number of phases is kept constant.

The relation (9-2) is known as the phase rule of Gibbs, and f is usually called the number of degrees of freedom of the system. It is important to note that the phase rule in the form (9-2) holds only under the following assumptions:

a. Surface contributions are negligible.

b. The only external force is a uniform normal pressure.

c. Interphase surfaces are deformable, permeable to all components, and heat-conducting.

Since $f = r + 2 - \nu$, the maximum number of degrees of freedom

$$f = r + 1 \tag{9-3}$$

corresponds to a homogeneous system;

$$f = r \tag{9-4}$$

corresponds to a two-phase system, etc. In the following sections, we consider the geometrical representation of the thermodynamic state of a heterogeneous system in a phase diagram space of $r + 1$ dimensions. In this space, $(r + 1)$-dimensional domains represent homogeneous states; r-dimensional domains represent states of coexistence of pairs of phases, . . . and zero-dimensional domains (invariant systems) represent states of coexistence of $r + 2$ phases.

The phase rule can be derived in an alternative fashion from a consideration of the Gibbs-Duhem equations (6-60) for the phases of the heterogeneous system and the restrictions imposed on the variations of the intensive variables $T^{(\alpha)}$, $p^{(\alpha)}$, and $\mu_i^{(\alpha)}$, $i = 1, \ldots, r$; $\alpha = 1, \ldots \nu$, by the equilibrium conditions. For each phase α of the system, there exists a Gibbs-Duhem equation of the form

$$\sum_{i=1}^{r} x_i^{(\alpha)}(d\mu_i^{(\alpha)} - \bar{v}_i^{(\alpha)}\, dp^{(\alpha)} + \bar{s}_i^{(\alpha)}\, dT^{(\alpha)}) = 0 \tag{9-5}$$

or

$$\sum_{i=1}^{r} (x_i^{(\alpha)}\, d\mu_i^{(\alpha)}) - v^{(\alpha)}\, dp^{(\alpha)} + s^{(\alpha)}\, dT^{(\alpha)} = 0 \tag{9-6}$$

Equations (9-5) and (9-6) are independent of the theory of heterogeneous equilibrium. If we consider changes in which heterogeneous equilibrium between the ν phases is preserved, then

$$\begin{aligned} dT^{(\alpha)} &= dT \\ dp^{(\alpha)} &= dp \qquad\qquad\qquad\qquad \alpha = 1, \ldots, \nu \\ d\mu_i^{(\alpha)} &= d\mu_i \qquad i = 1, \ldots, r \end{aligned} \tag{9-7}$$

where we have made use of Eqs. (9-1). Substitution of Eqs. (9-7) into Eqs. (9-5) and (9-6) results in

$$\sum_{i=1}^{r} (x_i^{(\alpha)}\, d\mu_i) - v^{(\alpha)}\, dp + s^{(\alpha)}\, dT = 0 \qquad \alpha = 1, \ldots, \nu \tag{9-8}$$

or

$$\sum_{i=1}^{r} x_i^{(\alpha)}(d\mu_i - \bar{v}_i^{(\alpha)}\, dp + \bar{s}_i^{(\alpha)}\, dT) = 0 \tag{9-9}$$

Equations (9-8) [or (9-9)] are a system of ν differential equations relating the $r + 2$ intensive variables $\mu_1, \ldots, \mu_r$, T, and p. The phase rule [Eq. (9-2)] is an immediate consequence of this system of differential equations.

9-2. UNIVARIANT SYSTEMS

In this section we consider systems in which the number of degrees of freedom, f, is one. These systems are termed univariant and represent states of coexistence of $r + 1$ phases.

In a univariant system, the Gibbs-Duhem equations take a particularly simple form. We may choose dT as the free variation and rewrite Eq. (9-8) in the form

$$-v^{(\alpha)} \frac{dp}{dT} + \sum_{i=1}^{r} x_i^{(\alpha)} \frac{d\mu_i}{dT} = -s^{\alpha} \qquad \alpha = 1, \ldots, r+1 \tag{9-10}$$

Equations (9-10) are a set of $r + 1$ linear algebraic equations for the $r + 1$ variables dp/dT, $d\mu_1/dT, \ldots, d\mu_r/dT$. The solution for dp/dT is

$$\frac{dp}{dT} = \frac{\begin{vmatrix} s^{(1)} & x_1^{(1)} & \cdots & x_r^{(1)} \\ \cdots & \cdots & \cdots & \cdots \\ s^{(r+1)} & x_1^{(r+1)} & \cdots & x_r^{(r+1)} \end{vmatrix}}{\begin{vmatrix} v^{(1)} & x_1^{(1)} & \cdots & x_r^{(1)} \\ \cdots & \cdots & \cdots & \cdots \\ v^{(r+1)} & x_1^{(r+1)} & \cdots & x_r^{(r+1)} \end{vmatrix}} \tag{9-11}$$

Equation (9-11) is the general Clapeyron equation for a univariant system. It must be remembered that the derivative dp/dT is under the restraint of heterogeneous equilibrium.

For a one-component univariant system, $r = 1$, $\nu = 2$, Eq. (9-11) reduces to

$$\frac{dp}{dT} = \frac{\begin{vmatrix} s^{(1)} & 1 \\ s^{(2)} & 1 \end{vmatrix}}{\begin{vmatrix} v^{(1)} & 1 \\ v^{(2)} & 1 \end{vmatrix}} = \frac{s^{(2)} - s^{(1)}}{v^{(2)} - v^{(1)}} \tag{9-12}$$

At equilibrium, $\mu^{(1)} = \mu^{(2)}$; thus

$$s^{(2)} - s^{(1)} = \frac{h^{(2)} - h^{(1)}}{T} \tag{9-13}$$

where we have made use of Eq. (6-13). Substitution of Eq. (9-13) into Eq. (9-12) results in

$$\frac{dp}{dT} = \frac{h^{(2)} - h^{(1)}}{T(v^{(2)} - v^{(1)})} = \frac{\Delta h^{(1\to 2)}}{T\,\Delta v^{(1\to 2)}} \tag{9-14}$$

where $\Delta h^{(1\to 2)}$ is the heat absorbed at constant pressure in transferring 1 mole from phase 1 to phase 2 in equilibrium with it and $\Delta v^{(1\to 2)}$ is the volume change per mole transferred. Equation (9-14) is the Clausius-Clapeyron equation.

The phase diagram for a typical one-component system is illustrated in Fig. 9-1. The solid, liquid, and vapor regions are one-phase systems for which $f = 2$. The curves, whose slopes are given by Eq. (9-14), represent states of coexistence of pairs of phases and are univariant. At the triple point, three phases coexist, and the system then is invariant.

It can be shown that an equation of the form of Eq. (9-12) applies to one-component, two-phase systems in which the restraint of heterogeneous equilibrium is not imposed. We consider a system in which the temperatures of the two phases are equal, $T^{(1)} = T^{(2)} = T$, and the pressures of the two phases are equal, $p^{(1)} = p^{(2)} = p$, but in which

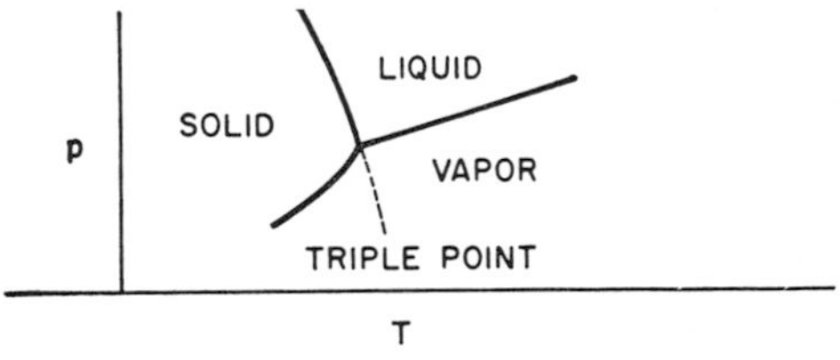

FIG. 9-1. Phase diagram for a one-component system.

the chemical potentials of the two phases need not be equal. We consider p, T, and $\mu^{(2)} - \mu^{(1)}$ to be the variables of interest and make use of Eq. (A-10) to obtain

$$\left(\frac{\partial p}{\partial T}\right)_{\mu^{(2)}-\mu^{(1)}} = -\frac{[\partial(\mu^{(2)} - \mu^{(1)})/\partial T]_p}{[\partial(\mu^{(2)} - \mu^{(1)})/\partial p]_T} = \frac{s^{(2)} - s^{(1)}}{v^{(2)} - v^{(1)}} \tag{9-15}$$

Thus, the variation of pressure with temperature at constant $\mu^{(2)} - \mu^{(1)}$ has the same form as in Eq. (9-12) where we have assumed heterogeneous equilibrium.

If the phases are in equilibrium,

$$\mu^{(2)} - \mu^{(1)} = 0 \tag{9-16}$$

and Eq. (9-15) becomes

$$\left(\frac{\partial p}{\partial T}\right)_{\mu^{(2)}-\mu^{(1)}=0} = \frac{\Delta h^{(1\to 2)}}{T\,\Delta v^{(1\to 2)}} \tag{9-17}$$

which is identical to Eq. (9-14).

9-3. THEORY OF PHASE DIAGRAMS

In this section we develop methods for describing states of coexistence of pairs of phases of a system by deriving an equation that relates the variables in the phase-diagram space of that system. The thermodynamic state of a heterogeneous system can be given a geometrical representation in an $(r + 1)$-dimensional phase-diagram space. It is convenient to choose T, p, $x_1^{(\beta)}, \ldots, x_{r-1}^{(\beta)}$ as the variables spanning the phase-diagram space. β is one of the virtual or real coexisting phases in the heterogeneous system, the states of which are represented in the phase-diagram space. For example, for $r = 1$, $v = 1$, one may use T and p as variables. For $r = 2$, $v = 1$, one may use T, p, and $x_2^{(1)}$ or T, p, and $x_1^{(1)}$ as variables.

In order to express the thermodynamic state of the heterogeneous system in terms of the $r + 1$ variables that we have chosen to span the phase-diagram space, we transform the set of v equations [Eq. (9-8)] relating the $r + 2$ variables $T, p, \mu_1, \ldots, \mu_r$ to a set of $v - 1$ equations relating the $r + 1$ variables $T, p, x_1^{(\beta)}, \ldots, x_{r-1}^{(\beta)}$. To do this, we express the differentials $d\mu_i$, $i = 1, \ldots, r$, in Eq. (9-8) in terms of dT, dp, and $dx_k^{(\beta)}$, $k = 1, \ldots, r - 1$, where β is the reference phase, virtual or real, such that all components are real components of β. We may write the differential of the chemical potential of component i in phase β in the form

$$d\mu_i^{(\beta)} = -\bar{s}_i^{(\beta)}\,dT + \bar{v}_i^{(\beta)}\,dp + \sum_{k=1}^{r-1}\left(\frac{\partial \mu_i^{(\beta)}}{\partial x_k^{(\beta)}}\right)_{T,p,x_{j\neq k}^{(\beta)}} dx_k^{(\beta)} \tag{9-18}$$

where the subscript $x^{(\beta)}_{j\neq k}$ implies that the mole fractions of $r - 2$ components are held fixed in the partial differentiation and we have used Eq. (6-56). For heterogeneous equilibrium,

$$d\mu_i^{(\alpha)} = d\mu_i^{(\beta)} \qquad \alpha = 1, \ldots, \nu \tag{9-19}$$

and thus

$$d\mu_i^{(\alpha)} = d\mu_i^{(\beta)} = -\bar{s}_i^{(\beta)}\, dT + \bar{v}_i^{(\beta)}\, dp + \sum_{k=1}^{r-1} G_{ik}^{(\beta)}\, dx_k^{(\beta)} \tag{9-20}$$

where

$$G_{ik}^{(\beta)} = \left(\frac{\partial \mu_i^{(\beta)}}{\partial x_k^{(\beta)}}\right)_{T,p,x^{(\beta)}_{j\neq k}} \tag{9-21}$$

Substitution of Eq. (9-20) into Eq. (9-9) results in

$$\sum_{k=1}^{r-1} G_k^{(\alpha\beta)}\, dx_k^{(\beta)} + \sum_{i=1}^{r} x_i^{(\alpha)}(\bar{s}_i^{(\alpha)} - \bar{s}_i^{(\beta)})\, dT + \sum_{i=1}^{r} x_i^{(\alpha)}(\bar{v}_i^{(\beta)} - \bar{v}_i^{(\alpha)})\, dp = 0 \qquad \alpha = 1, \ldots, \nu \tag{9-22}$$

where

$$G_k^{(\alpha\beta)} = \sum_{i=1}^{r} x_i^{(\alpha)} G_{ik}^{(\beta)} \tag{9-23}$$

Equation (9-22) is a set of equations equivalent to the set of Gibbs-Duhem equations subject to equilibrium [Eqs. (9-8) or (9-9)]. Since

$$G_k^{(\beta\beta)} = \sum_{i=1}^{r} x_i^{(\beta)} \left(\frac{\partial \mu_i^{(\beta)}}{\partial x_k^{(\beta)}}\right)_{T,p,x_{j\neq k}} = 0$$

by Eq. (6-61), Eq. (9-22) reduces to the identity $0 \equiv 0$ when $\alpha = \beta$. Thus, Eq. (9-22) is a system of $\nu - 1$ differential equations in $r + 1$ variables $(dT, dp, dx_1^{(\beta)}, \ldots, dx^{(\beta)}_{r-1})$. The phase rule can be derived from this set of equations since the number of degrees of freedom is given by

$$f = (r + 1) - (\nu - 1) = r + 2 - \nu \tag{9-24}$$

It is convenient to reexpress the coefficients of Eq. (9-22) in terms of quantities that are frequently measured experimentally. Since $\mu_i^{(\alpha)} = \mu_i^{(\beta)}$, we may write

$$\bar{s}_i^{(\alpha)} - \bar{s}_i^{(\beta)} = \frac{\bar{h}_i^{(\alpha)} - \bar{h}_i^{(\beta)}}{T} = \frac{\bar{L}_i^{(\beta\to\alpha)}}{T} \tag{9-25}$$

$\bar{L}_i^{(\beta\to\alpha)}$ is the differential heat of transfer at constant pressure of component i from phase β to α. It is the heat of transfer of 1 mole of component i from an infinite amount of phase β to an infinite amount of phase α. The quantity $L^{(\alpha\to\beta)}$ is defined by the relation

$$L^{(\alpha\to\beta)} = \sum_{i=1}^{r} x_i^{(\alpha)} \bar{L}_i^{(\alpha\to\beta)} \tag{9-26}$$

Therefore, $L^{(\alpha\to\beta)}$ is the mean molal differential heat of transfer from phase α to β. It is the heat absorbed when a mean mole of phase α is transferred to an infinite phase β at constant p. The quantity $\Delta v^{(\alpha\to\beta)}$ is defined by the relation

$$\Delta v^{(\alpha\to\beta)} = \sum_{i=1}^{r} x_i^{(\alpha)}(\bar{v}_i^{(\beta)} - \bar{v}_i^{(\alpha)}) = \sum_{i=1}^{r} x_i^{(\alpha)} \Delta\bar{v}_i^{(\alpha\to\beta)} \tag{9-27}$$

Thus, $\Delta v^{(\alpha\to\beta)}$ is the change in volume of the system when a mean mole of phase α is transferred to an infinite amount of phase β. Substitution of Eqs. (9-26) and (9-27) into Eq. (9-22) results in

$$\sum_{k=1}^{r-1} G_k^{(\alpha\beta)}\, dx_k^{(\beta)} - \frac{L^{(\alpha\to\beta)}}{T}\, dT + \Delta v^{(\alpha\to\beta)}\, dp = 0 \tag{9-28}$$

We can predict states of coexistence of pairs of phases by use of Eqs. (9-28) and experimental information concerning $G_k^{(\alpha\beta)}$, $L^{(\alpha\to\beta)}$, and $\Delta v^{(\alpha\to\beta)}$ as functions of $x_k^{(\beta)}$, T, and p.

9-4. APPLICATIONS OF THE GENERAL THEORY

In this section we discuss a number of applications of the general theory developed in Secs. 9-1 to 9-3. The main body of the section is devoted to a discussion of two-component, two-phase systems. The application of Eq. (9-28) to general two-component, two-phase systems is treated. In the following sections, a number of specific examples are presented in which various approximations are introduced.

In a one-component system, $r = 1$, and the phase rule [Eq. (9-2)] becomes

$$f = 3 - \nu \tag{9-29}$$

When $\nu = 1$, the system is homogeneous and no further discussion is required. In the two-phase system, $\nu = 2$, $f = 1$, and the system is univariant. Thus, the results of Sec. 9-2 may be applied directly. In this case, Eq. (9-28) becomes

$$-\frac{L^{(\alpha\to\beta)}}{T}\, dT + \Delta v^{(\alpha\to\beta)}\, dp = 0 \tag{9-30}$$

where $L^{(\alpha\to\beta)} = h^{(\beta)} - h^{(\alpha)}$ and $\Delta v^{(\alpha\to\beta)} = v^{(\beta)} - v^{(\alpha)}$. Equation (9-30) may be rearranged to yield

$$\frac{dp}{dT} = \frac{L^{(\alpha\to\beta)}}{T\,\Delta v^{(\alpha\to\beta)}} \tag{9-31}$$

which is identical to the Clausius-Clapeyron equation [Eq. (9-14)]. In the three-phase system, $\nu = 3, f = 0$, and the system is invariant. The system is represented as a point in the two-dimensional phase-diagram space (see Fig. 9-1).

For a two-component system, $r = 2$, and the phase rule [Eq. (9-2)] becomes

$$f = 4 - \nu \tag{9-32}$$

Thus, there are four possible cases: $\nu = 1, f = 3$; $\nu = 2, f = 2$; $\nu = 3, f = 1$; and $\nu = 4, f = 0$. When $\nu = 4$ the system is completely determined and is represented by a point in phase-diagram space. The case $\nu = 3$ has already been discussed in the general theory of univariant systems (Sec. 9-2). The case $\nu = 1$ represents a homogeneous system and, therefore, does not require further discussion. The case $\nu = 2$ will now be discussed in some detail. In order to simplify the notation, we define the symbols

$$\begin{aligned} x_2^{(1)} &= x_2 \qquad & x_1^{(1)} &= x_1 = 1 - x_2 \\ x_2^{(2)} &= y_2 \qquad & x_1^{(2)} &= y_1 = 1 - y_2 \end{aligned} \tag{9-33}$$

If phase 1 is chosen as the reference phase and T, p, and x_2 are the chosen variables, Eq. (9-28) becomes

$$G_2^{(21)}\,dx_2 - \frac{L^{(21)}}{T}\,dT + \Delta v^{(21)}\,dp = 0 \tag{9-34}$$

If phase 2 is chosen as the reference phase with T, p, and y_2 as variables, Eq. (9-28) becomes

$$G_2^{(12)}\,dy_2 - \frac{L^{(12)}}{T}\,dT + \Delta v^{(12)}\,dp = 0 \tag{9-35}$$

Equations (9-34) and (9-35) provide alternative equivalent descriptions of two-dimensional regions of coexistence of pairs of phases. Equation (9-34) is an equation for the definition of a two-dimensional surface in the phase-diagram space spanned by T, p, and x_2 corresponding to a two-phase region. Equation (9-35) is an equation for the definition of a two-dimensional surface in the phase-diagram space spanned by T, p, and y_2 corresponding to a two-phase region. In the usual phase diagram the spaces spanned by T, p, and x_2 and by T, p, and y_2 are superposed, and the surfaces described by Eqs. (9-34) and (9-35) appear on the same diagram. We note that a path through equilibrium states must be used in the integration of these equations.

We proceed with the analysis of Eqs. (9-34) and (9-35) by writing the terms occurring in them more explicitly. The explicit expressions for the coefficients of dT are

$$
\begin{aligned}
L^{(21)} &= -(y_1\bar{L}_1^{(12)} + y_2\bar{L}_2^{(12)}) \\
L^{(12)} &= x_1\bar{L}_1^{(12)} + x_2\bar{L}_2^{(12)} \\
\bar{L}_1^{(12)} &= \bar{h}_1^{(2)} - \bar{h}_1^{(1)} \\
\bar{L}_2^{(12)} &= \bar{h}_2^{(2)} - \bar{h}_2^{(1)}
\end{aligned}
\tag{9-36}
$$

Similar relations can be written for $\Delta v^{(21)}$ and $\Delta v^{(12)}$. Explicit expressions for the coefficient of dx_2 and dy_2 are

$$G_2^{(21)} = y_1 G_{12}^{(1)} + y_2 G_{22}^{(1)} \tag{9-37}$$

$$G_2^{(12)} = x_1 G_{12}^{(2)} + x_2 G_{22}^{(2)} \tag{9-38}$$

$$G_{12}^{(1)} = \left(\frac{\partial \mu_1^{(1)}}{\partial x_2}\right)_{T,p} \tag{9-39}$$

$$G_{22}^{(1)} = \left(\frac{\partial \mu_2^{(1)}}{\partial x_2}\right)_{T,p} \tag{9-40}$$

$$G_{12}^{(2)} = \left(\frac{\partial \mu_1^{(2)}}{\partial y_2}\right)_{T,p} \tag{9-41}$$

$$G_{22}^{(2)} = \left(\frac{\partial \mu_2^{(2)}}{\partial y_2}\right)_{T,p} \tag{9-42}$$

The Gibbs-Duhem equation [Eq. (9-5)] can be used to simplify the expressions for $G_2^{(21)}$ and $G_2^{(12)}$. Substitution of Eqs. (9-39) to (9-42) into Eq. (6-61) yields

$$x_1 G_{12}^{(1)} + x_2 G_{22}^{(1)} = 0 \tag{9-43}$$

$$y_1 G_{12}^{(2)} + y_2 G_{22}^{(2)} = 0 \tag{9-44}$$

Substitution of Eq. (9-43) into Eq. (9-37) results in

$$
\begin{aligned}
G_2^{(21)} &= \left(\frac{y_2 x_1 - y_1 x_2}{x_1}\right) G_{22}^{(1)} \\
&= \frac{y_2 - x_2}{x_1} G_{22}^{(1)}
\end{aligned}
\tag{9-45}
$$

Similarly, substitution of Eq. (9-44) into Eq. (9-38) results in

$$G_2^{(12)} = \frac{x_2 - y_2}{y_1} G_{22}^{(2)} \tag{9-46}$$

It is convenient to define the quantities

$$g_{22}^{(1)} = \frac{G_{22}^{(1)} x_2}{RT} \tag{9-47}$$

$$g_{22}^{(2)} = \frac{G_{22}^{(2)} y_2}{RT}$$

In order to appreciate the advantage of defining the new quantities, $g_{22}^{(1)}$ and $g_{22}^{(2)}$, we anticipate some future results. The chemical potential of component i in phase β can, in general, be written in the form

$$\mu_i^{(\beta)} = \mu_i^{\circ(\beta)}(T,p) + RT \log (f_i^{(\beta)} x_i^{(\beta)}) \tag{9-48}$$

where Eq. (9-48) defines the activity coefficient $f_i^{(\beta)}$ (see Sec. 11-1 for more details). Substitution of Eq. (9-48) into Eq. (9-21) yields

$$G_{ik}^{(\beta)} = \frac{RT}{x_i^{(\beta)}} \delta_{ik} + \frac{RT}{f_i^{(\beta)}} \left(\frac{\partial f_i^{(\beta)}}{\partial x_k^{(\beta)}} \right)_{T,p,x_{j \neq k}^{(\beta)}} \qquad i = 1, \ldots, r-1 \tag{9-49}$$

where $\delta_{ik} = 0$ when $i \neq k$ and $\delta_{ik} = 1$ when $i = k$. We note again that the subscript $x_{j \neq k}^{(\beta)}$ implies that the mole fractions x_j, $j = 1, \ldots, r-1$; $\neq$ k, are held fixed in the partial differentiation. Thus we find that, since

$$x_r^{(\beta)} = 1 - \sum_{k=1}^{r-1} x_k^{(\beta)} \tag{9-50}$$

and

$$\left(\frac{\partial x_r^{(\beta)}}{\partial x_k^{(\beta)}} \right)_{x_{j \neq k}^{(\beta)}} = -1 \tag{9-51}$$

the expression for $G_{rk}^{(\beta)}$ can be written

$$G_{rk}^{(\beta)} = -\frac{RT}{x_r^{(\beta)}} + \frac{RT}{f_r^{(\beta)}} \left(\frac{\partial f_r^{(\beta)}}{\partial x_k^{(\beta)}} \right)_{T,p,x_{j \neq k}^{(\beta)}} \qquad k = 1, \ldots, r-1 \tag{9-52}$$

Comparison of Eqs. (9-49) and (9-47) leads to the expression

$$g_{ii}^{(\beta)} = 1 + \left(\frac{\partial \log f_i^{(\beta)}}{\partial \log x_i^{(\beta)}} \right)_{T,p,x_{j \neq i}^{(\beta)}} \qquad i = 1, \ldots, r \tag{9-53}$$

In an ideal mixture, $f_i^{(\beta)} = 1$, $\partial f_i^{(\beta)} / \partial x_i^{(\beta)} = 0$, and Eq. (9-53) becomes

$$g_{ii}^{(\beta)} = 1 \tag{9-54}$$

It is advantageous to introduce the quantities $g_{ii}^{(\beta)}$ since they reduce to unity in the frequently utilized ideal-mixture approximation.

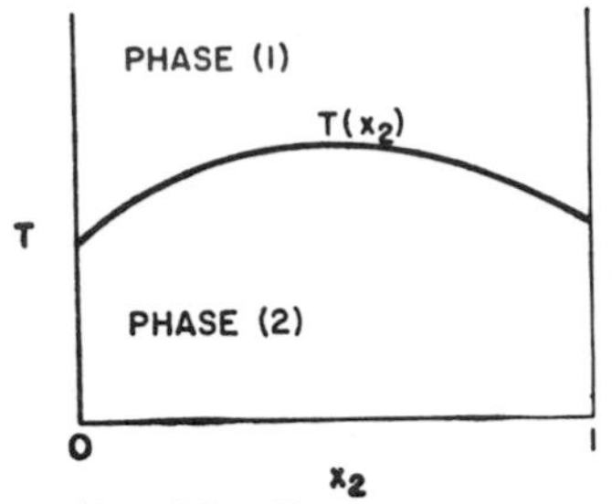

FIG. 9-2. Temperature-composition diagram for a two-component system.

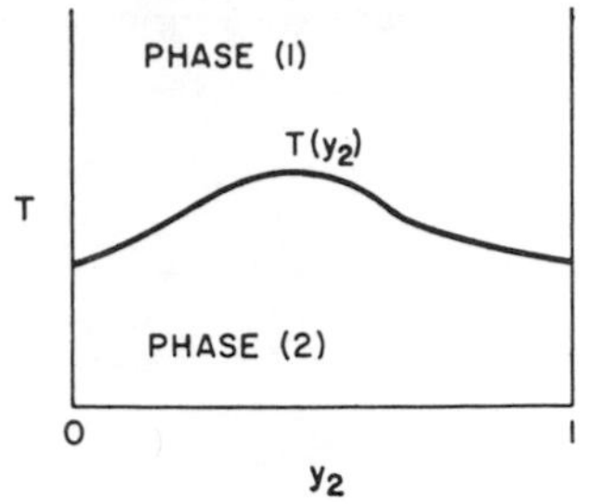

FIG. 9-3. Temperature-composition diagram for a two-component system.

Making use of Eqs. (9-36), (9-45) to (9-47), and the fundamental equations (9-34) and (9-35) we obtain

$$g_{22}^{(1)}\left(\frac{y_2 - x_2}{x_1x_2}\right) dx_2 + \frac{y_1\bar{L}_1 + y_2\bar{L}_2}{RT^2}\,dT - \frac{y_1\,\Delta\bar{v}_1 + y_2\,\Delta\bar{v}_2}{RT}\,dp = 0 \qquad (9\text{-}55)$$

$$g_{22}^{(2)}\left(\frac{y_2 - x_2}{y_1y_2}\right) dy_2 + \frac{x_1\bar{L}_1 + x_2\bar{L}_2}{RT^2}\,dT - \frac{x_1\,\Delta\bar{v}_1 + x_2\,\Delta\bar{v}_2}{RT}\,dp = 0 \qquad (9\text{-}56)$$

We have omitted the superscript (12) from the quantities $\bar{L}_1$, $\bar{L}_2$, $\Delta\bar{v}_1$, and $\Delta\bar{v}_2$ in Eqs. (9-55) and (9-56). In these equations and in the following the quantities $\bar{L}_1$, etc., are to be assumed to be $\bar{L}_1^{(12)}$, etc. Equations (9-55) and (9-56) are alternative, equivalent equations that define surfaces of coexistence of pairs of phases in a three-dimensional phase-diagram space.

The three-dimensional spaces spanned by T, p, and x_2, or by T, p, and y_2, are usually represented as projections on a plane by holding one variable constant. In these planes the projected surfaces described by Eqs. (9-55) and (9-56) become curves. The three-dimensional space may be projected onto the temperature-composition plane. In this plane the pressure is constant and we obtain temperature-composition diagrams at constant pressure. The curves of coexistence of pairs of phases are described by the equation

$$\left(\frac{\partial T}{\partial x_2}\right)_p = g_{22}^{(1)}\left(\frac{RT^2}{y_1\bar{L}_1 + y_2\bar{L}_2}\right)\left(\frac{x_2 - y_2}{x_1x_2}\right) \qquad (9\text{-}57)$$

in the T, p, x_2 space and by the equation

$$\left(\frac{\partial T}{\partial y_2}\right)_p = g_{22}^{(2)}\left(\frac{RT^2}{x_1\bar{L}_1 + x_2\bar{L}_2}\right)\left(\frac{x_2 - y_2}{y_1y_2}\right) \qquad (9\text{-}58)$$

in the T, p, y_2 space. When the three-dimensional phase-diagram space is projected onto the pressure-composition plane we obtain pressure-composition diagrams at constant temperature. The curves of coexistence of pairs of phases are described by

$$\left(\frac{\partial p}{\partial x_2}\right)_T = -\frac{RTg_{22}^{(1)}}{y_1\,\Delta\bar{v}_1 + y_2\,\Delta\bar{v}_2}\,\frac{x_2 - y_2}{x_1x_2} \tag{9-59}$$

in the T, p, x_2 space and by

$$\left(\frac{\partial p}{\partial y_2}\right)_T = -\frac{RTg_{22}^{(2)}}{x_1\,\Delta\bar{v}_1 + x_2\,\Delta\bar{v}_2}\,\frac{x_2 - y_2}{y_1y_2} \tag{9-60}$$

in the T, p, y_2 space. When the phase-diagram space is projected onto the pressure-temperature plane we obtain pressure-temperature diagrams at constant composition. The curves of coexistence of pairs of phases are described by

$$\left(\frac{\partial p}{\partial T}\right)_{x_2} = \frac{y_1\bar{L}_1 + y_2\bar{L}_2}{(y_1\,\Delta\bar{v}_1 + y_2\,\Delta\bar{v}_2)T} \tag{9-61}$$

in the T, p, x_2 space and by

$$\left(\frac{\partial p}{\partial T}\right)_{y_2} = \frac{x_1\bar{L}_1 + x_2\bar{L}_2}{(x_1\,\Delta\bar{v}_1 + x_2\,\Delta\bar{v}_2)T} \tag{9-62}$$

in the T, p, y_2 space.

From the theory of stability (Sec. 6-4) we know that $g_{22}^{(1)}$ and $g_{22}^{(2)}$ must be greater than zero except at certain rare unique critical points at which they may be zero. In this discussion, we shall assume that $g_{22}^{(1)}$ and $g_{22}^{(2)}$ are greater than zero. If these quantities were less than zero, the mixed phases would be unstable and would separate into pure phases. Thus, the temperature-composition curves [Eqs. (9-57) and (9-58)] and the pressure-composition curves [Eqs. (9-59) and (9-60)] have extreme, or inflection, points if, and only if, $x_2 = y_2$. A typical curve, $T(x_2)$, described by Eq. (9-57) is plotted in Fig. 9-2. A typical curve, $T(y_2)$ described by Eq. (9-58) is plotted in Fig. 9-3. Usually these curves are plotted on the same diagram, as in Fig. 9-4 or 9-5. The curves in

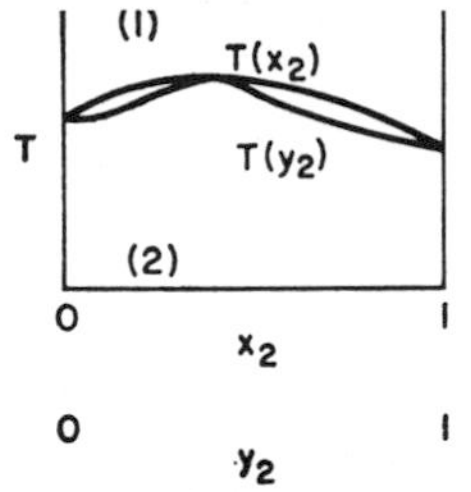

FIG. 9-4. Temperature - composition diagram for a two-component system.

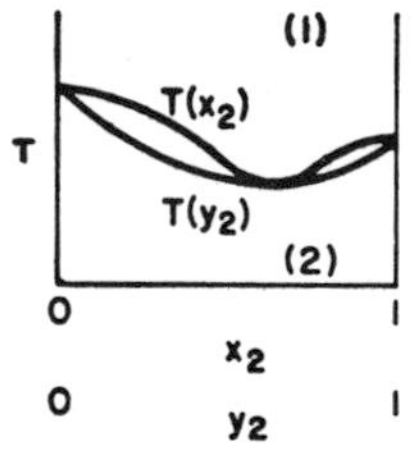

FIG. 9-5. Temperature - composition diagram for a two-component system.

Figs. 9-4 and 9-5 can be used to determine the value of y_2, the mole fraction of component 2 in phase 2, as a function of x_2, the mole fraction of component 2 in phase 1. At a given value of $x_2 = x_2^\circ$, the temperature of the system consisting of phases 1 and 2 in equilibrium at pressure p is given by $T(x_2^\circ)$. Since the phases are in equilibrium, $T(x_2) = T(y_2)$. The horizontal line through $T(x_2^\circ)$ intersects the curve of $T(y_2)$ at a point whose ordinate is $T(y_2^\circ) = T(x_2^\circ)$ and whose abscissa is y_2°, the value of y_2 corresponding to x_2° and p. Thus, it is clear that the curves $T(x_2)$ and $T(y_2)$ must touch when the phases are pure, that is, $x_2 = 1$ or 0; they must also touch at the extrema since the composition values are the same at these points. [Similar conclusions hold for the $p(x_2)$ and $p(y_2)$ curves.] Flat maxima and minima are drawn in Figs. 9-4 and 9-5 since $g_{22}^{(1)}$ and $g_{22}^{(2)}$ are always finite and no cusps may occur.

Integration of Eqs. (9-57) to (9-62) requires more information than is usually available. In the following sections we present a number of detailed discussions of the applications of Eqs. (9-57) to (9-62) to particular systems in which parts of the system may be considered to be ideal.

9-5. LIQUID-VAPOR EQUILIBRIUM AT CONSTANT PRESSURE

In this section we consider a two-component, two-phase liquid-vapor system. We assume that phase 1, the liquid, and phase 2, the vapor, are ideal. Hence, $g_{22}^{(1)} = 1$, $g_{22}^{(2)} = 1$, and $\bar{L}_1$, $\bar{L}_2$, $\Delta\bar{v}_1$, and $\Delta\bar{v}_2$ are independent of composition. Thus

$$\bar{L}_1 = L_1 = h_1^{(2)}(T) - h_1^{(1)}(T,p) \tag{9-63}$$

is the heat of vaporization of 1 mole of pure component 1 at temperature T and pressure p.

Equations (9-57) and (9-58) become

$$\left(\frac{\partial T}{\partial x_2}\right)_p = \frac{x_2 - y_2}{x_1 x_2} \frac{RT^2}{y_1 L_1 + y_2 L_2} \tag{9-64}$$

and

$$\left(\frac{\partial T}{\partial y_2}\right)_p = \frac{x_2 - y_2}{y_1 y_2} \frac{RT^2}{x_1 L_1 + x_2 L_2} \tag{9-65}$$

Equations (9-64) and (9-65) may be transformed to yield

$$x_1(y_1 L_1 + y_2 L_2)\, dT = \frac{x_2 - y_2}{x_2} RT^2\, dx_2 \tag{9-66}$$

and

$$y_1(x_1 L_1 + x_2 L_2)\, dT = \frac{x_2 - y_2}{y_2} RT^2\, dy_2 \tag{9-67}$$

or

$$(y_1 x_1 L_1 - y_1 x_1 L_2 + x_1 L_2)\, dT = (x_2 - y_2) RT^2\, d \log x_2 \tag{9-68}$$

and

$$(y_1 x_1 L_1 - y_1 x_1 L_2 + y_1 L_2)\, dT = (x_2 - y_2) RT^2\, d \log y_2 \tag{9-69}$$

Subtraction of Eq. (9-68) from (9-69) results in

$$(y_1 - x_1)L_2\, dT = RT^2(x_2 - y_2)(d \log y_2 - d \log x_2) \tag{9-70}$$

Since
$$y_1 - x_1 = x_2 - y_2 \tag{9-71}$$

Equation (9-70) becomes

$$\frac{d \log (y_2/x_2)}{d(1/RT)} = -L_2 \tag{9-72}$$

In a similar manner, we obtain the equation

$$\frac{d \log (y_1/x_1)}{d(1/RT)} = -L_1 \tag{9-73}$$

Equation (9-72) can be integrated formally to yield

$$\frac{y_2}{x_2} = \exp\left[\int_T^{T_2} L_2(T')\, d\left(\frac{1}{RT'}\right)\right] \tag{9-74}$$

where $T = T(y_2) = T(x_2)$, $T_2(p)$ is the boiling point of pure liquid 2 at pressure p, and the coefficient of the exponential term is unity since $(v_2/x_2) \to 1$ as $x_2 \to 1$. In many systems, $L_1(T)$ and $L_2(T)$ are relatively insensitive to changes in the temperature and we may assume that

$$L_1(T) = L_1(T_1) = L_1 \tag{9-75}$$

$$L_2(T) = L_2(T_2) = L_2 \tag{9-76}$$

where $T_1(p)$ is the boiling point of pure liquid 1 at pressure p. Insertion of Eq. (9-76) into Eq. (9-74) yields

$$\frac{y_2}{x_2} = \exp\left[\frac{L_2}{R}\left(\frac{1}{T_2} - \frac{1}{T}\right)\right] \tag{9-77}$$

In a similar fashion, we arrive at the result

$$\frac{y_1}{x_1} = \exp\left[\frac{L_1}{R}\left(\frac{1}{T_1} - \frac{1}{T}\right)\right] \tag{9-78}$$

Equation (9-78) can be written in terms of x_2 and y_2 in the form

$$\frac{1 - y_2}{1 - x_2} = \exp\left[\frac{L_1}{R}\left(\frac{1}{T_1} - \frac{1}{T}\right)\right] \tag{9-79}$$

Substituting Eq. (9-79) into Eq. (9-77), and solving for x_2, we find

$$x_2 = \frac{\exp\left[L_1/R(1/T_1 - 1/T)\right] - 1}{\exp\left[L_1/R(1/T_1 - 1/T)\right] - \exp\left[L_2/R(1/T_2 - 1/T)\right]} \tag{9-80}$$

Carrying out similar substitutions for y_2, we obtain

$$y_2 = \frac{\exp\,[L_1/R(1/T_1 - 1/T)] - 1}{\exp\,[(L_1/R)(1/T_1 - 1/T_2) + (L_2 - L_1)/RT] - 1} \tag{9-81}$$

Equations (9-80) and (9-81) provide explicit expressions for x_2 and y_2 as functions of T and implicit expressions for T as functions of x_2 and y_2. Thus, temperature-composition diagrams similar to Fig. 9-6 can be constructed from knowledge of the boiling points and heats of vaporization at the boiling points of pure liquids 1 and 2.

Equation (9-77) can be obtained in a more elementary fashion. The chemical potential of component 2 in an ideal-gas mixture is given by the expression

$$\mu_2{}^{(2)} = \mu_2^*(T) + RT\log(py_2) \tag{9-82}$$

The chemical potential of component 2 in an ideal-liquid mixture is given by the expression

$$\mu_2{}^{(1)} = \mu_2^\circ(T,p) + RT\log x_2 \tag{9-83}$$

At equilibrium,

$$\mu_2^*(T) + RT\log(py_2) = \mu_2^\circ(T,p) + RT\log x_2 \tag{9-84}$$

Rearrangement of Eq. (9-84) yields

$$\frac{y_2}{x_2} = \exp\left[\frac{\mu_2^\circ(T,p) - \mu_2{}^g(T,p)}{RT}\right] \tag{9-85}$$

where

$$\mu_2{}^{(g)}(T,p) = \mu_2^*(T) + RT\log p \tag{9-86}$$

is the chemical potential of pure gas 2 and μ_2° is the chemical potential of pure liquid 2. Making use of the relation

$$\left[\frac{\partial(\mu_2/RT)}{\partial T}\right]_p = -\frac{h_2}{RT^2} \tag{9-87}$$

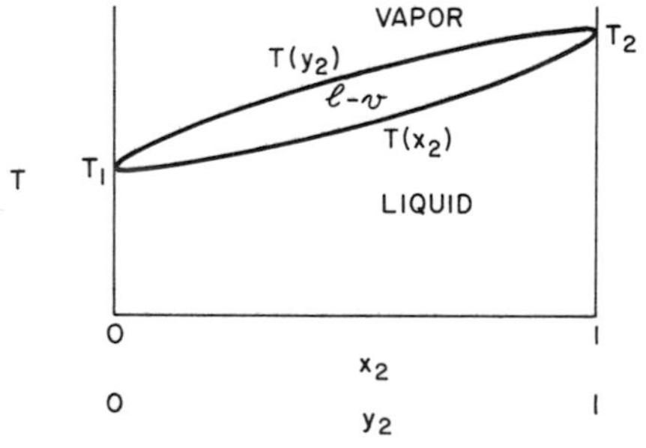

FIG. 9-6. Temperature-composition diagram for a two-component liquid-vapor system.

Equation (9-85) can be rewritten in the form

$$\frac{y_2}{x_2} = \exp\left[\int_T^{T_2} (h_2^{(g)} - h_2^{(l)})\, d\left(\frac{1}{RT'}\right)\right] \tag{9-88}$$

which is identical to Eq. (9-74).

It is possible to solve Eqs. (9-64) and (9-65) for y_2 as a function of x_2, by eliminating T. In the ideal case, we obtain

$$\left(\frac{dy_2}{dx_2}\right)_p = \frac{y_2 y_1}{x_2 x_1} \frac{x_1 L_1 + x_2 L_2}{y_1 L_1 + y_2 L_2} \tag{9-89}$$

Equation (9-89) is useful in the discussion of the theory of distillation processes.

9-6. LIQUID-VAPOR EQUILIBRIUM AT CONSTANT TEMPERATURE

In this section we consider a two-component, two-phase liquid-vapor system at constant temperature. We assume that the liquid phase 1 and the vapor phase 2 are ideal. Hence, $g_{22}^{(1)} = g_{22}^{(2)} = 1$ and $\bar{v}_1^{(2)} = \bar{v}_2^{(2)} = RT/p$. In addition, we assume that the pressure is low so that $\bar{v}_1^{(2)} \gg \bar{v}_1^{(1)}$ and $\bar{v}_2^{(2)} \gg \bar{v}_2^{(1)}$. Under these conditions, Eqs. (9-59) and (9-60) reduce to

$$\left(\frac{\partial p}{\partial x_2}\right)_T = -p\,\frac{x_2 - y_2}{x_1 x_2} \tag{9-90}$$

$$\left(\frac{\partial p}{\partial y_2}\right)_T = -p\,\frac{x_2 - y_2}{y_1 y_2} \tag{9-91}$$

Combination of Eqs. (9-90) and (9-91) results in

$$\left(\frac{\partial y_2}{\partial x_2}\right)_T = \frac{y_1 y_2}{x_1 x_2} \tag{9-92}$$

Integration of Eq. (9-92) yields

$$\log\frac{1 - y_2}{y_2} = \log\frac{1 - x_2}{x_2} - \log \beta(T) \tag{9-93}$$

where $\beta(T)$ is a constant of integration. Equation (9-93) can be re-arranged in the form

$$\beta\,\frac{1 - y_2}{y_2} = \frac{1 - x_2}{x_2} \tag{9-94}$$

which can be solved for y_2 to give

$$y_2 = \frac{\beta x_2}{1 + (\beta - 1)x_2} \tag{9-95}$$

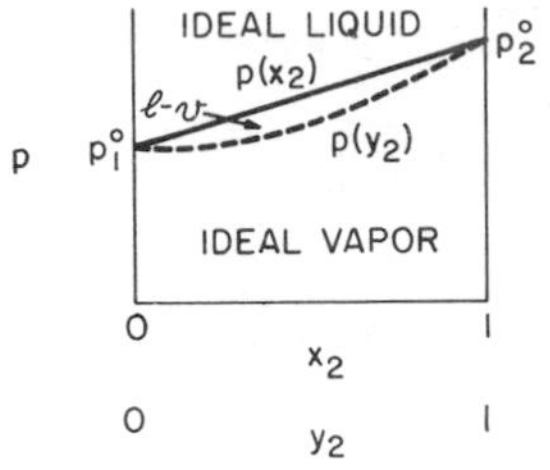

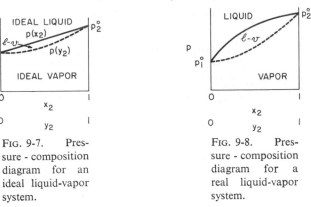

FIG. 9-7. Pressure - composition diagram for an ideal liquid-vapor system.

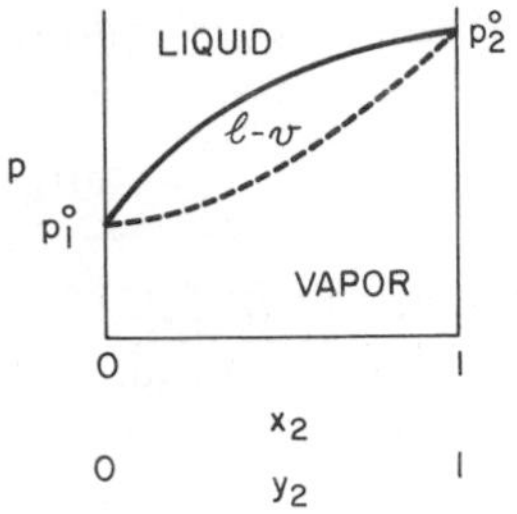

FIG. 9-8. Pressure - composition diagram for a real liquid-vapor system.

Substitution of Eq. (9-95) into Eq. (9-90) and rearrangement result in

$$d \log p = \frac{(\beta - 1)\, dx_2}{1 + (\beta - 1)x_2} \tag{9-96}$$

Integration of Eq. (9-96) along a path at constant temperature yields

$$\log p = \log [1 + (\beta - 1)x_2] + \log \alpha \tag{9-97}$$

where $\alpha(T)$ is an integration constant. Equation (9-97) can be rewritten in the form

$$p = \alpha[1 + (\beta - 1)x_2] \tag{9-98}$$

In order to evaluate the constants of integration in Eq. (9-98) we investigate its values for pure components 1 and 2. When $x_2 = 0$, Eq. (9-98) becomes

$$p = p_1^\circ = \alpha \tag{9-99}$$

where p_1° is the pressure of pure component 1 at temperature T for liquid-vapor equilibrium. When $x_2 = 1$, Eq. (9-98) becomes

$$p = p_2^\circ = \beta\alpha \tag{9-100}$$

and

$$\beta = \frac{p_2^\circ}{p_1^\circ} \tag{9-101}$$

where p_2° is the pressure of pure component 2 at temperature T for liquid-vapor equilibrium. Substitution of Eqs. (9-99) and (9-101) into Eq. (9-95) yields

$$y_2 = \frac{p_2^\circ x_2}{p_1^\circ + (p_2^\circ - p_1^\circ)x_2} \tag{9-102}$$

which can be inverted to yield

$$x_2 = \frac{p_1^\circ y_2}{p_2^\circ + (p_1^\circ - p_2^\circ)y_2} \tag{9-103}$$

The pressure can be obtained as a function of x_2 from Eq. (9-98) in the form

$$p(x_2) = p_1^\circ + (p_2^\circ - p_1^\circ)x_2 = x_1 p_1^\circ + x_2 p_2^\circ \tag{9-104}$$

The pressure can be obtained as a function of y_2 by substituting Eq. (9-103) into Eq. (9-104), in the form

$$p(y_2) = \frac{p_1^\circ p_2^\circ}{p_2^\circ + (p_1^\circ - p_2^\circ)y_2} = \frac{p_1^\circ p_2^\circ}{y_1 p_2^\circ + y_2 p_1^\circ} \tag{9-105}$$

Equations (9-104) and (9-105) provide the basis for a pressure-composition diagram for an ideal system. Figure 9-7 is a plot of these equations while Figs. 9-8 and 9-9 represent typical nonideal cases.

9-7. LIQUID-SOLID EQUILIBRIUM AT CONSTANT PRESSURE

In this section, we consider a system consisting of two substances which are immiscible in the solid state but which are miscible throughout the entire composition range in the liquid phase. The temperature-composition diagram of this system is represented in Fig. 9-10. Phase 2 is pure solid 1 or pure solid 2, while phase 1 is the liquid.

We first consider the equilibrium between the liquid solution and pure solid 1; in this case, $y_1 = 1$ and $y_2 = 0$. Under these conditions, Eq. (9-57) becomes

$$\left(\frac{\partial T}{\partial x_2}\right)_p = g_{22}{}^{(1)} \frac{RT^2}{x_1 \bar{L}_1} \tag{9-106}$$

where
$$\bar{L}_1 = \bar{h}_1{}^{(2)} - \bar{h}_1{}^{(1)} = h_1{}^{(s)} - \bar{h}_1{}^{(l)} \tag{9-107}$$

is the heat evolved on solution of 1 mole of solid 1 in an infinite amount of saturated solution. When we consider the equilibrium between the liquid solution and pure solid 2, $y_2 = 1$, $y_1 = 0$, and Eq. (9-57) becomes

$$\left(\frac{\partial T}{\partial x_2}\right)_p = -g_{22}{}^{(1)} \frac{RT^2}{x_2 \bar{L}_2} \tag{9-108}$$

where
$$\bar{L}_2 = \bar{h}_2{}^{(2)} - \bar{h}_2{}^{(1)} = h_2{}^{(s)} - \bar{h}_2{}^{(l)} \tag{9-109}$$

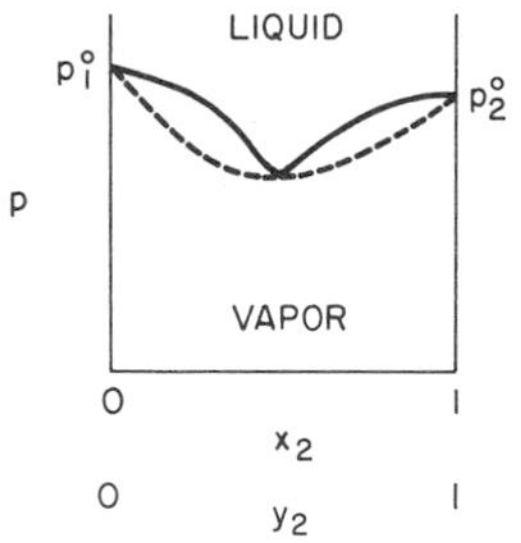

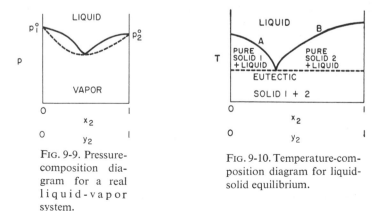

FIG. 9-9. Pressure-composition diagram for a real liquid-vapor system.

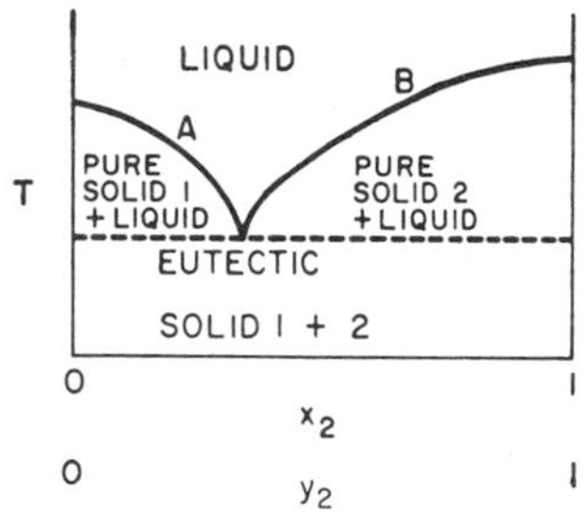

FIG. 9-10. Temperature-composition diagram for liquid-solid equilibrium.

If $\bar{L}_2$ is positive, the solubility of component 2 decreases with increasing temperature. $\bar{L}_2$ is often called the "last" heat of solution, i.e., the differential heat of solution into saturated solution, and for most electrolytes is negative.

If we use an ideal-liquid approximation, $g_{22}^{(1)} = 1$, $\bar{h}_2^{(1)} = h_2^{(1)}(T,p)$, and $-\bar{L}_2 = -L_2 = -h_2^{(s)} + h_2^{(l)}$ is the molar heat of fusion of pure liquid 2 at T and p. Equation (9-108) becomes

$$\left(\frac{\partial T}{\partial x_2}\right)_p = -\frac{RT^2}{x_2\bar{L}_2} = -\frac{RT^2}{x_2 L_2} \tag{9-110}$$

or

$$\left(\frac{\partial \log x_2}{\partial T}\right)_p = -\frac{L_2}{RT^2} \tag{9-111}$$

If we approximate $L_2(T,p)$ by $L_2(T_2,p)$, where T_2 is the melting point of pure solid 2 at pressure p, Eq. (9-111) can be easily integrated to yield

$$\log x_2 = \frac{L_2}{R}\left(\frac{1}{T} - \frac{1}{T_2}\right) \tag{9-112}$$

where $T = T(x_2)$. Rearrangement of Eq. (9-112) results in

$$T = \frac{T_2}{(RT_2/L_2)\log x_2 + 1} \tag{9-113}$$

$T = T(x_2)$ is the temperature at which pure solid 2 is in equilibrium with the liquid solution with mole fraction x_2 at pressure p. Thus, T is the freezing point of the liquid solution with mole fraction x_2. Equation (9-113) is the equation for curve B in Fig. 9-10. Similarly, from Eq. (9-106), we obtain the equation for curve A in Fig. 9-10 in the form

$$T = \frac{T_1}{1 + (RT_1/L_1)\log(1 - x_2)} \tag{9-114}$$

where T_1 is the freezing point of pure liquid 1 at pressure p. At the eutectic point, where three phases, solid 1, solid 2, and liquid, are in equilibrium, Eqs. (9-113) and (9-114) must be satisfied simultaneously.

Most of the elementary physical chemistry of solutions comes out of Eqs. (9-113) or (9-114). It is of interest to consider Eq. (9-114) when $x_2 \ll 1$. In this case we can approximate $\log(1 - x_2)$ by $-x_2$, and Eq. (9-114) becomes

$$T - T_1 = \frac{RT_1T}{L_1} x_2 \tag{9-115}$$

which can be approximated by

$$T - T_1 = \frac{RT^2}{L_1} x_2 \tag{9-116}$$

The quantity L_1 is usually negative, and Eq. (9-116) is the familiar van't Hoff law for freezing-point depression.

9-8. SOLID-LIQUID EQUILIBRIUM WITH SOLID COMPOUND AT CONSTANT PRESSURE

In this section we consider a two-component system consisting of a liquid mixture and three immiscible solid phases: pure solids 1 and 2 and a compound of composition $(X_1)_{\nu_1}(X_2)_{\nu_2}$. The temperature-composition diagram of this system is represented in Fig. 9-11. In this case, phase 1 is the liquid mixture and phase 2 is pure solid 1, pure solid 2, or solid compound of mole fraction $y_2 = y_2^* = \nu_2/(\nu_1 + \nu_2)$. Substitution of y_2^* into Eq. (9-57) results in

$$\left(\frac{\partial T}{\partial x_2}\right)_p = \frac{(\nu_1 + \nu_2)(x_2) - \nu_2}{x_1 x_2} \frac{g_{22}{}^{(1)} R T^2}{\nu_1 \bar{L}_1 + \nu_2 \bar{L}_2} \tag{9-117}$$

Equation (9-117) represents the curve *ACB*, in Fig. 9-11, of coexistence of the liquid solution and the solid compound.

In the ideal case, $g_{22}{}^{(1)} = 1$, and Eq. (9-117) becomes

$$\left(\frac{\partial T}{\partial x_2}\right)_p = -\frac{(\nu_1 + \nu_2)x_2 - \nu_2}{x_1 x_2} \frac{R T^2}{L_{12}} \tag{9-118}$$

where $L_{12} = -(\nu_1 \bar{L}_1 + \nu_2 \bar{L}_2)$ is the heat of fusion of the solid compound into the ideal liquid. Integration of Eq. (9-118) under the assumption that L_{12} is independent of T results in

$$\frac{L_{12}}{R}\left(\frac{1}{T} - \frac{1}{T_{12}}\right) = \int_{\nu_2/(\nu_1+\nu_2)}^{x_2} \left[\frac{\nu_1 + \nu_2}{1 - x_2} - \frac{\nu_2}{x_2(1 - x_2)}\right] dx_2 \tag{9-119}$$

where T_{12} is the melting point of the solid compound into a liquid of the same composition at pressure p. Equation (9-119) can be solved for T to yield

$$T = \frac{T_{12}}{1 - (RT_{12}/L_{12}) \log \{[(\nu_1 + \nu_2/\nu_1)x_1]^{\nu_1}[(\nu_1 + \nu_2/\nu_2)x_2]^{\nu_2}\}} \tag{9-120}$$

when $x_1 = \dfrac{\nu_1}{\nu_1 + \nu_2} = y_1^*$ and $x_2 = \dfrac{\nu_2}{\nu_1 + \nu_2} = y_2^*$, $T = T_{12}$

the melting point of the solid compound.

The solid compound in Fig. 9-11 is said to have a congruent melting point since it melts into a liquid of the same composition as the compound. A solid compound is said to have an incongruent melting point if it does not melt into a liquid phase of the same composition but decomposes. It is of interest that solid-compound formation can occur with ideal-liquid behavior.

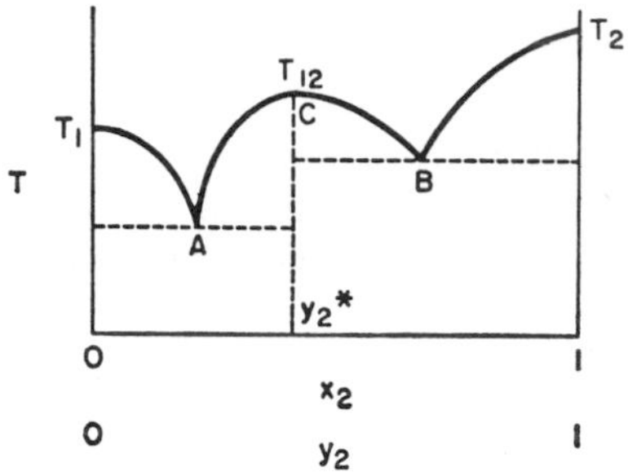

FIG. 9-11. Temperature-composition diagram for solid-liquid equilibrium with solid compound.

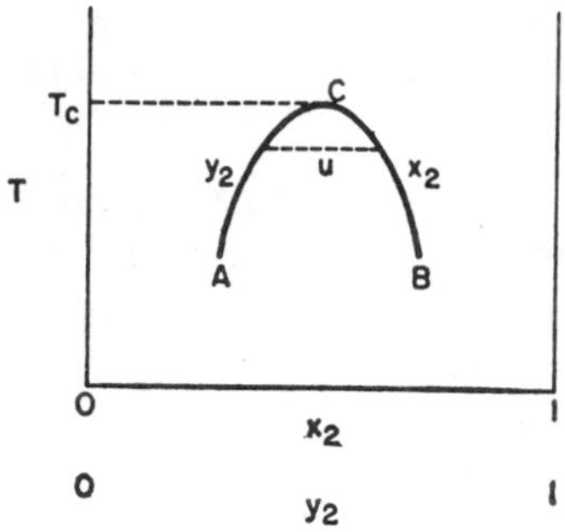

FIG. 9-12. Temperature-composition diagram for nonideal liquid-liquid equilibrium.

9-9. NONIDEAL LIQUID-LIQUID EQUILIBRIUM AT CONSTANT PRESSURE

In this section we consider a system of two components in two partially miscible liquid phases. The temperature-composition diagram of this system is represented in Fig. 9-12. The liquids are completely miscible above the critical temperature T_c. The curve AC represents the equilibrium temperature as a function of the composition of liquid phase 2; the curve BC represents the equilibrium temperature as a function of the composition of the liquid phase 1.

We shall use the explicit conditions for heterogeneous equilibrium in order to derive the equations describing temperature-composition equilibrium curves. At equilibrium,

$$\begin{aligned} \mu_2^{(1)}(T,p,x_2) &= \mu_2^{(2)}(T,p,y_2) \\ \mu_1^{(1)}(T,p,x_2) &= \mu_1^{(2)}(T,p,y_2) \end{aligned} \qquad (9\text{-}121)$$

Using the Margules expansion for the chemical potential of a component in a liquid mixture (see Sec. 11-6), we may write

$$\mu_2^{(1)} = \mu_2^{(l)}(T,p) + RT \log x_2 + \alpha x_1^2 + O(x_1^3) \qquad (9\text{-}122a)$$

$$\mu_1^{(1)} = \mu_1^{(l)}(T,p) + RT \log x_1 + \alpha x_2^2 + O(x_2^3) \qquad (9\text{-}122b)$$

Substitution of Eqs. (9-122a) and (9-122b) and similar relations for $\mu_1^{(2)}$ and $\mu_2^{(2)}$ into Eq. (9-121) yields

$$\log x_2 + \frac{\alpha}{RT} x_1^2 = \log y_2 + \frac{\alpha}{RT} y_1^2 \qquad (9\text{-}123a)$$

$$\log x_1 + \frac{\alpha}{RT} x_2^2 = \log y_1 + \frac{\alpha}{RT} y_2^2 \qquad (9\text{-}123b)$$

If we assume that the curve ACB in Fig. 9-12 is symmetric about its mid-point, $x_2 = y_2 = 0.5$, we can write $x_1 = y_2$ and $x_2 = y_1$. Under these conditions, Eqs. (9-123*a*) and (9-123*b*) become identical, and we may write

$$\log x_2 + \frac{\alpha}{RT} x_1^2 = \log x_1 + \frac{\alpha}{RT} x_2^2 \tag{9-124}$$

or

$$\log \frac{x_2}{x_1} = \frac{\alpha}{RT}(x_2 - x_1) \tag{9-125}$$

If u is set equal to $x_2 - y_2 = x_2 - x_1$, Eq. (9-125) becomes

$$\log \frac{1+u}{1-u} = \frac{\alpha}{RT} u \tag{9-126}$$

or

$$u = \tanh \frac{\alpha u}{2RT} \tag{9-127}$$

If we let $Z = \alpha u/2RT$, Eq. (9-127) can be rewritten in the form

$$\frac{2RT}{\alpha} Z = \tanh Z \tag{9-128}$$

Equation (9-128) relates the difference in composition of the two liquid phases to the temperature T. Equation (9-128) is usually solved graphically by plotting $w = \tanh Z$ and $w = (2RT/\alpha)Z$ and noting the points of intersection of the two curves. These curves are plotted in Fig. 9-13. If $(2RT/\alpha) > 1$, the two curves intersect only at the point $u = 0$; i.e., the two phases always have the same composition and, therefore, are miscible. Because of our symmetry assumption, $x_2 = x_1$ in this case. For $(2RT/\alpha) < 1$, Eq. (9-128) also has a nonzero solution and the system is heterogeneous. Thus, a nonideal liquid solution will have a critical mixing temperature if α is positive. At the critical temperature, $\alpha/2RT_c = 1$ and $T_c = \alpha/2R$.

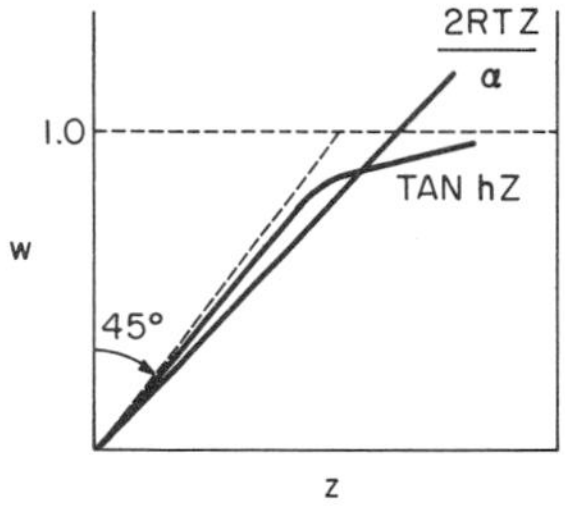

FIG. 9-13. Plot of $w = \tanh Z$ and $w = (2RT/\alpha)Z$. The dashed line at 45° to the axis is a plot of $w = (2RT_c/\alpha)Z$.

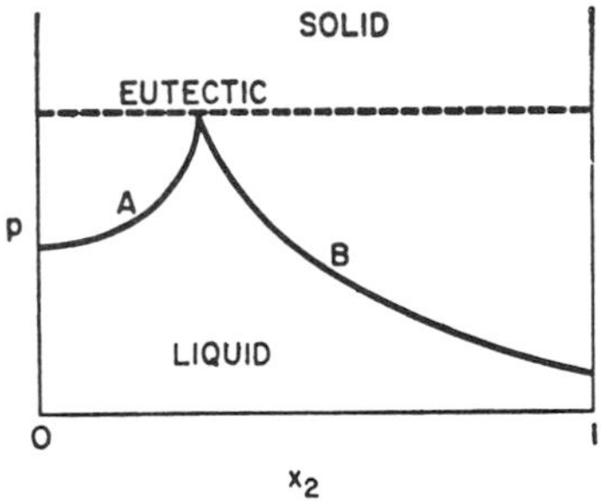

FIG. 9-14. Pressure-composition diagram for liquid-solid equilibrium.

The assumption of symmetry holds reasonably well for molecules of approximately the same size; in polymer solutions, it is necessary to use volume fractions instead of mole fractions to maintain the symmetric form (Flory-Huggins theory).

9-10. LIQUID-SOLID EQUILIBRIUM AT CONSTANT TEMPERATURE

In this section we consider the same system as in Sec. 9-7. The pressure-composition diagram of this system is represented in Fig. 9-14. The form of the pressure-composition curves in Fig. 9-14 will be derived by making use of Eqs. (9-59) and (9-60).

Consider curve A representing equilibrium between pure solid 1, $y_2 = 0$, and the liquid solution. In this case,

$$\Delta\bar{v}_1 = v_1^{(s)} - \bar{v}_1^{(l)} \tag{9-129}$$

and Eq. (9-59) becomes

$$\left(\frac{\partial p}{\partial x_2}\right)_T = \frac{g_{22}^{(l)}RT}{x_1(\bar{v}_1^{(l)} - v_1^{(s)})} \tag{9-130}$$

Along curve B, $y_2 = 1$, and Eq. (9-59) reduces to

$$\left(\frac{\partial p}{\partial x_2}\right)_T = -\frac{g_{22}^{(l)}RT}{x_2(\bar{v}_2^{(l)} - v_2^{(s)})} \tag{9-131}$$

If $\bar{v}_2^{(l)} - v_2^{(s)} > 0$ and $\bar{v}_1^{(l)} - v_1^{(s)} > 0$, a pressure-composition diagram similar to Fig. 9-14 is obtained. This is generally the case. Rearrangement of Eq. (9-131) results in

$$\left(\frac{\partial \log x_2}{\partial p}\right)_T = -\frac{\bar{v}_2^{(l)} - v_2^{(s)}}{g_{22}^{(l)}RT} \tag{9-132}$$

Since $g_{22}^{(l)} > 0$, an increase in pressure causes a decrease in the solubility of component 2 if $\bar{v}_2^{(l)} > v_2^{(s)}$. This is an example of the Le Châtelier principle (Sec. 8-1).

For an ideal solution, $g_{22}^{(l)} = 1$, and $\bar{v}_2^{(l)} = v_2^{(l)}$. In this case, Eq. (9-132) becomes

$$\left(\frac{\partial \log x_2}{\partial p}\right)_T = -\frac{\Delta v_2^{(f)}}{RT} \tag{9-133}$$

where $\Delta v_2^{(f)} = v_2^{(l)} - v_2^{(s)}$ is the volume increment of fusion of pure component 2 at temperature T. If $\Delta v_2^{(f)}$ is independent of pressure, Eq. (9-133) can be easily integrated to yield

$$\log\frac{x_2}{x_2^\circ} = -\frac{\Delta v_2^{(f)}}{RT}(p - p^\circ) \tag{9-134}$$

where x_2° is the mole fraction of component 2 in the liquid solution at the reference pressure p°.

The variation of the eutectic point in this system obeys the generalized Clapeyron equation for univariant systems. This discussion concludes the quantitative treatment of phase diagrams in terms of the general equations of heterogeneous equilibrium.

9-11. LIQUID-VAPOR EQUILIBRIUM

In this section we consider the equilibrium between a condensed phase and vapor. We derive the Duhem-Margules equation and investigate its application to the determination of vapor fugacities.

We consider an r-component system composed of a liquid and a vapor phase in equilibrium. The chemical potential of component i in the vapor phase is given by Eq. (7-155) in the form

$$\mu_i^{(g)} = \mu_i^*(T) + RT \log p_i^* \tag{9-135}$$

Consequently, the total differential of $\mu_i^{(g)}$ can be written

$$d\mu_i^{(g)} = RTd \log p_i^* + [R \log p_i^* - s_i^*(T)]\, dT \tag{9-136}$$

where Eq. (7-192) has been used. At equilibrium,

$$\mu_i^{(l)} = \mu_i^{(g)} \tag{9-137}$$

and thus

$$\bar{h}_i^{(l)} - T\bar{s}_i^{(l)} = RT \log p_i^* - Ts_i^* + h_i^* \tag{9-138}$$

where we have used Eq. (6-13). Substitution of Eq. (9-138) into Eq. (9-136) results in

$$d\mu_i^{(g)} = RTd \log p_i^* + \left[\frac{\bar{h}_i^{(l)} - h_i^*}{T} - \bar{s}_i^{(l)}\right] dT \tag{9-139}$$

In the field of equilibrium states, $d\mu_i^{(g)} = d\mu_i^{(l)}$, and Eq. (9-139) can be substituted into the Gibbs-Duhem equation [Eq. (9-9)] for the liquid phase to obtain

$$\sum_{i=1}^{r} x_i(d\mu_i^{(g)} + \bar{s}_i^{(l)}\, dT - \bar{v}_i^{(l)}\, dp) = 0 \tag{9-140}$$

or

$$\sum_{i=1}^{r} x_i d \log p_i^* - \frac{L^*}{RT^2}\, dT - \frac{v^{(l)}}{RT}\, dp = 0 \tag{9-141}$$

In Eq. (9-141), x_i is the mole fraction of component i in the liquid phase,

$$L^* = \sum_{i=1}^{r} x_i L_i^*$$

where

$$L_i^* = h_i^* - h_i^{(l)}$$

is the differential heat of vaporization of i at temperature T from the liquid at pressure p to the gas at zero pressure, and $v^{(l)}$ is the mean molal

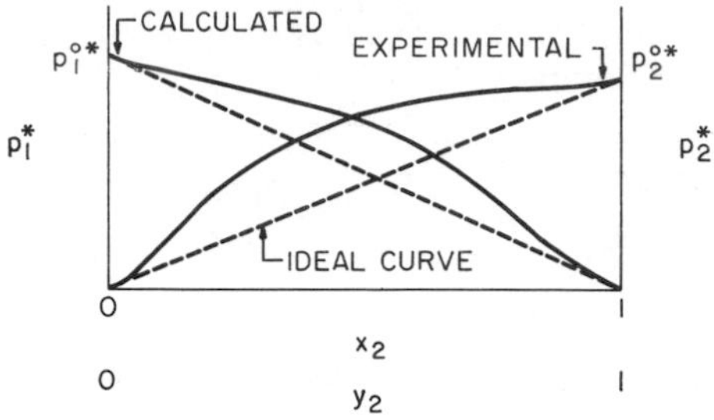

FIG. 9-15. Plot of experimental p_2^* and calculated p_1^* versus the mole fraction of component 2.

volume of the liquid phase. Equation (9-141) is called the Duhem-Margules equation. It differs from the Gibbs-Duhem equation in that it contains the conditions for heterogeneous equilibrium.

The Duhem-Margules equation is usually written in either isothermal or isobaric forms. It is most frequently used in the determination of the fugacities of vapor in equilibrium with liquid. At constant temperature Eq. (9-141) reduces to

$$\sum_{i=1}^{r} x_i d \log p_i^* - \frac{v^{(l)}}{RT} dp = 0 \tag{9-142}$$

Equation (9-142) is frequently approximated by

$$\sum_{i=1}^{r} x_i d \log p_i^* = 0 \tag{9-143}$$

when $pv^{(l)}/RT \ll 1$. It is clear that dp and dT cannot both be set equal to zero in Eq. (9-141) if we reserve the right to vary the $r - 1$ composition variables independently since we are dealing with a two-phase, r-component system that has r degrees of freedom. If we do not wish to neglect the dp term in Eq. (9-142), we may set

$$dp = \sum_{i=1}^{r} \left(\frac{\partial p}{\partial x_i}\right)_{T, x_{j \neq i}} dx_i \tag{9-144}$$

and obtain $(\partial p/\partial x_i)_{T, x_{j \neq i}}$ from the equations for heterogeneous equilibrium. A knowledge of the fugacity of $r - 1$ components permits the evaluation of the fugacity of the rth component from Eq. (9-142) or (9-143).

If the vapor phase is ideal,

$$p_i^* = p_i = py_i \tag{9-145}$$

where Eq. (7-164), Dalton's law, has been used and where p is the total pressure and y_i is the mole fraction of component i in the gas phase. Substitution of Eq. (9-145) into Eq. (9-143) yields

$$\sum_{i=1}^{r} x_i d \log (py_i) = 0 \tag{9-146}$$

For a binary system, knowledge of p as a function of x_2 is sufficient to determine p_1 and p_2 from Eq. (9-146).

For a binary solution ($r = 2$), Eq. (9-143) takes the form

$$d \log p_2^* = -\frac{x_1}{x_2}\, d \log p_1^* \tag{9-147}$$

Equation (9-147) can be used to determine the fugacities as a function of the liquid composition. Integration of Eq. (9-147) yields

$$\log \frac{p_2^*}{p_2^{\circ *}} = -\int_0^{p_1^*} \frac{x_1}{(1 - x_1)p_1^*}\, dp_1^* \tag{9-148}$$

where $p_2^{\circ *}$ is the vapor fugacity of pure component 2 at temperature T in equilibrium with the liquid. The integration in Eq. (9-148) is over a constant-temperature path. The right-hand side of Eq. (9-148) is usually evaluated by graphical methods, and results similar to those of Fig. 9-15 are obtained. The experimental data that enter into the calculation are plotted as p_1^* versus $x_1/(1 - x_1)p_1^*$ as illustrated in Fig. 9-16. The lower limit as $p_1^* \to 0$ can be obtained by using a Henry's law extrapolation. Henry's law is discussed in Sec. 11-4 and predicts

$$\lim_{x_1 \to 0} \frac{p_1^*}{x_1} = K(T) \tag{9-149}$$

In this way, values of p_2^* can be computed.

The method above can be improved for numerical integration by integrating only over the deviations from ideality of the liquid. If $p_2^{\circ *}$ is the vapor fugacity of component 2 when $x_2 = 1$, and $p_1^{\circ *}$ is the vapor fugacity of component 1 when $x_1 = 1$, Eq. (9-147) can be written in the form

$$d \log \frac{p_2^*}{p_2^{\circ *} x_2} = -\frac{x_1}{x_2}\, d \log \frac{p_1^*}{p_1^{\circ *} x_1} \tag{9-150}$$

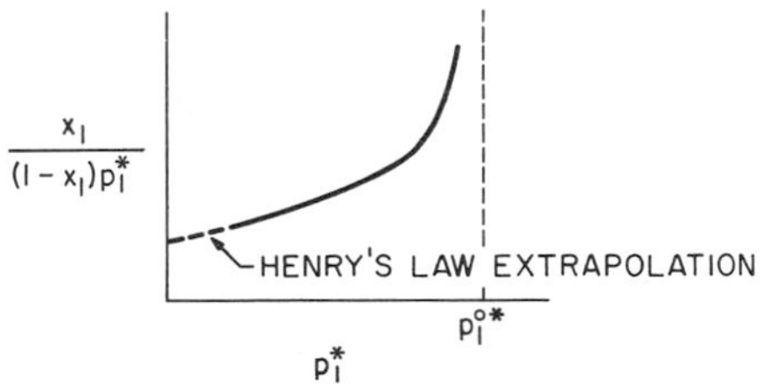

FIG. 9-16. Plot of p_1^* versus $x_1/(1 - x_1)p_1^*$.

where we have used the fact that

$$x_1 d\log x_1 + x_2 d\log x_2 = 0 \tag{9-151}$$

and the approximation of Eq. (9-143) for pure systems,

$$d\log p_2^{\circ*} = d\log p_1^{\circ*} = 0 \tag{9-152}$$

When the liquid is ideal, Eq. (9-137) reduces to

$$\mu_i^\circ(T,p) + RT\log x_i = \mu_i^*(T) + RT\log p_i^* \tag{9-153}$$

When $x_i = 1$, Eq. (9-153) becomes

$$\mu_i^\circ(T,p) = \mu_i^*(T) + RT\log p_i^{\circ*} \tag{9-154}$$

Comparison of Eqs. (9-153) and (9-154) yields the result

$$p_i^* = x_i p_i^{\circ*} \tag{9-155}$$

for the ideal liquid. Thus $p_1^*/p_1^{\circ*}x_1$ is the ratio of the fugacity of component 1 in the real system to the fugacity of component 1 in the system in which the liquid is ideal. It is convenient to introduce the symbol $u_i = p_i^*/p_i^{\circ*}x_i$. Equation (9-150) can be integrated to yield

$$\log u_2 = -\int_{x_1'=0}^{x_1'=x_1} \frac{x_1'}{x_2'}\, d\log u_1 \tag{9-156}$$

The lower limit of integration is evaluated by using Henry's law:

$$\lim_{x_1\to 0} \frac{p_1^*}{x_1} = K(T) \tag{9-157}$$

Equation (9-156) is now written as

$$\log u_2 = -\int_{\log[K(T)/p_1^{\circ*}]}^{\log(p_1^*/p_1^{\circ*}x_1)} \frac{x_1'}{x_2'}\, d\log u_1 \tag{9-158}$$

Using tabulated values of x_1/x_2 versus $\log(p_1^*/p_1^{\circ*}x_1)$, we can carry out a graphical integration. For positive deviations from ideality, that is, $u_1 > 1$, a graph similar to that in Fig. 9-17 is obtained. The area is negative, since we integrate from right to left. For negative deviations from ideality, $u_1 < 1$, and the area of integration is positive (see Fig. 9-18). Thus, in two-component nonideal solutions, the deviations from ideality of the components have the same sign.

The Duhem-Margules equation [Eq. (9-141)] at constant pressure becomes

$$\sum_{i=1}^{r} x_i d\log p_i^* - \frac{L^*}{RT^2}\, dT = 0 \tag{9-159}$$

For a system consisting of pure component i, Eq. (9-159) reduces to

$$d \log p_i^{\circ *} - \frac{L_i^*}{RT^2} dT = 0 \qquad (9\text{-}160)$$

where $L_i^* = h_i^* - h_i^{(l)}$ is the molal heat of vaporization of pure liquid i to vapor at zero pressure. Multiplication of Eq. (9-160) by x_i and summation over r components result in

$$\sum_{i=1}^{r} x_i d \log p_i^{\circ *} - \sum_{i=1}^{r} \frac{x_i L_i^*}{RT^2} dT = 0 \qquad (9\text{-}161)$$

Subtraction of Eq. (9-161) from Eq. (9-160) yields

$$\sum_{i=1}^{r} x_i d \log \frac{p_i^*}{p_i^{\circ *}} + \frac{\sum_{i=1}^{r} x_i(\bar{h}_i^{(l)} - h_i^{(l)})\, dT}{RT^2} = 0 \qquad (9\text{-}162)$$

where $\sum_{i=1}^{r} x_i(\bar{h}_i^{(l)} - h_i^{(l)})$ is the mean molal heat of mixing of the liquid solution. This is often a very small quantity; hence an approximation to Eq. (9-162) which is often useful is

$$\sum_{i=1}^{r} x_i d \log \frac{p_i^*}{p_i^{\circ *}} = 0 \qquad (9\text{-}163)$$

If the vapor phase is ideal, Eq. (9-163) reduces to

$$\sum_{i=1}^{r} x_i d \log \frac{p_i}{p_i^{\circ}} = 0 \qquad (9\text{-}164)$$

where p_i is the partial pressure of i in the gas mixture and p_i° is the vapor pressure of pure liquid i. Equations (9-163) and (9-164) are useful in the discussion of distillation processes.

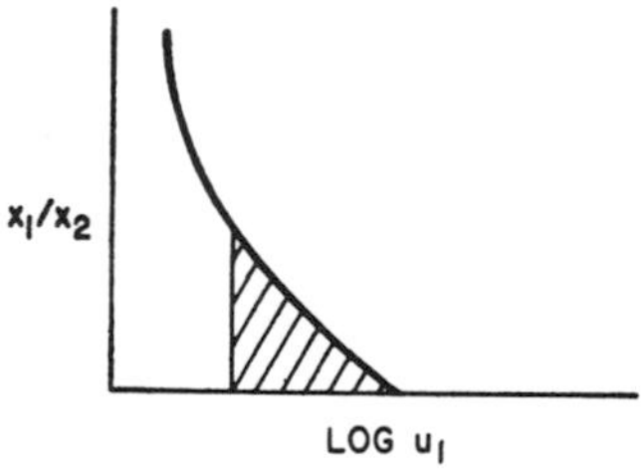

FIG. 9-17. Plot of log u_1 versus x_1/x_2.

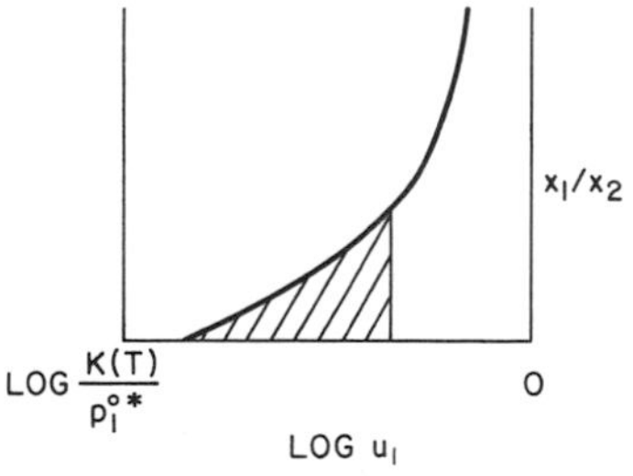

FIG. 9-18. Plot of log u_1 versus x_1/x_2.

9-12. DEPENDENCE OF VAPOR FUGACITY ON TEMPERATURE, PRESSURE, AND COMPOSITION

In this section, we consider a binary solution in equilibrium with vapor. We shall investigate in some detail the dependence of the vapor fugacities on temperature, pressure, and composition.

The total derivative of the chemical potential of component 2 in the liquid (l) phase may be written

$$d\mu_2^{(l)} = -\bar{s}_2^{(l)}\, dT + \bar{v}_2^{(l)}\, dp + G_{22}^{(l)}\, dx_2 \tag{9-165}$$

where

$$G_{22}^{(l)} = \left(\frac{\partial \mu_2^{(l)}}{\partial x_2}\right)_{T,p} \tag{9-166}$$

The total derivative of the chemical potential of component 2 in the vapor phase may be written in the form

$$d\mu_2^{(g)} = RTd\log p_2^* + (R\log p_2^* - s_2^*)\, dT$$

$$= RTd\log p_2^* + \left(\frac{\bar{h}_2^{(l)} - h_2^*}{T} - \bar{s}_2^{(l)}\right) dT \tag{9-167}$$

where Eq. (9-139) has been used. Making use of Eqs. (9-165) and (9-167) and the fact that $d\mu_2^{(g)} = d\mu_2^{(l)}$, we can write

$$d\log p_2^* = \frac{\bar{L}_2^*}{RT^2}\, dT + \frac{\bar{v}_2^{(l)}}{RT}\, dp + g_{22}^{(l)}\, d\log x_2 \tag{9-168}$$

where

$$\bar{L}_2^* = h_2^* - \bar{h}_2^{(l)} \tag{9-169}$$

and

$$g_{22}^{(l)}\frac{RT}{x_2} = G_{22}^{(l)} \tag{9-170}$$

A similar equation can be written for component 1. It is clear by application of the phase rule that T, p, and x_2 cannot all be varied independently in this two-component, two-phase system.

At constant temperature, Eq. (9-168) becomes

$$\left(\frac{\partial \log p_2^*}{\partial p}\right)_T = \frac{\bar{v}_2^{(l)}}{RT}\left[1 + \frac{g_{22}^{(l)}RT}{\bar{v}_2^{(l)}x_2}\left(\frac{\partial x_2}{\partial p}\right)_T\right] \tag{9-171}$$

The quantity $(\partial x_2/\partial p)_T$ is obtained from pressure-composition diagrams. If vapor 1 is very slightly soluble in liquid 2, that is, $x_1 \ll 1$, we may assume that

$$\left|\left(\frac{\partial \log x_2}{\partial \log p}\right)_T\right| = \left|\frac{1}{x_2}\left(\frac{\partial x_1}{\partial \log p}\right)_T\right| \ll 1 \tag{9-172}$$

In this case, $\left| g_{22}{}^{(l)} \frac{RT}{p\bar{v}_2{}^{(l)}} \left(\frac{\partial \log x_2}{\partial \log p}\right)_T \right| < 1$

and Eq. (9-171) can be approximated by

$$\left(\frac{\partial \log p_2^*}{\partial p}\right)_T = \frac{\bar{v}_2{}^{(l)}}{RT} \tag{9-173}$$

For an ideal vapor, Eq. (9-173) becomes

$$\left(\frac{\partial \log p_2}{\partial p}\right)_T = \frac{\bar{v}_2{}^{(l)}}{RT} \tag{9-174}$$

It should be noted here that Eqs. (9-173) and (9-174) are expressions for derivatives of vapor fugacity in two-phase systems; they should not be confused with similar expressions for homogeneous systems in which two variables may be held constant. In a homogeneous system consisting of a two-component gaseous phase

$$\log p_2^* = \frac{\mu_2 - \mu_2^*(T)}{RT} \tag{9-175}$$

and

$$\left(\frac{\partial \log p_2^*}{\partial p}\right)_{T,y_2} = \frac{\bar{v}_2{}^{(g)}}{RT} \tag{9-176}$$

where y_2 is the mole fraction of component 2 in the vapor. Equation (9-176) has a form similar to Eq. (9-173) but it describes a different physical situation.

At constant composition, Eq. (9-168) can be rearranged to yield

$$\left(\frac{\partial \log p_2^*}{\partial T}\right)_{x_2} = \frac{\bar{L}_2^*}{RT^2}\left[1 + \frac{T\bar{v}_2{}^{(l)}}{\bar{L}_2^*}\left(\frac{\partial p}{\partial T}\right)_{x_2}\right] \tag{9-177}$$

Equation (9-177) describes the variation of vapor fugacity with temperature when the liquid composition is held constant and the total pressure is adjusted so as to preserve equilibrium. The quantity $(\partial p/\partial T)_{x_2}$ can be obtained from the slope of a pressure-temperature diagram. When p is small,

$$\frac{T\bar{v}_2{}^{(l)}}{\bar{L}_2^*}\left(\frac{\partial p}{\partial T}\right)_{x_2} = \frac{p\bar{v}_2{}^{(l)}}{RT}\left(\frac{\partial \log p}{\partial T}\right)_{x_2}\frac{RT^2}{\bar{L}_2^*} \ll 1 \tag{9-178}$$

and Eq. (9-177) can be approximated by

$$\left(\frac{\partial \log p_2^*}{\partial T}\right)_{x_2} = \frac{\bar{L}_2^*}{RT^2} \tag{9-179}$$

For an ideal vapor, Eq. (9-179) reduces to

$$\left(\frac{\partial \log p_2}{\partial T}\right)_{x_2} = \frac{\bar{L}_2^*}{RT^2} \tag{9-180}$$

As noted above, Eq. (9-179) should not be confused with the equation for a homogeneous phase

$$\left(\frac{\partial \log p_2^*}{\partial T}\right)_{p,y_2} = \frac{h_2^* - \bar{h}_2^{(g)}}{RT^2} \tag{9-181}$$

where $h_2^* - \bar{h}_2^{(g)}$ is the differential heat of transfer from the gas mixture to pure gas at zero pressure.

The derivative of the fugacity with respect to pressure at constant composition can be obtained from Eq. (9-168) in the form

$$\left(\frac{\partial \log p_2^*}{\partial p}\right)_{x_2} = \frac{\bar{v}_2^{(l)}}{RT}\left[1 + \frac{\bar{L}_2^*}{T\bar{v}_2^{(l)}}\left(\frac{\partial T}{\partial p}\right)_{x_2}\right] \tag{9-182}$$

In this case, $(g_2^*/T\bar{v}_2^{(l)})(\partial T/\partial p)_{x_2}$ is usually the dominant term.

The derivative of the fugacity with respect to composition at constant temperature can be obtained from Eq. (9-168) in the form

$$\left(\frac{\partial \log p_2^*}{\partial \log x_2}\right)_T = g_{22}^{(l)}\left[1 + \frac{\bar{v}_2^{(l)}}{g_{22}^{(l)}RT}\left(\frac{\partial p}{\partial \log x_2}\right)_T\right] \tag{9-183}$$

Since

$$\frac{\bar{v}_2^{(l)}}{g_{22}^{(l)}RT}\left(\frac{\partial p}{\partial \log x_2}\right)_T = x_2\frac{p\bar{v}_2^{(l)}}{RT}\frac{1}{g_{22}^{(l)}}\left(\frac{\partial \log p}{\partial x_2}\right)_T \tag{9-184}$$

and $(x_2/g_{22}^{(l)})(\partial \log p/\partial x_2)_T$ is of the order of unity at low pressures and $p\bar{v}_2^{(l)}/RT \ll 1$, Eq. (9-183) can be simplified to yield

$$\left(\frac{\partial \log p_2^*}{\partial \log x_2}\right)_T = g_{22}^{(l)} \tag{9-185}$$

Equation (9-185) reduces to

$$\left(\frac{\partial \log p_2^*}{\partial \log x_2}\right)_T = 1 \tag{9-186}$$

for the ideal liquid. Equation (9-186) can be integrated to yield

$$p_2^* = K_2(T)x_2 \tag{9-187}$$

where $K_2(T)$ is a constant of integration. Equation (9-187) is Henry's law. In this approximation, the fugacity is independent of the pressure. When $x_2 = 1$, Eq. (9-187) becomes

$$p_2^{\circ *} = K_2(T) \tag{9-188}$$

and thus Eq. (9-187) can be rewritten in the form

$$p_2^* = p_2^{\circ *} x_2 \tag{9-189}$$

Equation (9-168) can be utilized to determine how the vapor composition varies with temperature at constant fugacity. We find

$$\left(\frac{\partial \log x_2}{\partial T}\right)_{p_2^*} = -\frac{\bar{L}_2^*}{g_{22}^{(l)}RT^2}\left[1 + \frac{\bar{v}_2^{(l)}T}{\bar{L}_2^*}\left(\frac{\partial p}{\partial T}\right)_{p_2^*}\right] \tag{9-190}$$

If $p\bar{v}_2^{(l)}/RT \ll 1$, Eq. (9-190) reduces to

$$\left(\frac{\partial \log x_2}{\partial T}\right)_{p_2^*} = -\frac{\bar{L}_2^*}{g_{22}^{(l)}RT^2} \tag{9-191}$$

In the ideal-liquid approximation, Eq. (9-191) reduces to

$$\left(\frac{\partial \log x_2}{\partial T}\right)_{p_2^*} = -\frac{L_2^*}{RT^2} \tag{9-192}$$

In a similar manner, the expression

$$\left(\frac{\partial \log x_2}{\partial p}\right)_{p_2^*} = -\frac{\bar{v}_2^{(l)}}{g_{22}^{(l)}RT}\left[1 + \frac{\bar{L}_2^*}{T\bar{v}_2^{(l)}}\left(\frac{\partial T}{\partial p}\right)_{p_2^*}\right] \tag{9-193}$$

is obtained. If $p\bar{v}_2^{(l)}/RT \ll 1$, Eq. (9-193) reduces to

$$\left(\frac{\partial \log x_2}{\partial p}\right)_{p_2^*} = -\frac{\bar{L}_2^*}{g_{22}^{(l)}RT^2}\left(\frac{\partial T}{\partial p}\right)_{p_2^*} \tag{9-194}$$

This completes our discussion of the fugacity of binary solutions.

10 THERMODYNAMICS OF SURFACES

In this chapter, we discuss the thermodynamic properties of surface phases. In the previous chapters we have assumed that heterogeneous systems consist of a number of completely homogeneous phases separated by sharply defined mathematical surfaces. It is clear from either molecular or macroscopic considerations that this assumption cannot rigorously apply. Molecules in the vicinity of the interface between any two phases experience a different environment from molecules in the bulk of the phases. Thus, the densities of the various components and the densities of energy and entropy in the vicinity of the interface will be different from the corresponding densities in the bulk phases. However, the influence of the interface does not extend for more than a few molecular dimensions (about 10^{-7} cm) into the phases, and the phases may therefore be assumed to be uniform except in the immediate neighborhood of the interfaces. The interface between two phases is in reality a thin region in which the physical properties vary continuously from the bulk properties of one phase to the bulk properties of the other phase.

The treatment of surface phases presented here is essentially that of Gibbs. (The reader is referred to the book: J. Willard Gibbs, "Collected Works," vol. I, pp. 219–328, Yale University Press, New Haven, Conn., 1948, for more details.) In Sec. 10-1, we derive the fundamental equations for the thermodynamic treatment of surface phenomena. In Sec. 10-2, we consider the dependence of the various surface properties on the position of the dividing surface. Section 10-3 is devoted to a study of the temperature and component derivatives of the surface tension.

10-1. FUNDAMENTAL EQUATIONS

We consider a two-phase, r-component equilibrium system. We find it useful to introduce the concept of the Gibbs dividing surface. The dividing surface s is a precisely defined geometrical surface which is in the interfacial region between phases α and β. The position of this surface is as yet to some extent arbitrary but its shape and, therefore, the direction of its normals are completely determined by the shape of the interfacial region. We consider a closed surface generated by a moving normal to s and denote the part of s included by the closed surface by σ with area a. The closed surface is of such an extent that it includes portions of the homogeneous bulk phase α and β. We now divide the volume enclosed by the closed surfaces into three parts by two surfaces one on each side of σ parallel to σ (Fig. 10-1). These surfaces are close to σ but are placed so that regions 1 and 2 are homogeneous and region 3 contains the interphase region. We assume that the extensive properties of the volume enclosed by the closed surface can be adequately described by relations of the type

$$E = E^{(1)} + E^{(2)} + E^{(3)} \tag{10-1}$$

where E is the total energy, $E^{(1)}$ is the energy of region 1, $E^{(2)}$ is the energy of region 2, and $E^{(3)}$ is the energy of region 3. The quantities $E^{(1)}$, $E^{(2)}$, and $E^{(3)}$ can be varied independently.

The condition for internal equilibrium of region 3 subject to a variation in which the boundaries are held fixed is given by

$$(\delta E^{(3)})_{S^{(3)},n^{(3)}} \geqslant 0 \tag{10-2}$$

Thus, we may write

$$\delta E^{(3)} = T^{(3)}\,\delta S^{(3)} + \sum_{i=1}^{r} \mu_i^{(3)}\,\delta n_i^{(3)} \tag{10-3}$$

for reversible variations in which the boundaries are fixed. The criterion for heterogeneous equilibrium for the region in the closed surface is

$$(\delta E)_{S,n} \geqslant 0 \tag{10-4}$$

for variations in which the closed surface is held fixed. The conditions for heterogeneous equilibrium for variations in which all surfaces are held fixed are

$$\begin{aligned} T^{(\alpha)} &= T^{(1)} = T^{(3)} = T^{(2)} = T^{(\beta)} = T \\ \mu_i^{(\alpha)} &= \mu_i^{(1)} = \mu_i^{(3)} = \mu_i^{(2)} = \mu_i^{(\beta)} = \mu_i \qquad i = 1, \ldots, r \end{aligned} \tag{10-5}$$

where we have used arguments similar to those of Sec. 6-3. Equations (10-5) hold when all phases are heat-conducting and allow the diffusion

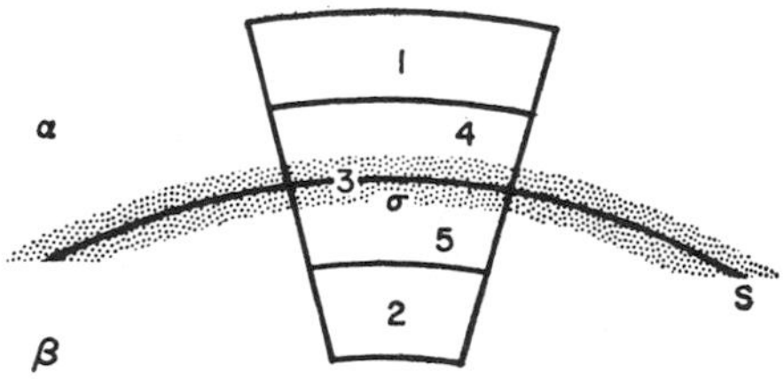

FIG. 10-1. The dividing surface.

of all components and all components are real components of all the phases. Thus, the conditions on temperature and chemical potentials for heterogeneous equilibrium derived in Sec. 6-3 in which surface phases were disregarded also apply when the effects of the surface are taken into account.

We shall now define thermodynamic variables of the surface by the following procedure. Region 3 is divided into two regions, 4 and 5, by the surface σ. We consider a hypothetical system in which the material in region 4(5) has the same values of T, p, μ_i, energy density, entropy density, and component density as the bulk phase $\alpha(\beta)$. We define the quantities

$$E^\sigma = E^{(3)} - E^{(4)} - E^{(5)}$$

$$S^\sigma = S^{(3)} - S^{(4)} - S^{(5)}$$

$$n_i^\sigma = n_i^{(3)} - n_i^{(4)} - n_i^{(5)} \qquad i = 1, \ldots, r \tag{10-6}$$

where the quantities denoted by the superscripts (4) and (5) are those for the hypothetical system described above. We may now write

$$\delta E^\sigma = T\,\delta S^\sigma + \sum_{i=1}^{r} \mu_i\,\delta n_i^\sigma \tag{10-7}$$

for reversible variations in which the surfaces are fixed. The quantity E^σ is the difference in energy between the real system with an interphase region and a hypothetical system in which the phases α and β are completely uniform up to the dividing surface. Thus we may call E^σ the energy of the surface, S^σ the entropy of the surface, etc. The quantity

$$E_\sigma = \frac{E^\sigma}{a} \tag{10-8}$$

is the superficial energy density,

$$S_\sigma = \frac{S^\sigma}{a} \tag{10-9}$$

is the superficial entropy density, and

$$\Gamma_i = \frac{n_i^\sigma}{a} \qquad i = 1, \ldots, r \tag{10-10}$$

is the superficial density of component i. The quantities E^σ, E_σ, etc., are determined partly by the state of the system of interest and partly by the imaginary surfaces introduced which lie within the nonhomogeneous interface region. Thus we must consider the dependence of these quantities on variations in the position and form of the surface σ which determines all the surfaces in the nonhomogeneous region.

We consider σ to be so small that its principal curvature may be considered uniform.† In this case, the variations in the position and form of σ can be described in terms of variations of its area a and its principal curvatures c_1 and c_2. Thus we may write

$$\delta E^\sigma = T\,\delta S^\sigma + \sum_{i=1}^{r} \mu_i\,\delta n_i^\sigma + \gamma\,\delta a + C_1\,\delta c_1 + C_2\,\delta c_2 \qquad (10\text{-}11)$$

where we have used Eq. (10-7) and where γ, C_1, and C_2 are functions of the thermodynamic variables and the position and form of σ. It can be shown that, for any interface whose thickness is small compared with the radii of curvature, Eq. (10-11) can be rewritten in the form

$$\delta E^\sigma = T\,\delta S^\sigma + \sum_{i=1}^{r} \mu_i\,\delta n_i^\sigma + \gamma\,\delta a \qquad (10\text{-}12)$$

when the surface σ is chosen in an appropriate fashion and lies within the interface. Equation (10-12) holds for all positions of a plane dividing surface. The quantity γ is the surface tension. The surface tension has been shown by experiment to be independent of the radii of curvature when the condition

$$R_1, R_2 \gg \tau \qquad (10\text{-}13)$$

is met. The quantities $R_1 = 1/c_1$ and $R_2 = 1/c_2$ are the radii of curvature of the surface and τ is the thickness of the interface. Systems in which Eq. (10-13) does not apply must be treated with care and may not be amenable to simple thermodynamic analysis.

We shall now investigate the conditions for heterogeneous equilibrium on the pressures of the homogeneous phases α and β. The criterion for equilibrium for region 3 is given by

$$(\delta E^{(3)})_{S^{(3)},n^{(3)}} \geqslant 0 \qquad (10\text{-}14)$$

when the bounding surface is fixed. We may use Eq. (10-6) to write

$$\delta E^{(3)} = \delta E^\sigma + \delta E^{(4)} + \delta E^{(5)} \qquad (10\text{-}15)$$

where
$$\delta E^\sigma = T\,\delta S^\sigma + \sum_{i=1}^{r} \mu_i\,\delta n_i^\sigma + \gamma\,\delta a \qquad (10\text{-}16)$$

by Eq. (10-12) and where

$$\delta E^{(4)} = T\,\delta S^{(4)} - p^{(4)}\,\delta V^{(4)} + \sum_{i=1}^{r} \mu_i\,\delta n_i^{(4)} \qquad (10\text{-}17)$$

and
$$\delta E^{(5)} = T\,\delta S^{(4)} - p^{(5)}\,\delta V^{(5)} + \sum_{i=1}^{r} \mu_i\,\delta n_i^{(5)} \qquad (10\text{-}18)$$

† The reader is referred to the book: L. P. Eisenhart, "Introduction to Differential Geometry," Princeton University Press, Princeton, N.J., 1947, for a discussion of the geometrical properties of surfaces.

Regions 4 and 5 are supposed to have properties which are identical with those of bulk phases α and β, respectively. Thus we may write

$$p^{(4)} = p^{(\alpha)} \tag{10-19}$$

and

$$p^{(5)} = p^{(\beta)} \tag{10-20}$$

Substitution of Eqs. (10-15) to (10-20) into Eq. (10-14) yields

$$\gamma\,\delta a - p^{(\alpha)}\,\delta V^{(4)} - p^{(\beta)}\,\delta V^{(5)} \geqslant 0 \tag{10-21}$$

when the bounding surface is fixed. Equation (10-21) is equivalent to

$$\gamma\,\delta a - p^{(\alpha)}\,\delta V^{(4)} - p^{(\beta)}\,\delta V^{(5)} = 0 \tag{10-22}$$

since all variations may be positive or negative. It is clear from Eq. (10-22) why γ is called the surface tension. Equation (10-22) has the same form as if a membrane having a tension γ, uniform in all directions, existed at the dividing surface. We now consider the set of variations in which all parts of the surface σ move a uniform normal distance δN. In these variations

$$\delta a = (c_1 + c_2)a\,\delta N \tag{10-23}$$

and

$$\delta V^{(4)} = -\delta V^{(5)} = a\,\delta N \tag{10-24}$$

Substitution of Eqs. (10-23) and (10-24) into Eq. (10-21) results in

$$[\gamma(c_1 + c_2) - p^{(\alpha)} + p^{(\beta)}]a\,\delta N \geqslant 0 \tag{10-25}$$

In order for Eq. (10-25) to hold for all conceivable variations δN

$$\gamma(c_1 + c_2) = p^{(\alpha)} - p^{(\beta)} \tag{10-26}$$

where the curvatures are positive when their centers lie in phase α. Equation (10-26) is the equilibrium condition on the pressures of phases α and β. It provides the basis for the capillary-rise method for the measurement of γ. For a plane surface,

$$c_1 = c_2 = 0 \tag{10-27}$$

and Eq. (10-26) becomes

$$p^{(\alpha)} = p^{(\beta)} \tag{10-28}$$

which is identical to the condition of Sec. 6-3.

The Helmholtz free energy of the surface is defined by the relation

$$A^\sigma = E^\sigma - TS^\sigma \tag{10-29}$$

Use of Eqs. (10-29) and (10-12) results in

$$\delta A^\sigma = -S^\sigma\,\delta T + \sum_{i=1}^{r} \mu_i\,\delta n_i^\sigma + \gamma\,\delta a \tag{10-30}$$

It is clear from Eq. (10-30) that γ is the isothermal work of formation of a unit area of interface. The Gibbs free energy of the surface is defined by

$$F^\sigma = E^\sigma - TS^\sigma - \gamma a \tag{10-31}$$

Use of Eqs. (10-31) and (10-30) yields

$$\delta F^\sigma = -S^\sigma\,\delta T + \sum_{i=1}^{r} \mu_i\,\delta n_i^\sigma - a\,\delta\gamma \tag{10-32}$$

It is experimentally determined that F^σ is a linear homogeneous function of the n_i^σ, $i = 1, \ldots, r$, at constant T and γ. Thus we may write

$$F^\sigma = \sum_{i=1}^{r} \mu_i n_i^\sigma \tag{10-33}$$

Differentiation of Eq. (10-33) and comparison with Eq. (10-32) lead to

$$\sum_{i=1}^{r} n_i^\sigma\,\delta\mu_i + S^\sigma\,\delta T + a\,\delta\gamma = 0 \tag{10-34}$$

Equation (10-34) is the analogue of the Gibbs-Duhem equation (6-59). Division of Eq. (10-34) by a and use of Eqs. (10-9) and (10-10) result in

$$\sum_{i=1}^{r} \Gamma_i\,\delta\mu_i + S_\sigma\,\delta T + \delta\gamma = 0 \tag{10-35}$$

The number of degrees of freedom in the r-component system consisting of two phases and an interface region is determined by the following considerations:

a. The intensive properties of phases α and β are determined by $T^{(\alpha)}$, $p^{(\alpha)}$, $x_1^{(\alpha)}, \ldots, x_{r-1}^{(\alpha)}$ and $T^{(\beta)}$, $p^{(\beta)}$, $x_1^{(\beta)}, \ldots, x_{r-1}^{(\beta)}$. The intensive properties of the surface are determined by T^σ, γ, $x_1^\sigma, \ldots, x_{r-1}^\sigma$. Thus, there are $3(r + 1)$ intensive variables.

b. The restrictions imposed upon the variables by the conditions of heterogeneous equilibrium are those of Eq. (10-5). Thus, there are $(r + 1)2$ restrictions.

c. The number of degrees of freedom is given by

$$3(r+1) - 2(r+1) = r + 1 \tag{10-36}$$

If the curvatures of the surface are fixed, there are r degrees of freedom in the system. This result is identical to that of Eq. (9-2) which was derived neglecting surface phases.

10-2. PROPERTIES OF THE SURFACE

In this section we specialize our treatment to a plane interface. We investigate the dependence of the various quantities E^σ, S^σ, n_i^σ, E_σ, S_σ, Γ_i, and γ on the position of the dividing surface. It is clear that if the plane dividing surface is moved a distance λ into phase β the quantities E_σ, S_σ, Γ_i will be changed by the respective amounts $\lambda(e_v{}^{(\beta)} - e_v{}^{(\alpha)})$, $\lambda(s_v{}^{(\beta)} - s_v{}^{(\alpha)})$, and $\lambda(\rho_i{}^{(\beta)} - \rho_i{}^{(\alpha)})$, where $e_v{}^{(\beta)} = E^{(\beta)}/V^{(\beta)}$ is the energy density of the homogeneous phase β, $e_v{}^{(\alpha)} = E^{(\alpha)}/V^{(\alpha)}$ is the energy density of the homogeneous phase α, $s_v{}^{(\beta)} = S^{(\beta)}/V^{(\beta)}$, $s_v{}^{(\alpha)} = S^{(\alpha)}/V^{(\alpha)}$, $\rho_i{}^{(\beta)} = n_i{}^{(\beta)}/V^{(\beta)}$, and $\rho_i{}^{(\alpha)} = n_i{}^{(\alpha)}/V^{(\alpha)}$. Thus, the surface quantities for which the corresponding densities in phases α and β are identical are invariant with respect to the position of the surface. The surface tension γ will be changed by

$$\Delta\gamma = \lambda(e_v{}^{(\beta)} - e_v{}^{(\alpha)}) - T\lambda(s_v{}^{(\beta)} - s_v{}^{(\alpha)}) - \sum_{i=1}^{r} \mu_i\lambda(\rho_i^{(\beta)} - \rho_i{}^{(\alpha)}) \quad (10\text{-}37)$$

where we have used Eq. (10-31). Integral forms of the first law for phases α and β may be written

$$-p^{(\alpha)} = e_v{}^{(\alpha)} - Ts_v{}^{(\alpha)} - \sum_{i=1}^{r} \mu_i\rho_i{}^{(\alpha)} \quad (10\text{-}38)$$

and

$$-p^{(\beta)} = e_v{}^{(\beta)} - Ts_v{}^{(\beta)} - \sum_{i=1}^{r} \mu_i\rho_i{}^{(\beta)} \quad (10\text{-}39)$$

Substitution of Eqs. (10-38) and (10-39) into Eq. (10-37) yields

$$\Delta\gamma = \lambda(p^{(\alpha)} - p^{(\beta)}) \quad (10\text{-}40)$$

At equilibrium, $p^{(\alpha)} = p^{(\beta)}$ for plane surfaces, and Eq. (10-40) becomes

$$\Delta\gamma = 0 \quad (10\text{-}41)$$

Thus the value of the surface tension is independent of the position of the dividing surface when this surface is plane.

It is sometimes convenient to choose the position of the dividing surface so that one of the quantities E_σ, S_σ, or Γ_i is zero. This can be done except when the corresponding densities in the two phases are identical. For example, we may choose the dividing surface to be such that Γ_1 vanishes. In this case, Eq. (10-35) becomes

$$d\gamma = -S_{\sigma(1)}\, dT - \sum_{i=2}^{r} \Gamma_{i(1)}\, d\mu_i \quad (10\text{-}42)$$

where the subscript 1 implies that the surface is chosen such that $\Gamma_1 = 0$. The quantity

$$\left(\frac{\partial\gamma}{\partial\mu_2}\right)_{T,\mu_3,\ldots,\mu_r} = -\Gamma_{2(1)} \quad (10\text{-}43)$$

is invariant to the position of the dividing surface. This can be easily shown by considering Eq. (10-35) for an arbitrary surface. At constant T and $\mu_3, \ldots, \mu_r$ Eq. (10-35) becomes

$$d\gamma = -\Gamma_1\, d\mu_1 - \Gamma_2\, d\mu_2 \tag{10-44}$$

Differentiation of Eq. (10-38) and (10-39) at constant T and $\mu_3, \ldots, \mu_r$ yields

$$dp^{(\alpha)} = \rho_1{}^{(\alpha)}\, d\mu_1 + \rho_2{}^{(\alpha)}\, d\mu_2 \tag{10-45}$$

and

$$dp^{(\beta)} = \rho_1{}^{(\beta)}\, d\mu_1 + \rho_2{}^{(\beta)}\, d\mu_2 \tag{10-46}$$

where we have made use of Eq. (6-48).

At equilibrium, $dp^{(\alpha)} = dp^{(\beta)}$, and we may combine Eqs. (10-45) and (10-46) to obtain

$$d\mu_1 = \frac{\rho_2{}^{(\beta)} - \rho_2{}^{(\alpha)}}{\rho_1{}^{(\alpha)} - \rho_1{}^{(\beta)}}\, d\mu_2 \tag{10-47}$$

Substitution of Eq. (10-47) into Eq. (10-44) and division by $d\mu_2$ result in

$$\left(\frac{\partial \gamma}{\partial \mu_2}\right)_{T,\mu_3,\ldots,\mu_r} = -\Gamma_2 - \frac{\rho_2{}^{(\beta)} - \rho_2{}^{(\alpha)}}{\rho_1{}^{(\alpha)} - \rho_1{}^{(\beta)}}\,\Gamma_1 \tag{10-48}$$

The distance between the surface considered here and the surface for which $\Gamma_1 = 0$ is $\Gamma_1/(\rho_1{}^{(\alpha)} - \rho_1{}^{(\beta)})$. When the surface is moved in this way Γ_2 becomes

$$\Gamma_{2(1)} = \Gamma_2 + \frac{\rho_2{}^{(\beta)} - \rho_2{}^{(\alpha)}}{\rho_1{}^{(\alpha)} - \rho_1{}^{(\beta)}}\,\Gamma_1 \tag{10-49}$$

Thus, Eq. (10-48) may be rewritten in the form

$$\left(\frac{\partial \gamma}{\partial \mu_2}\right)_{T,\mu_3,\ldots,\mu_r} = -\Gamma_{2(1)} \tag{10-50}$$

which is identical to Eq. (10-43).

We conclude that the surface tension and its derivatives with respect to quantities characteristic of the bulk phases are independent of the choice of the dividing surface for a plane interface.

10-3. SURFACE TENSION

In this section we present relationships for the derivatives of the surface tension with respect to various intensive properties of the system. We restrict our considerations to systems in which the phases α and β are fluid systems and in which the interface is planar.

The fundamental equations that we shall use are

$$d\gamma = -S_\sigma\, dT - \sum_{i=1}^{r} \Gamma_i\, d\mu_i \tag{10-51}$$

which follows from Eq. (10-35) and

$$\sum_{k=1}^{r-1} G_k^{(\beta\alpha)}\, dx_k^{(\alpha)} + \sum_{i=1}^{r} x_i^{(\beta)}(\bar{s}_i^{(\beta)} - \bar{s}_i^{(\alpha)})\, dT + \sum_{i=1}^{r} x_i^{(\beta)}(\bar{v}_i^{(\alpha)} - \bar{v}_i^{(\beta)})\, dp = 0 \tag{10-52}$$

where

$$G_k^{(\beta\alpha)} = \sum_{i=1}^{r} x_i^{(\beta)} \left(\frac{\partial \mu_i^{(\alpha)}}{\partial x_k^{(\alpha)}}\right)_{T,p,x_{j\pm k}^{(\alpha)}} \tag{10-53}$$

which follow from Eqs. (9-22) and (9-23) upon interchange of α and β. Use of the equilibrium relation

$$d\mu_i = d\mu_i^{(\alpha)} = d\mu_i^{(\beta)} \tag{10-54}$$

and substitution of Eq. (9-18) into Eq. (10-51) yield

$$d\gamma = \Big(\sum_{i=1}^{r} \Gamma_i \bar{s}_i^{(\alpha)} - S_\sigma\Big)\, dT - \sum_{i=1}^{r} \Gamma_i \bar{v}_i^{(\alpha)}\, dp - \sum_{i=1}^{r} \Gamma_i \sum_{k=1}^{r-1} G_{ik}^{(\alpha)}\, dx_k^{(\alpha)} \tag{10-55}$$

There are r degrees of freedom in the system of interest, and the right-hand side of Eq. (10-55) contains the variations of $r + 1$ quantities. Thus, the restrictions of Eq. (10-52) must be taken into account when computing derivatives of γ.

The partial derivative of γ with respect to T at constant $x^{(\alpha)}$ is given by

$$\left(\frac{\partial \gamma}{\partial T}\right)_{x^{(\alpha)}} = \sum_{i=1}^{r} \Gamma_i \bar{s}_i^{(\alpha)} - S_\sigma - \sum_{i=1}^{r} \Gamma_i \bar{v}_i^{(\alpha)} \left(\frac{\partial p}{\partial T}\right)_{x^{(\alpha)}} \tag{10-56}$$

The quantity $(\partial p/\partial T)_{x^{(\alpha)}}$ is determined from Eq. (10-52) to be

$$\left(\frac{\partial p}{\partial T}\right)_{x^{(\alpha)}} = \frac{\sum_{i=1}^{r} x_i^{(\beta)}(\bar{s}_i^{(\beta)} - \bar{s}_i^{(\alpha)})}{\sum_{i=1}^{r} x_i^{(\beta)}(\bar{v}_i^{(\beta)} - \bar{v}_i^{(\alpha)})} \tag{10-57}$$

Substitution of Eq. (10-57) into Eq. (10-56) yields

$$\left(\frac{\partial \gamma}{\partial T}\right)_{x^{(\alpha)}} = \sum_{i=1}^{r} \Gamma_i \bar{s}_i^{(\alpha)} - S_\sigma - \left(\sum_{i=1}^{r} \Gamma_i \bar{v}_i^{(\alpha)}\right) \frac{\sum_{j=1}^{r} x_j^{(\beta)}(\bar{s}_j^{(\beta)} - \bar{s}_j^{(\alpha)})}{\sum_{j=1}^{r} x_j^{(\beta)}(\bar{v}_j^{(\beta)} - \bar{v}_j^{(\alpha)})} \tag{10-58}$$

If we assume that phase β is a vapor phase and phase α is a liquid phase and $T \ll T_c$, the critical temperature, then

$$\bar{v}_i^{(\beta)} \gg \bar{v}_i^{(\alpha)} \qquad i = 1, \ldots, r \tag{10-59}$$

and Eq. (10-58) may be rewritten

$$-\left(\frac{\partial \gamma}{\partial T}\right)_{x^{(\alpha)}} = S_\sigma - \sum_{i=1}^{r} \Gamma_i \bar{s}_i^{(\alpha)} \tag{10-60}$$

The right-hand side of Eq. (10-60) is the entropy of a unit area of surface minus the entropy of the surface material content of liquid. $(\partial\gamma/\partial T)_{x^{(\alpha)}}$ is negative for liquid-vapor systems. The surface tension vanishes at the critical point. Equation (10-60) may be rewritten by use of the relation

$$T\bar{s}_i^{(\alpha)} = -\mu_i + \bar{e}_i^{(\alpha)} + p\bar{v}_i^{(\alpha)} \tag{10-61}$$

in the form

$$-\left(\frac{\partial \gamma}{\partial T}\right)_{x^{(\alpha)}} = S_\sigma + \frac{1}{T}\sum_{i=1}^{r} \Gamma_i \mu_i - \frac{1}{T}\sum_{i=1}^{r} \Gamma_i \bar{e}_i^{(\alpha)} \tag{10-62}$$

where we have neglected the terms containing $\bar{v}_i^{(\alpha)}$. Division of Eq. (10-31) by a and use of Eq. (10-33) result in

$$\gamma = -\sum_{i=1}^{r} \Gamma_i \mu_i - TS_\sigma + E_\sigma \tag{10-63}$$

Substitution of Eq. (10-63) into Eq. (10-62) and rearrangement yield

$$\gamma - T\left(\frac{\partial \gamma}{\partial T}\right)_{x^{(\alpha)}} = E_\sigma - \sum_{i=1}^{r} \Gamma_i \bar{e}_i^{(\alpha)} \tag{10-64}$$

Equation (10-64) may be looked upon as a form of the first law for the process in which a unit area of surface is created isothermally and reversibly. The work done on the system in this process is γ, and the heat absorbed by the system is $-T(\partial\gamma/\partial T)_{x^{(\alpha)}}$. In a one-component system, Eq. (10-58) becomes

$$\begin{aligned}\frac{d\gamma}{dT} &= \Gamma s^{(\alpha)} - S_\sigma - \Gamma v^{(\alpha)} \frac{s^{(\beta)} - s^{(\alpha)}}{v^{(\beta)} - v^{(\alpha)}} \\ &= \Gamma \frac{s^{(\alpha)} v^{(\beta)} - s^{(\beta)} v^{(\alpha)}}{v^{(\beta)} - v^{(\alpha)}} - S_\sigma \end{aligned} \tag{10-65}$$

For the liquid-vapor system, Eq. (10-65) reduces to

$$\frac{d\gamma}{dT} = \Gamma s^{(\alpha)} - S_\sigma \tag{10-66}$$

We shall now compute the dependence of γ on the mole fraction of component 1 in phase α when T and $x_2^{(\alpha)}, \ldots, x_{r-1}^{(\alpha)}$ are fixed. The partial derivative of γ with respect to $x_1^{(\alpha)}$ can be obtained from Eq. (10-55) in the form

$$\left(\frac{\partial \gamma}{\partial x_1^{(\alpha)}}\right)_{T,x_2^{(\alpha)},\ldots,x_{r-1}^{(\alpha)}} = -\sum_{i=1}^{r} \Gamma_i \bar{v}_i^{(\alpha)} \left(\frac{\partial p}{\partial x_1^{(\alpha)}}\right)_{T,x_2^{(\alpha)},\ldots,x_{r-1}^{(\alpha)}} - \sum_{i=1}^{r} \Gamma_i G_{i1}^{(\alpha)} \tag{10-67}$$

The partial derivative of p can be obtained from Eq. (10-52) as

$$\left(\frac{\partial p}{\partial x_1^{(\alpha)}}\right)_{T,x_2^{(\alpha)},\ldots,x_{r-1}^{(\alpha)}} = -\frac{G_1^{(\beta\alpha)}}{\Delta v^{(\beta\alpha)}} \tag{10-68}$$

where
$$\Delta v^{(\beta\alpha)} = \sum_{i=1}^{r} x_i^{(\beta)}(\bar{v}_i^{(\alpha)} - \bar{v}_i^{(\beta)}) \tag{10-69}$$

and
$$G_1^{(\beta\alpha)} = \sum_{i=1}^{r} x_i^{(\beta)} G_{i1}^{(\alpha)} \tag{10-70}$$

Substitution of Eq. (10-68) into Eq. (10-67) yields

$$\left(\frac{\partial \gamma}{\partial x_1^{(\alpha)}}\right)_{T,x_{j\neq 1}^{(\alpha)}} = \sum_{i=1}^{r} \Gamma_i \bar{v}_i^{(\alpha)} \frac{G_1^{(\beta\alpha)}}{\Delta v^{(\beta\alpha)}} - \sum_{i=1}^{r} \Gamma_i G_{i1}^{(\alpha)} \tag{10-71}$$

where we have used the abbreviation $x_{j\neq 1}^{(\alpha)}$ to stand for the set of variables $x_2^{(\alpha)}, \ldots, x_{r-1}^{(\alpha)}$. Equation (10-71) can be simplified greatly in the case of a liquid-vapor interface. We shall assume that phase α is the liquid phase and that phase β is the vapor phase. We may neglect the first term on the right-hand side of Eq. (10-71) and rewrite it in the form

$$\left(\frac{\partial \gamma}{\partial x_1^{(\alpha)}}\right)_{T,x_{j\neq 1}^{(\alpha)}} = -\sum_{i=1}^{r} \Gamma_i \left(\frac{\partial \mu_i^{(\alpha)}}{\partial x_1^{(\alpha)}}\right)_{T,p,x_{j\neq 1}^{(\alpha)}} \tag{10-72}$$

In an ideal solution,

$$\mu_i^{(\alpha)} = \mu_i^{\circ}(T,p) + RT \log x_i^{(\alpha)} \tag{10-73}$$

and
$$\left(\frac{\partial \mu_i^{(\alpha)}}{\partial x_1^{(\alpha)}}\right)_{T,p,x_{j\neq 1}^{(\alpha)}} = \frac{RT}{x_1}\delta_{i1} - \frac{RT}{x_r}\delta_{ir} \tag{10-74}$$

Substitution of Eq. (10-74) into Eq. (10-72) yields

$$\left(\frac{\partial \gamma}{\partial x_1^{(\alpha)}}\right)_{T,x_{j\neq 1}^{(\alpha)}} = RT\left(\frac{\Gamma_r}{x_r} - \frac{\Gamma_1}{x_1}\right) \tag{10-75}$$

Thus the quantity $\Gamma_r/x_r - \Gamma_1/x_1$ can be determined by measurements of the dependence of γ on $x_1^{(\alpha)}$. This quantity is invariant to the position of the dividing surface.

It is sometimes convenient to rewrite Eq. (10-67) in a form involving the properties of the vapor phase. We make use of Eq. (10-51) to write

$$\left(\frac{\partial \gamma}{\partial x_1^{(\alpha)}}\right)_{T,x_{j\neq 1}^{(\alpha)}} = -\sum_{i=1}^{r} \Gamma_i \left(\frac{\partial \mu_i^{(\beta)}}{\partial x_1^{(\alpha)}}\right)_{T,x_{j\neq 1}^{(\alpha)}} \tag{10-76}$$

Substitution of Eq. (9-135) into Eq. (10-76) results in

$$\left(\frac{\partial \gamma}{\partial x_1^{(\alpha)}}\right)_{T,x_{j\neq 1}^{(\alpha)}} = -RT \sum_{i=1}^{r} \Gamma_i \left(\frac{\partial \log p_i^*}{\partial x_1^{(\alpha)}}\right)_{T,x_{j\neq 1}^{(\alpha)}} \tag{10-77}$$

In a binary mixture, Eq. (10-77) becomes

$$\left(\frac{\partial \gamma}{\partial x_1^{(\alpha)}}\right)_T = -RT\left[\Gamma_1\left(\frac{\partial \log p_1^*}{\partial x_1^{(\alpha)}}\right)_T + \Gamma_2\left(\frac{\partial \log p_2^*}{\partial x_1^{(\alpha)}}\right)_T\right]$$

$$= -RT\left[\Gamma_1 - \frac{x_1^{(\alpha)}}{1 - x_1^{(\alpha)}}\Gamma_2\right]\left(\frac{\partial \log p_1^*}{\partial x_1^{(\alpha)}}\right)_T \tag{10-78}$$

where we have used the approximation of Eq. (9-143). Thus, measurements of p_1^* and γ over a range of compositions yield a value for $\Gamma_1 - (x_1^{(\alpha)}/1 - x_1^{(\alpha)})\Gamma_2$.

We remark that stability considerations require γ to be positive.

11 CHEMICAL POTENTIALS OF NONELECTROLYTE SOLUTIONS

In this chapter, we consider a liquid system consisting of r components. Such a system is termed a liquid solution. The system is a nonelectrolyte solution if all the components exist in solution as uncharged species rather than as charged ions. In most solutions, one of the components predominates. This component is called the solvent and the other components are called solutes.

In this chapter, we apply some of the general principles developed heretofore to a study of the bulk thermodynamic properties of nonelectrolyte solutions. In Sec. 11-1 we discuss conventions for the description of chemical potentials in nonelectrolyte solutions and introduce the concept of an ideal component. In Sec. 11-2, we demonstrate how the concept of solution molecular weight can be introduced into thermodynamics in a natural fashion. Section 11-3 is devoted to a study of the properties of ideal solutions. In Sec. 11-4, we discuss the properties of solutions that can be considered to be ideal when they are dilute but are not necessarily ideal when they are more concentrated. In Sec. 11-5, regular solutions are defined and some of their properties are derived. Section 11-6 is devoted to a study of some of the approximations that prove useful in the derivation of the properties of real solutions. Finally, in Sec. 11-7, some of the experimental techniques utilized for the measurement of chemical potentials and activity coefficients of components in solution are described.

11-1. CONVENTIONS AND GENERAL FORMULATION

In order to aid in the investigation of the dependence of the chemical potentials of the components of a liquid phase on composition, it is convenient to define an ideal substance. An ideal substance is defined in such a way that its chemical potential has a simple functional dependence on a concrete composition variable. Under appropriate conditions, the properties of a large class of real substances must be adequately represented by the properties of the ideal substance. It is found by experiment and from molecular considerations that a suitable form of the chemical potential of an ideal component i can be written

$$\mu_i = \mu_i^\circ(T,p) + RT \log x_i \tag{11-1}$$

where $\mu_i^\circ(T,p)$ is some reference value of the chemical potential.

The excess chemical potential of component i, μ_i^E represents the difference between the chemical potential of component i in the real solution and the chemical potential of i considered as an ideal component. Thus, μ_i^E can be written as

$$\mu_i^E = \mu_i - [RT \log x_i + \mu_i^\circ(T,p)] \tag{11-2}$$

The activity coefficient of component i, f_i, may be defined in terms of its excess chemical potential in the form

$$f_i = e^{\mu_i^E/RT} = \frac{1}{x_i} e^{(\mu_i - \mu_i^\circ)/RT} \tag{11-3}$$

where f_i is the activity coefficient with respect to the mole fraction. Combination of Eqs. (11-1) and (11-3) results in

$$\mu_i = \mu_i^\circ(T,p) + RT \log (f_i x_i) \tag{11-4}$$

It is sometimes convenient to make use of the activity of component i, a_i, defined by the relation

$$a_i = f_i x_i \tag{11-5}$$

In order completely to determine the excess chemical potential, the activity coefficient, or the activity, the convention used to define the reference value of the chemical potential and the composition units used, must be specified.

There are two definitions of $\mu_i^\circ(T,p)$ in common use. One of the conventions for the choice of $\mu_i^\circ(T,p)$ for an r-component solution is

$$\mu_i^\circ(T,p) = \mu_i^{(l)}(T,p) \qquad i = 1, \ldots, r \tag{11-6}$$

where $\mu_i^{(l)}$ is the chemical potential of pure liquid i at T and p. The other convention distinguishes between the solvent and solute components. In this convention,

$$\mu_i^\circ(T,p) = \mu_i^{(l)}(T,p) \qquad i = 1 \tag{11-7}$$

$$\mu_i^\circ(T,p) = \lim_{x_1 \to 1} (\mu_i - RT \log x_i) \qquad i = 2, \ldots, r \tag{11-8}$$

where 1 is the solvent component, the component present at highest concentration, and $i = 2, \ldots, r$ are the solute components. We shall see later that the limit in Eq. (11-8) does not exist when the molecular weight of component i is arbitrarily assigned. The solution molecular weight of i, M_i, must be chosen in such a way that this limit does exist. We note that the convention of Eqs. (11-7) and (11-8) leads to standard states which are fictitious. They are the states which would exist if the components $2, \ldots, r$ retained the ideal properties of the dilute state up to the pure state of component 1. These states are commonly referred to as infinitely dilute states. It is evident that, for the convention of Eq. (11-6),

$$\lim_{x_i \to 1} f_i = 1 \qquad i = 1, \ldots, r \tag{11-9}$$

and that for the convention of Eqs. (11-7) and (11-8),

$$\lim_{x_1 \to 1} f_i = 1 \qquad i = 1, \ldots, r \tag{11-10}$$

A large number of concentration units are used in the definition of the chemical potential. In the following paragraphs, we discuss the activity coefficients and standard chemical potentials for some commonly used units. The chemical potential of component i can be written in terms of m_i, the gross molality or formality of i, that is, the number of moles of i per thousand grams of solvent [Eq. (2-3)] in the form

$$\mu_i = RT \log (\gamma_i m_i) + \mu^{(m)\circ}(T,p) \tag{11-11}$$

where γ_i, the activity coefficient of component i with respect to the molality, is defined by Eq. (11-11). Only the convention of Eqs. (11-7) and (11-8) is of use in this case since the choice of m_i as a concentration unit implies that one of the components is the solvent. Making use of Eqs. (11-7), (11-8), and (11-11), we find that

$$\mu_1{}^{(m)\circ} = \mu_1{}^{(m)\prime}(T,p) \tag{11-12}$$

for the solvent and

$$\mu_i^{(m)\circ} = \lim_{x_1 \to 1} (\mu_i - RT \log m_i) \qquad i = 2, \ldots, r \tag{11-13}$$

for the solute components. Thus

$$\lim_{x_1 \to 1} \gamma_i = 1 \qquad i = 1, \ldots, r \tag{11-14}$$

We may easily find the relation between μ_i° and $\mu_i{}^{(m)\circ}$ and that between f_i and γ_i by use of the relationship

$$x_i = \frac{M_1}{1000} \frac{m_i}{1 + (M_1/1000) \sum_{k=2}^{r} m_k} \tag{11-15}$$

Comparison of Eqs. (11-4) and (11-11) and use of Eq. (11-15) yield

$$\mu_i^\circ + RT \log \left[f_i \frac{M_1}{1000} \frac{m_i}{1 + (M_1/1000) \sum_{k=2}^{r} m_k} \right] = \mu_i^{(m)\circ} + RT \log (\gamma_i m_i) \tag{11-16}$$

It is clear from Eqs. (11-16) and (11-14) that

$$\gamma_i = \frac{f_i}{1 + (M_1/1000) \sum_{k=2}^{r} m_k} \tag{11-17}$$

and

$$\mu_i^{(m)\circ} = \mu_i^\circ + RT \log \frac{M_1}{1000} \tag{11-18}$$

The chemical potential of component i can be written in terms of c_i, the molarity, i.e., the number of moles of component i per liter of solution (Sec. 2-3) in the form

$$\mu_i = \mu_i^{(c)\circ}(T,p) + RT \log (\alpha_i c_i) \tag{11-19}$$

where α_i, the activity coefficient of component i with respect to molarity, is defined by Eq. (11-19). In this case, both conventions may be used in choosing $\mu_i^{(c)\circ}(T,p)$. When the convention of Eq. (11-6) is used, we have

$$\mu_i^{(c)\circ} = \mu_i^{(c)(l)} \tag{11-20}$$

When the convention of Eqs. (11-7) and (11-8) is used, we have

$$\mu_1^{(c)\circ} = \mu_1^{(c)(l)} \tag{11-21}$$

for the solvent and

$$\mu_i^{(c)\circ} = \lim_{x_1 \to 1} (\mu_i - RT \log c_i) \qquad i = 2, \ldots, r \tag{11-22}$$

for the solute components. Rearrangement of Eq. (2-29) for a two-component system yields the relation

$$c_i = \frac{x_i 1000}{x_1 \bar{v}_1 + x_2 \bar{v}_2} \tag{11-23}$$

Comparison of Eqs. (11-4) and (11-19) results in

$$\mu_i^{(c)\circ} + RT \log \left(\alpha_i \frac{x_i 1000}{x_1 \bar{v}_1 + x_2 \bar{v}_2} \right) = \mu_i^\circ + RT \log (f_i x_i) \tag{11-24}$$

After some algebraic manipulation, Eq. (11-24) yields the relations

$$\alpha_2 = \frac{\bar{v}_1}{v_1^{(l)}} \frac{1000 f_2}{1000 + (\bar{v}_1 - \bar{v}_2) c_2} \tag{11-25}$$

and

$$\mu_2^{(c)\circ} = \mu_2^\circ + RT \log \frac{v_1^{(l)}}{1000} \tag{11-26}$$

when the convention of Eq. (11-22) is used. The quantity $v_1^{(l)}$ is the molal volume of pure component 1.

The volume fraction of component i, ϕ_i, is defined by the relation

$$\phi_i = c_i \bar{v}_i \tag{11-27}$$

ϕ_i is the volume of component i per liter of solution and is a useful composition unit for polymer solutions. The chemical potential of component i can be written in terms of ϕ_i in the form

$$\mu_i = RT \log (\alpha_i \phi_i) + \mu_i^{(v)\circ} \tag{11-28}$$

where α_i is defined by Eq. (11-19). It is clear from Eqs. (11-19), (11-27), and (11-28) that

$$\mu_i^{(v)\circ} = \mu_i^{(c)\circ} - RT \log \bar{v}_i \tag{11-29}$$

As in the case of molarity, both conventions may be used to establish the value of $\mu_i^{(v)\circ}(T,p)$. When the convention of Eq. (11-6) is used, Eq. (11-29) becomes

$$\mu_i^{(v)\circ} = \mu_i^{(c)(l)} - RT \log v_i^{(l)} \tag{11-30}$$

where $v_i^{(l)}$ is the molar volume of pure component i.

Finally, we mention the representation of the nonideality of component i in terms of the osmotic coefficient g_i. The osmotic coefficient of component i is defined by the relation

$$\mu_i = RTg_i \log x_i + \mu_i^\circ(T,p) \tag{11-31}$$

The convention of Eq. (11-6) leads to the relations

$$\lim_{x_i \to 1} g_i = 1 \qquad i = 1, \ldots, r \tag{11-32}$$

The convention of Eqs. (11-7) and (11-8) leads to the relations

$$\lim_{x_1 \to 1} g_i = 1 \qquad i = 1, \ldots, r \tag{11-33}$$

The osmotic coefficient is advantageous for the consideration of the nonideality of the solvent in dilute solutions. In dilute solutions, the activity coefficient of the solvent is close to unity even for appreciable deviations from ideality.

11-2. MOLECULAR WEIGHTS IN SOLUTION

In this section, we consider the concept of solution molecular weights for the solute species. We first prove that it is possible to select molecular weights for the solutes such that Raoult's law holds for the solvent at infinite dilution. Then we demonstrate that this choice of molecular weight is the one necessary for the existence of the limiting operation in Eq. (11-8).

We consider a binary solution in equilibrium with vapor. Let M_1 be the molecular weight arbitrarily assigned to the solvent 1. Let M_2 be the molecular weight for the solute 2 presently to be assigned so that

$$\lim_{x_2 \to 0} \frac{p_1^{\circ *} - p_1^*}{x_2 p_1^{\circ *}} = 1 \tag{11-34}$$

where x_2 is the mole fraction of 2 in the liquid, p_1^* is the fugacity of vapor 1 in equilibrium with the solution, and $p_1^{\circ *}$ is the fugacity of the vapor in equilibrium with pure solvent at the same T. Equation (11-34) is an expression of Raoult's law at infinite dilution. The molecular weight for which Eq. (11-34) holds is the definition of the molecular weight of the solute. We shall see that the criterion of Eq. (11-34) determines only the ratio of the molecular weights of the solvent and the solute. Thus, the solution molecular weight of the solute is dependent upon the molecular weight assigned to the solvent.

A condition for equilibrium between the liquid and vapor phases is given by

$$\mu_1 = \mu_1^{(v)} \tag{11-35}$$

where μ_1 is the chemical potential of component 1 in the liquid phase and

$$\mu_1^{(v)} = \mu_1^*(T) + b_1 RT \log p_1^* \tag{11-36}$$

where $\mu_1^{(v)}$ is the chemical potential of component 1 in the vapor phase. In Eq. (11-36), b_1 is some numerical factor depending upon the choice of M_1. If M_1 is chosen as the gram-molecular weight, as it is from now on, $b_1 = 1$ (see the discussion in Sec. 1-3). It should be noted that, in the general expressions derived heretofore, the molecular weights are unspecified. However, wherever R appears in a formula, some specification of the molecular weight has been made.

Differentiation of Eq. (11-35) with respect to x_2 at constant T results in

$$\left(\frac{\partial \mu_1}{\partial x_2}\right)_T = RT \left(\frac{\partial \log p_1^*}{\partial x_2}\right)_T \tag{11-37}$$

Substitution of Eq. (9-183) into Eq. (11-37) yields

$$\left(\frac{\partial \mu_1}{\partial x_2}\right)_T = -\frac{RT}{x_1}\left[g_{11}^{(l)} + \frac{x_1 \bar{v}_1^{(l)}}{RT}\left(\frac{\partial p}{\partial x_1}\right)_T\right] \tag{11-38}$$

where we have made use of the relation

$$\left(\frac{\partial \log p_1^*}{\partial x_1}\right)_T = -\left(\frac{\partial \log p_1^*}{\partial x_2}\right)_T \tag{11-39}$$

Since $(x_1\bar{v}_1^{(l)}/RT)(\partial p/\partial x_1)_T$ is of the order of $p\bar{v}_1^{(l)}/RT$ which is much less than unity and $g_{11}^{(l)}$ is of the order of unity, Eq. (11-38) can be approximated by

$$\left(\frac{\partial \mu_1}{\partial x_2}\right)_T = -\frac{RT}{x_1} g_{11}^{(l)} \tag{11-40}$$

Substitution of Eqs. (9-47) and (9-40) into Eq. (11-40) leads to

$$\left(\frac{\partial \mu_1}{\partial x_2}\right)_T = -\left(\frac{\partial \mu_1}{\partial x_1}\right)_{T,p} = \left(\frac{\partial \mu_1}{\partial x_2}\right)_{T,p} \tag{11-41}$$

The system under consideration consists of two components and two phases. Thus there are two degrees of freedom. The derivative $(\partial\mu_1/\partial x_2)_T$ is evaluated by considering the variation of μ_1 when x_2 is varied at constant T while preserving equilibrium between liquid and vapor phases. The pressure of the system is a function of T and x_2 and varies when x_2 varies. The derivative $(\partial\mu_1/\partial x_2)_{T,p}$ appearing in Eq. (11-41) is evaluated by considering the variation of μ_1 when x_2 is varied at constant T and p without preserving equilibrium between liquid and vapor phases. We shall make use of the approximation inherent in Eq. (11-41) to study the choice of M_2. At the end of the section, we shall briefly discuss the use of the exact expression, Eq. (11-38), in the determination of M_2.

We define the quantity $\alpha(T,p)$ by the relation

$$\lim_{x_2\to 0}\left(\frac{\partial \mu_1}{\partial x_2}\right)_{T,p} = -\lim_{x_1\to 1}\left(\frac{\partial \mu_1}{\partial x_1}\right)_{T,p} = -\alpha(T,p) \tag{11-42}$$

A condition for stability of the binary solution is

$$\alpha \geqslant 0 \tag{11-43}$$

where we have made use of the discussion of Sec. 6-4. It is empirically found that, in general, α is not equal to zero and we therefore assume that $\alpha > 0$. If z_2 is the weight fraction of component 2 in solution, then

$$z_2 = \frac{w_2}{w_1 + w_2} = \frac{x_2}{x_2 + (M_1/M_2)x_1} \tag{11-44}$$

Equation (11-42) can be written in the form

$$\alpha(T,p) = -RT \lim_{x_2\to 0}\left[\left(\frac{\partial \log p_1^*}{\partial z_2}\right)_T\left(\frac{\partial z_2}{\partial x_2}\right)_T\right] \tag{11-45}$$

where we have made use of Eqs. (11-37) and (11-41). The variation of z_2 with x_2 is determined from Eq. (11-44) to be

$$\left(\frac{\partial z_2}{\partial x_2}\right)_T = \frac{M_1/M_2}{[x_2 + (M_1/M_2)x_1]^2} \tag{11-46}$$

Substitution of Eq. (11-46) into Eq. (11-45) yields

$$\alpha(T,p) = RT\frac{M_2}{M_1}\,a(T,p) \tag{11-47}$$

where

$$a(T,p) = -\lim_{x_2\to 0}\left(\frac{\partial \log p_1^*}{\partial z_2}\right)_T \tag{11-48}$$

The quantity $a(T,p)$ can be measured making no assumption concerning solution molecular weight.

The solution molecular weight of component 2 is chosen to be

$$M_2 = \frac{M_1}{a(T,p)} \tag{11-49}$$

Substitution of Eq. (11-49) into Eq. (11-47) yields

$$\alpha(T,p) = RT \tag{11-50}$$

and thus

$$\lim_{x_2\to 0}\left(\frac{\partial \log p_1^*}{\partial x_2}\right)_T = -1 \tag{11-51}$$

If we assume that the fugacity of component 1 is an analytic function of x_2, we can write

$$p_1^* = p_1^{\circ *} - b(T)x_2 + O(x_2{}^2) \tag{11-52}$$

for small x_2. The derivative of $\log p_1^*$ with respect to x_2 at constant T is determined from Eq. (11-52) to be

$$\left(\frac{\partial \log p_1^*}{\partial x_2}\right)_T = -\frac{b + O(x_2)}{p_1^{\circ *} - bx_2 + O(x_2{}^2)} \tag{11-53}$$

The limit as x_2 tends to zero of Eq. (11-53) is easily obtained in the form

$$\lim_{x_2\to 0}\frac{1}{p_1^*}\left(\frac{\partial p_1^*}{\partial x_2}\right)_T = -\frac{b}{p_1^{\circ *}} \tag{11-54}$$

Comparison of Eqs. (11-54) and (11-51) leads to the conclusion that $b = p_1^{\circ *}$. Substitution of this expression for b into Eq. (11-52) gives

$$p_1^* = p_1^{\circ *}(1 - x_2) + O(x_2{}^2) \tag{11-55}$$

Equation (11-55) is an expression of Raoult's law. Equation (11-55) can be rearranged to yield

$$\frac{p_1^{\circ *} - p_1^*}{x_2 p_1^{\circ *}} = 1 + O(x_2) \tag{11-56}$$

Hence

$$\lim_{x_2 \to 0} \frac{p_1^{\circ *} - p_1^*}{x_2 p_1^{\circ *}} = 1 \tag{11-57}$$

if M_2 is chosen to be given by the relation

$$M_2 = \frac{M_1}{a(T,p)} \tag{11-58}$$

We shall now demonstrate that if M_2 is determined by Eq. (11-58) the limit in Eq. (11-8) exists. At equilibrium between liquid and vapor, we have

$$\mu_2 = \mu_2^{(v)} \tag{11-59}$$

where

$$\mu_2 = \mu_2^\circ + RT \log (f_2 x_2) \tag{11-60}$$

is the chemical potential of component 2 in the liquid solution and

$$\mu_2^{(v)} = \mu_2^*(T) + b_2 RT \log p_2^* \tag{11-61}$$

is the chemical potential of component 2 in the vapor. The quantity b_2 is a numerical factor depending upon the choice of M_2.

The quantity μ_2° can be written in the form

$$\mu_2^\circ = \mu_2^*(T) + \lim_{x_2 \to 0} RT \log \frac{(p_2^*)^{b_2}}{x_2} \tag{11-62}$$

where we have made use of Eqs. (11-8), (11-59), (11-60), and (11-61). Thus μ_2° exists if $\lim_{x_2 \to 0} \log[(p_2^*)^{b_2}/x_2]$ exists. Equation (9-142) can be written in the form

$$x_1\, d \log p_1^* + x_2 b_2\, d \log p_2^* - \frac{v^{(l)}}{RT}\, dp = 0 \tag{11-63}$$

when M_2 is not the gram-molecular weight of component 2. The last term in Eq. (11-63) is of order $[pv^{(l)}/RT]\, d \log p$ and can be considered to be negligible compared with the other terms. Use of the approximate form of Eq. (11-63) and the relation

$$x_1\, d \log x_1 + x_2\, d \log x_2 = 0 \tag{11-64}$$

results in

$$d \log \frac{(p_2^*)^{b_2}}{x_2} = -\frac{x_1}{x_2}\, d \log \frac{p_1^*}{x_1} \tag{11-65}$$

Integration of Eq. (11-65) from the fixed point x_2° to x_2 results in

$$\log \frac{(p_2^*)^{b_2}}{x_2} = -\int_{x_2^\circ}^{x_2} \frac{x_1'}{x_2'}\, d \log \frac{p_1'^*}{x_1'} + C(T) \tag{11-66}$$

where $C(T)$ is independent of the composition variables, the primes denote variables of integration, and the integration is over an equilibrium path at constant T. Thus

$$\lim_{x_2 \to 0} \log \frac{(p_2^*)^{b_2}}{x_2} = D + \int_0^{\mathscr{E}} \frac{x_1'}{x_2'}\, d \log \frac{p_1^*}{x_1'} \tag{11-67}$$

where

$$D = \int_{\mathscr{E}}^{x_2^\circ} \frac{x_1'}{x_2'}\, d \log \frac{p_1^*}{x_1'} + C(T) \tag{11-68}$$

is finite and $\mathscr{E} > 0$ is small enough so that Eq. (11-55) holds. The integrand in Eq. (11-67) can be expanded in the form

$$\frac{x_1'}{x_2'} \left[\frac{-p_1^{\circ *} + O(x_2')}{p_1^{\circ *} - x_2' p_1^{\circ *} + O(x_2'^2)} + \frac{1}{1 - x_2'} \right] dx_2' \tag{11-69}$$

where Eq. (11-55) has been used. Equation (11-69) can be rearranged to yield

$$\frac{x_1'}{x_2'} \frac{O(x_2')}{(1 - 2x_2')p_1^{\circ *} + O(x_2'^2)}\, dx_2' = \frac{x_1' O(1)}{(1 - 2x_2')p_1^{\circ *} + O(x_2'^2)}\, dx_2' \tag{11-70}$$

The integrand in Eq. (11-70) is finite throughout the finite range of integration. Thus $\lim_{x_2 \to 0} [(p_2^*)^{b_2}/x_2]$ exists and, therefore, μ_2° exists. We have completed the proof of the statement that, if the solution molecular weight of component 2 is chosen according to Eq. (11-49), then Raoult's law [Eq. (11-55)] holds for the solvent in infinite dilution and the limit in Eq. (11-8) exists. We note that, for an ideal solution, M_2 is the gram-molecular weight of component 2.

We shall briefly indicate the results of the more exact analysis that uses Eq. (11-38). Substitution of Eq. (11-37) into Eq. (11-38) yields

$$x_1 \left(\frac{\partial \log p_1^*}{\partial x_2} \right)_T = \frac{x_1}{RT} \left(\frac{\partial \mu_1}{\partial x_2} \right)_{T,p} + \frac{\bar{v}_1^{(l)} x_1}{RT} \left(\frac{\partial p}{\partial x_2} \right)_T \tag{11-71}$$

Use of Eqs. (11-42), (11-71), and (11-46) results in the expression

$$\begin{aligned} \alpha(T,p) &= -\lim_{x_2 \to 0} \left(\frac{\partial \mu_1}{\partial x_2} \right)_{T,p} = \lim_{x_2 \to 0} \left[-RT \left(\frac{\partial \log p_1^*}{\partial x_2} \right)_T + v_1^{(l)} \left(\frac{\partial p}{\partial x_2} \right)_T \right] \\ &= \lim_{x_2 \to 0} \left[-RT \left(\frac{\partial \log p_1^*}{\partial z_2} \right)_T + v_1^{(l)} \left(\frac{\partial p}{\partial z_2} \right)_T \right] \frac{M_2}{M_1} \end{aligned} \tag{11-72}$$

Again, we choose M_2 such that $\alpha(T,p) = RT$. If p_1^* can be written in the form of Eq. (11-52), Eq. (11-72) becomes

$$\alpha = RT = \frac{bRT}{p_1^{\circ *}} - v_1^{(l)} \lim_{x_1 \to 1} \left(\frac{\partial p}{\partial x_1}\right)_T \tag{11-73}$$

Equation (11-73) can be inverted to yield an expression for b in the form

$$b = p_1^{\circ *}\left[1 + \frac{v_1^{(l)}}{RT} \lim_{x_1 \to 1} \left(\frac{\partial p}{\partial x_1}\right)_T\right] \tag{11-74}$$

Substitution of Eq. (11-74) into Eq. (11-52) yields

$$p_1^* = p_1^{\circ *}(1 - x_2) - \frac{x_2 v_1^{(l)}}{RT} \lim_{x_1 \to 1} \left(\frac{\partial p}{\partial x_1}\right)_T + O(x_2^2) \tag{11-75}$$

Thus Raoult's law is not exactly obeyed. However, since

$$\frac{x_2 v_1^{(l)}}{RT} \lim_{x_1 \to 1} \left(\frac{\partial p}{\partial x_1}\right)_T \sim \frac{p v_1^{(l)}}{RT} \ll 1,$$

Eq. (11-75) can be approximated by

$$p_1^* = p_1^{\circ *}(1 - x_2) \tag{11-76}$$

which is an expression of Raoult's law. We find that the choice of M_2 given by Eq. (11-49) is the one necessary for the existence of μ_2°. Equation (11-63) can be integrated to yield the expression

$$\log \frac{(p_2^*)^{b_2}}{x_2} = -\int_{x_2^\circ}^{x_2} \left(\frac{x_1'}{x_2'}\, d \log \frac{p_1^*}{x_1'} - \frac{v^{(l)}}{RTx_2'}\, dp'\right) + C(T) \tag{11-77}$$

where the integration is over an equilibrium path of constant T. Near the origin, $x_2 = 0$, the integrand of Eq. (11-77) reduces to a term of order unity. In order to derive this result we have used the expression

$$dp = \left(\frac{\partial p}{\partial x_2}\right)_T dx_2 \tag{11-78}$$

and the facts that

$$v^{(l)} = x_1 \bar{v}_1^{(l)} + x_2 \bar{v}_2^{(l)} \tag{11-79}$$

and $\lim_{x_2 \to 0} v^{(l)} = v_1^{(l)}$. Thus the integrand of Eq. (11-77) is finite throughout the range of integration, $\lim_{x_2 \to 0} \log [(p_2^*)^{b_2}/x_2]$ exists, and therefore μ_2° exists. In the following discussions we shall tacitly assume that M_2 is the gram-molecular weight and thus $b_2 = 1$. Generalization to other values of M_2 is a simple task.

11-3. IDEAL SOLUTIONS

We now turn our attention to the application of the general theory of chemical potentials to ideal solutions. Ideal solutions are of interest because all nonelectrolyte solutions become ideal at high dilution and some solutions remain ideal throughout the entire range of composition. For an ideal solution, the two conventions for choosing $\mu_i^\circ(T,p)$ yield the same result. Thus

$$\mu_i = \mu_i^{(l)}(T,p) + RT \log x_i \tag{11-80}$$

We first prove that, if a solution is ideal with respect to $r - 1$ of its components, it is ideal with respect to component r. At constant temperature and pressure, the Gibbs-Duhem equation [Eq. (6-59)] becomes

$$\sum_{i=1}^{r} x_i \, d\mu_i = 0 \tag{11-81}$$

Differentiation of Eq. (11-80), holding T and p fixed, leads to

$$d\mu_i = \frac{RT}{x_i} dx_i \qquad i = 1, \ldots, r - 1 \tag{11-82}$$

Substitution of Eq. (11-82) into Eq. (11-81) gives

$$x_r \, d\mu_r + \sum_{i=1}^{r-1} RT \, dx_i = 0 \tag{11-83}$$

Differentiation of

$$\sum_{i=1}^{r} x_i = 1 \tag{11-84}$$

yields

$$dx_r + \sum_{i=1}^{r-1} dx_i = 0 \tag{11-85}$$

When Eq. (11-85) is substituted into Eq. (11-83) the result is

$$d\mu_r = RT \frac{dx_r}{x_r} \tag{11-86}$$

Integration of Eq. (11-86) gives

$$\mu_r = RT \log x_r + \mu_r^\circ(T,p) \tag{11-87}$$

where $\mu_r^\circ(T,p)$ is a constant of integration. Equation (11-87) holds for $x_r = 1$ and thus

$$\mu_r^\circ = \mu_r^{(l)}(T,p) \tag{11-88}$$

Substitution of Eq. (11-88) into Eq. (11-87) yields an expression for μ_r identical in form to Eq. (11-80). Therefore, component r is ideal.

We next consider the heat of solution and volume increment of solution for the case of ideal solutions. The partial molal enthalpy of component i is given by Eq. (7-142) in the form

$$\bar{h}_i = -T^2\left[\frac{\partial(\mu_i/T)}{\partial T}\right]_{p,x} = -T^2\left[\frac{\partial(\mu_i^{(l)}/T)}{\partial T}\right]_p$$

$$= h_i^{(l)}(T,p) \tag{11-89}$$

where $h_i^{(l)}$ is the molal enthalpy of pure liquid i. The heat of mixing of the pure liquids at constant p is

$$\Delta H = \sum_{i=1}^{r} n_i)\bar{h}_i - h_i^{(l)}) = 0 \tag{11-90}$$

The partial molal volume of component i is given by Eq. (6-54) in the form

$$\bar{v}_i = \left(\frac{\partial \mu_i}{\partial p}\right)_{T,x} = \left(\frac{\partial \mu_i^{(l)}}{\partial p}\right)_T = v_i^{(l)} \tag{11-91}$$

where $v_i^{(l)}$ is the molal volume of pure liquid i. The volume increment of solution from the pure liquids is

$$\Delta V = \sum_{i=1}^{r} n_i(\bar{v}_i - v_i^{(l)}) = 0 \tag{11-92}$$

We next consider expressions for the fugacities of the vapor in equilibrium with the ideal liquid solution. At equilibrium between liquid and vapor

$$\mu_i^{(v)} = \mu_i \qquad i = 1, \ldots, r \tag{11-93}$$

Substitution of the explicit expressions for $\mu_i^{(v)}$ [Eq. (7-155)] and μ [Eq. (11-80)] into Eq. (11-93) results in

$$\mu_i^*(T) + RT \log p_i^* = \mu_i^{(l)}(T,p) + RT \log x_i \tag{11-94}$$

Equation (11-94) can be solved to yield an explicit expression for the fugacity of component i in the form

$$p_i^* = x_i \exp\left[\frac{\mu_i^{(l)}(T,p) - \mu_i^*(T)}{RT}\right] \tag{11-95}$$

When $x_i = 1$, Eq. (11-95) reduces to

$$p_i^* = p_i^{\circ *} = \exp\left[\frac{\mu_i^{(l)}(T,p) - \mu_i^*(T)}{RT}\right] \tag{11-96}$$

where $p_i^{\circ *}$ is the vapor fugacity of pure liquid i at temperature T. Substitution of Eq. (11-96) into Eq. (11-95) yields the expression

$$p_i^* = x_i p_i^{\circ *} \qquad i = 1, \ldots, r \tag{11-97}$$

Equation (11-97) is Raoult's law. If the vapor phase is ideal, Eq. (11-97) becomes

$$p_i = x_i p_i^{\circ} \tag{11-98}$$

where p_i is the vapor pressure of component i of the liquid solution of mole fraction x_i and where p_i° is the vapor pressure of pure liquid i at temperature T.

11-4. MODERATELY DILUTE IDEAL SOLUTIONS

In this section we discuss the properties of solutions which are not ideal throughout the entire range of composition but which are ideal only when moderately dilute. For these solutions, the chemical potentials of components 1, . . . , r can be written in the form

$$\mu_1 = RT \log x_1 + \mu_1^{(l)} \qquad 1 - \varepsilon \leqslant x_1 \leqslant 1 \tag{11-99}$$

$$\mu_i = RT \log x_i + \mu_i^{\circ}(T, p) \qquad i = 2, \ldots, r \tag{11-100}$$

when x_1 is in the range $1 - \varepsilon \leqslant x_1 \leqslant 1$, where ε is a small positive quantity. In Eq. (11-100)

$$\mu_i^{\circ} = \lim_{x_1 \to 1} (\mu_i - RT \log x_i) \tag{11-101}$$

Making use of Eqs. (6-54) and (7-142), we find that in the moderately dilute solution

$$\bar{h}_1 = h_1^{(l)} \qquad \bar{v}_1 = v_1^{(l)} \tag{11-102}$$

$$\bar{h}_i = \bar{h}_i^{\circ}(T,p) \qquad \bar{v}_i = \bar{v}_i^{\circ}(T,p) \qquad i = 2, \ldots, r \tag{11-103}$$

where
$$\bar{h}_i^{\circ} = \lim_{x_1 \to 1} \bar{h}_i \tag{11-104}$$

and
$$\bar{v}_i^{\circ}(T,p) = \lim_{x_1 \to 1} \bar{v}_i \tag{11-105}$$

The quantity $\bar{h}_i^{\circ}(\bar{v}_i^{\circ})$ is the partial molal enthalpy (molal volume) of component i in the hypothetical infinitely dilute state. Thus the heat of solution from the pure liquids at constant pressure is

$$\Delta H = \sum_{i=2}^{r} n_i(\bar{h}_i^{\circ} - h_i^{(l)}) \tag{11-106}$$

and the volume increment of solution is

$$\Delta V = \sum_{i=2}^{r} n_i(\bar{v}_i^\circ - v_i^{(l)}) \tag{11-107}$$

We next consider the properties of the fugacities of the vapor phase in equilibrium with the moderately dilute ideal solution. For vapor-liquid equilibrium,

$$RT \log p_1^* + \mu_1^*(T) = RT \log x_1 + \mu_1^{(l)}(T,p) \tag{11-108}$$

and

$$RT \log p_i^* + \mu_i^*(T) = RT \log x_i + \mu_i^\circ(T,p) \qquad i = 2, \ldots, r \tag{11-109}$$

Equation (11-109) can be solved for the fugacity in the form

$$p_i^* = x_i \exp\left(\frac{\mu_i^\circ - \mu_i^*}{RT}\right) \tag{11-110}$$

Thus

$$p_i^* = x_i k_i(T,p) \qquad i = 2, \ldots, r \tag{11-111}$$

where

$$k_i(T,p) = e^{(\mu_i^\circ - \mu_i^*)/RT} \tag{11-112}$$

Equation (11-111) is Henry's law. As in the case of ideal solutions,

$$p_1^* = x_1 p_1^{\circ *} \tag{11-113}$$

Thus, the solvent obeys Raoult's law.

11-5. REGULAR SOLUTIONS

Hildebrand has found experimentally that a large number of binary mixtures show a behavior which can be represented quite well by the laws of regular solutions. A regular solution is, by definition, one in which the partial entropies of the various components have ideal forms. In this section, we discuss some of the properties of regular solutions.

In an ideal solution,

$$\mu_i = RT \log x_i + \mu_i^{(l)}(T,p) \tag{11-114}$$

The partial molal entropy of component i is given by

$$\bar{s}_i = -\left(\frac{\partial \mu_i}{\partial T}\right)_{p,x} = -R \log x_i + s_i^{(l)} \tag{11-115}$$

The entropy of mixing of the ideal mixture is

$$\Delta s = \sum_{i=1}^{r} n_i(\bar{s}_i - s_i^{(l)}) = -R \sum_{i=1}^{r} n_i \log x_i \tag{11-116}$$

A solution in which the partial entropies are given by Eq. (11-115) is a regular solution.

Use of Eq. (11-115) and the relation

$$\mu_i^{(l)} = h_i^{(l)} - Ts_i^{(l)} \tag{11-117}$$

yields

$$\mu_i = \bar{h}_i - T\bar{s}_i = RT \log x_i + (\bar{h}_i - h_i^{(l)}) + \mu_i^{(l)}(T,p) \tag{11-118}$$

as an expression for the chemical potential of component i in a regular solution. Comparison of Eq. (11-118) with Eq. (11-4) gives

$$RT \log f_i = \bar{h}_i - h_i^{(l)} \tag{11-119}$$

as an expression for the excess chemical potential of component i. Differentiation of Eq. (11-118) with respect to T at constant p and x results in

$$\bar{s}_i = -\left(\frac{\partial \mu_i}{\partial T}\right)_{p,x} = -R \log x_i + s_i^{(l)} - (\bar{c}_{p_i} - c_{p_i}^{(l)}) \tag{11-120}$$

Substitution of Eq. (11-115) into Eq. (11-120) yields the result

$$\bar{c}_{p_i} = c_{p_i}^{(l)} \tag{11-121}$$

Thus the partial molal heat capacity at constant pressure of component i in the regular solution is the same as the molal heat capacity of pure liquid i. Differentiation of Eq. (11-118) with respect to p at constant T and x yields

$$\bar{v}_i = v_i^{(l)} + \left(\frac{\partial \bar{h}_i}{\partial p}\right)_{T,x} - \left(\frac{\partial h_i^{(l)}}{\partial p}\right)_T \tag{11-122}$$

Use of Eq. (6-27) in the form

$$\left(\frac{\partial \bar{h}_i}{\partial p}\right)_{T,x} = \bar{v}_i - T\left(\frac{\partial \bar{v}_i}{\partial T}\right)_{p,x} \tag{11-123}$$

and Eq. (11-122) results in

$$\left(\frac{\partial \bar{v}_i}{\partial T}\right)_{p,x} = \left(\frac{\partial v_i^{(l)}}{\partial T}\right)_{p,x} \tag{11-124}$$

Equations (11-121) and (11-124) are statements of two of the many properties of regular solutions that are identical with the properties of ideal solutions.

We next turn our attention to a consideration of some of the properties of regular solutions that differ from ideal solutions. We consider a binary solution. In this case, the Margules formalism for the expansion of the activity coefficient in powers of the mole fraction (Sec. 11-6) and use of Eq. (11-119) give

$$\bar{h}_1 - h_1^{(l)} = B_1 x_2^2 + C_1 x_2^3 + \cdots \tag{11-125}$$

and

$$\bar{h}_2 - h_2^{(l)} = (B_1 + \tfrac{3}{2}C_1)x_1^2 - C_1 x_1^3 + \cdots \tag{11-126}$$

where B_1 and C_1 are, in general, functions of T and p.

Since the laws of regular solutions closely approximate those derived by statistical mechanics for lattice models of the liquid state in which the partial molal volume of component i in the mixture is equal to the molal volume of pure liquid i, it is sometimes assumed that $\bar{v}_i = v_i^{(l)}$. In this case, reference to Eqs. (11-121) and (11-122) shows that B_1 and C_1 are constants independent of T and p. A particularly simple and frequently applicable result is obtained if C_1 is set equal to zero. Systems for which $C_1 = 0$ are called symmetric solutions. In this case, Eqs. (11-125) and (11-126) reduce to

$$\mu_1^E = B_1 x_2^2 \tag{11-127}$$

$$\mu_2^E = B_1 x_1^2 \tag{11-128}$$

The integral heat of solution per mean mole of a symmetric solution becomes

$$\Delta h = \sum_{i=1}^{r} x_i(\bar{h}_i - h_i^{(l)}) = B_1 x_1 x_2^2 + B_1 x_2 x_1^2 = B_1 x_1 x_2 \tag{11-129}$$

Consequently,

$$B_1 = 4\Delta h_{\frac{1}{2}} \tag{11-130}$$

where $\Delta h_{\frac{1}{2}}$ is the integral heat of solution per mean mole for an equimolar mixture. (More details concerning the properties of regular solutions can be found in the book: J. Hildebrand and R. Scott, "Solubility of Nonelectrolytes," Reinhold Publishing Corporation, New York, 1950.)

11-6. REAL SOLUTIONS

In this section, we consider a real mixture of two components. We describe Margules expansions for the logarithms of the activity coefficients and investigate relations between the coefficients in the expansions of $\log f_1$ and $\log f_2$ imposed by the Gibbs-Duhem equation.

The chemical potentials of components 1 and 2 of the real solution can be written in the form

$$\mu_1 = RT \log (f_1 x_1) + \mu_1^{(l)}(T,p) \tag{11-131}$$

and

$$\mu_2 = RT \log (f_2 x_2) + \mu_2^{(l)}(T,p) \tag{11-132}$$

where we have used the convention of Eq. (11-6) to determine the standard chemical potential. We assume, in agreement with experimental evidence, that $\log f_1$ and $\log f_2$ are analytic functions of x_2 and x_1 in the region $0 < x_1, x_2 < 1$. Thus we can write

$$\mu_1^E = RT \log f_1 = A_1 x_2 + B_1 x_2^2 + C_1 x_2^3 + \cdots \qquad x_2 < 1 \tag{11-133}$$

and

$$\mu_2^E = RT \log f_2 = A_2 x_1 + B_2 x_1^2 + C_2 x_1^3 + \cdots \qquad x_1 < 1 \tag{11-134}$$

where A_1, A_2, etc., are functions of T and p only. There are no constant terms in the power series of Eqs. (11-133) and (11-134) because $\lim_{x_2 \to 0} f_1 = 1$ and $\lim_{x_1 \to 0} f_2 = 1$. Expansions of the type of Eqs. (11-133) and (11-134) are known as Margules expansions.

We make use of the Gibbs-Duhem equation at constant T and p in the form

$$RT(x_1 d \log f_1 + x_2 d \log f_2) = 0 \tag{11-135}$$

to determine relationships between the coefficients in Eq. (11-133) and (11-134). Substitution of Eqs. (11-133) and (11-134) into Eq. (11-135) and use of the equations

$$x_2 = 1 - x_1 \qquad dx_2 = -dx_1 \tag{11-136}$$

results in

$$\begin{aligned} &A_2 + (2B_2 - A_2)x_1 + (3C_2 - 2B_2)x_1^2 - 3C_2 x_1^3 + \cdots \\ &\qquad = (A_1 + 2B_1 + 3C_1)x_1 - (2B_1 + 6C_1)x_1^2 + 3C_1 x_1^3 + \cdots \end{aligned} \tag{11-137}$$

In Eq. (11-137) we have retained only the first three terms in Eqs. (11-133) and (11-134). Equating coefficients of powers of x_1 on both sides of Eq. (11-137), we obtain

$$\begin{aligned} A_2 &= 0 \\ 2B_2 - A_2 &= A_1 + 2B_1 + 3C_1 \\ 3C_2 - 2B_2 &= -2B_1 - 6C_1 \\ 3C_1 &= -3C_2 \end{aligned} \tag{11-138}$$

Equations (11-138) can be rearranged to yield

$$\begin{aligned} A_2 &= 0 = A_1 \\ B_2 &= \tfrac{3}{2}C_1 + B_1 \\ C_2 &= -C_1 \end{aligned} \tag{11-139}$$

Substitution of Eqs. (11-139) into Eqs. (11-133) and (11-134) results in

$$RT \log f_1 = B_1 x_2^2 + C_1 x_2^3 + \cdots \tag{11-140}$$

$$RT \log f_2 = (B_1 + \tfrac{3}{2}C_1)x_1^2 - C_1 x_1^3 + \cdots \tag{11-141}$$

Equations (11-140) and (11-141) are the bases of the thermodynamic treatment of the properties of real solutions. Note that linear terms in the mole fractions do not occur in Eqs. (11-140) and (11-141).

11-7. MEASUREMENT OF CHEMICAL POTENTIAL

Many experimental techniques are used to determine the values of excess chemical potentials or activity coefficients. In this section we briefly discuss the relationships between the activity coefficients and information derived from measurement of

a. Vapor fugacities
b. Freezing point and boiling point
c. Solubility
d. Partition coefficient
e. Osmotic pressure
f. Light scattering

11-7a. Vapor Fugacity

The condition for equilibrium with respect to component i in liquid and gaseous phases is

$$\mu_i(\text{liquid}) = \mu_i(\text{gas}) \tag{11-142}$$

Substitution of the explicit expressions for the chemical potential of component i in the liquid and gaseous phases into Eq. (11-142) results in

$$RT \log (f_i x_i) + \mu_i^{(l)} = RT \log p_i^* + \mu_i^* \tag{11-143}$$

Equation (11-143) can be rearranged to yield an explicit expression for the activity coefficient of component i in the form

$$f_i x_i = p_i^* e^{(1/RT)(\mu_i^* - \mu_i^{(l)})} \tag{11-144}$$

Since the convention of Eq. (11-6) has been used in Eq. (11-143), $f_i = 1$ when $x_i = 1$. Thus, when $x_i = 1$, Eq. (11-144) becomes

$$\frac{1}{p_i^{\circ *}} = e^{(1/RT)(\mu_i^* - \mu_i^{(l)})} \tag{11-145}$$

Substitution of Eq. (11-145) into Eq. (11-144) yields

$$f_i x_i = \frac{p_i^*}{p_i^{\circ *}} \tag{11-146}$$

Thus, the activity coefficient of component i in solution is determined from knowledge derived from measurements of the vapor fugacity of component i in equilibrium with the liquid solution. If the vapor fugacities of components other than i are known, the vapor fugacity of i can be determined by application of the Gibbs-Duhem equation and, again, the activity coefficient of component i can be found.

11-7b. Freezing Point

A condition for equilibrium between the liquid solution and pure solid solvent 1 is

$$\mu_1^{(s)}(T,p) = \mu_1^{(l)}(T,p) + RT \log (f_1 x_1) \tag{11-147}$$

where $\mu_1^{(s)}$ is the chemical potential of the pure solid solvent. If T_1 is the melting point of pure solvent at pressure p, then

$$\mu_1^{(s)}(T_1,p) = \mu_1^{(l)}(T_1,p) \tag{11-148}$$

Division of Eq. (11-147) by T and of Eq. (11-148) by T_1 and subtraction of the resulting equations gives

$$\frac{\mu_1^{(s)}(T,p)}{T} - \frac{\mu_1^{(s)}(T_1,p)}{T_1} = \frac{\mu_1^{(l)}(T,p)}{T} - \frac{\mu_1^{(l)}(T_1,p)}{T_1} + R \log (f_1 x_1) \tag{11-149}$$

Equation (11-149) can be rearranged to yield an explicit expression for $\log (f_1 x_1)$ in the form

$$\log (f_1 x_1) = \int_{T_1}^{T} \frac{h_1^{(l)} - h_1^{(s)}}{RT'^2}\, dT' = \int_{T_1}^{T} \frac{L_f\, dT'}{RT'^2} \tag{11-150}$$

where $L_f = h_1^{(l)} - h_1^{(s)}$ is the molar heat of fusion of pure solvent and the integration is along a path at constant p. The relationship

$$\left[\frac{\partial(\mu_1/T)}{\partial T}\right]_p = -\frac{h_1}{T^2} \tag{11-151}$$

has been used in the derivation of Eq. (11-150).

Expansion of $L_f(T,p)$ about $L_f(T_1,p)$ and substitution of the result into Eq. (11-150) lead to

$$\log (f_1 x_1) = -\int_0^{\theta} \frac{L_f^\circ + \Delta C_p^\circ \theta' + O(\theta'^2)}{R(T_1 - \theta')^2}\, d\theta' \tag{11-152}$$

where $L_f^\circ = L_f(T_1,p)$, $\Delta C_p^\circ = (\partial L_f/\partial T)_p$ evaluated at $T = T_1$, $\theta' = T_1 - T'$, and $\theta = T_1 - T$.

Substitution of the expansion

$$\frac{1}{(T_1 - \theta)^2} = \frac{1}{T_1^2}\left[1 + \frac{2\theta}{T_1} + O(\theta^2)\right] \tag{11-153}$$

into Eq. (11-152) and integration of the resulting expression yield

$$\log (f_1 x_1) = -\frac{L_f^\circ}{RT_1}\frac{\theta}{T_1} - \left(\frac{\Delta C_p^\circ}{2R} + \frac{L_f^\circ}{RT_1}\right)\left(\frac{\theta}{T_1}\right)^2 + O\left(\left(\frac{\theta}{T_1}\right)^3\right) \tag{11-154}$$

Equation (11-154) can be rewritten in the form

$$\log (f_1 x_1) = -\Delta_1 \theta - \Delta_2 \theta^2 \tag{11-155}$$

where

$$\Delta_1 = +\frac{L_f^\circ}{RT_1^{\,2}} \tag{11-156}$$

and

$$\Delta_2 = \frac{1}{RT_1^{\,2}} \left(\frac{\Delta C_p^\circ}{2} + \frac{L_f^\circ}{T_1} \right) \tag{11-157}$$

The quantities Δ_1 and Δ_2 can be determined from the properties of pure systems containing only component 1. They are functions of pressure alone. Equation (11-155) is an expression for $\log (f_1 x_1)$ as a function of pressure p and freezing-point depression θ. Thus, measurement of the temperature at which solid component 1 first appears in the system at pressure p is sufficient to determine f_1. Equation (11-155) is useful when the solution is dilute and $\theta/T_1 \ll 1$.

In a binary solution, the activity coefficient of component 2 can be determined from Eq. (11-155) by use of the Gibbs-Duhem equation. Since, in the applications of this method, the solution is dilute with respect to component 2 it will be most useful to determine γ_2, the activity coefficient of component 2 with respect to the molality. At constant pressure, the Gibbs-Duhem equation may be written

$$x_1\, d\mu_1 + x_2\, d\mu_2 + s\, dT = 0 \tag{11-158}$$

where

$$s = x_1 \bar{s}_1 + x_2 \bar{s}_2 \tag{11-159}$$

It is not possible to apply the Gibbs-Duhem equation at constant T and p to this system because of the requirement of equilibrium between the solution and pure solid 1. Substitution of Eq. (11-147) for μ_1 and Eq. (11-11) for μ_2 into Eq. (11-158) results in

$$x_1 RT\, d \log (f_1 x_1) + x_2 RT\, d \log (\gamma_2 m_2)$$
$$= [-s - x_1 R \log (f_1 x_1) + x_1 s_1^{(l)} - x_2 R \log (\gamma_2 m_2) + x_2 s_2^{(m)\circ}]\, dT \tag{11-160}$$

where we have made use of the facts that

$$\left(\frac{\partial \mu_1^{(l)}}{\partial T} \right)_p = -s_1^{(l)} \tag{11-161}$$

and

$$\left(\frac{\partial \mu_2^{(m)\circ}}{\partial T} \right)_p = -s_2^{(m)\circ} \tag{11-162}$$

The right-hand side of Eq. (11-160) can be transformed into

$$\left[\frac{x_1(h_1^{(l)} - \bar{h}_1)}{T} + \frac{x_2(h_2^{(\circ)} - \bar{h}_2)}{T} \right] dT = -\frac{\bar{L}}{T}\, dT \tag{11-163}$$

where we have made use of the results

$$h_1^{(l)} - \bar{h}_1 = \mu_1^{(l)} + Ts_1^{(l)} - [\mu_1^{(l)} + RT \log (f_1 x_1) + T\bar{s}_1] \qquad (11\text{-}164)$$

and

$$h_2^{(\circ)} - \bar{h}_2 = \mu_2^{m(\circ)} + Ts_2^{m(\circ)} - [\mu_2^{m(\circ)} + RT \log (\gamma_2 m_2) + T\bar{s}_2] \qquad (11\text{-}165)$$

The quantity

$$\bar{L} = x_1(\bar{h}_1 - h_1^{(l)}) + x_2(\bar{h}_2 - h_2^{(\circ)}) \qquad (11\text{-}166)$$

is the mean molal heat of mixing of pure component 1 and component 2 in its hypothetical ideal state. In general, $\bar{L}$ is small, and the term on the right-hand side of Eq. (11-160) can be neglected. In this approximation, Eq. (11-160) becomes

$$d \log (\gamma_2 m_2) = -\frac{x_1}{x_2} d \log (f_1 x_1) = \frac{-1000}{m_2 M_1} d \log (f_1 x_1) \qquad (11\text{-}167)$$

where

$$m_2 = \frac{1000}{M_1} \frac{n_2}{n_1} \qquad (11\text{-}168)$$

The differential of Eq. (11-155) at constant p is given by

$$d \log (f_1 x_1) = -\Delta_1 \, d\theta - 2\Delta_2 \theta \, d\theta \qquad (11\text{-}169)$$

Substitution of Eq. (11-169) into Eq. (11-167) results in

$$\begin{aligned} d \log \gamma_2 &= \frac{1000\Delta_1 \, d\theta}{m_2 M_1} + \frac{2000\Delta_2 \theta \, d\theta}{m_2 M_1} - d \log m_2 \\ &= \frac{1}{\lambda m_2} d\theta - d \log m_2 + \frac{2000}{m_2 M_1} \Delta_2 \theta \, d\theta \\ &= -dj - \frac{j}{m_2} dm_2 + \frac{2000\Delta_2 \theta \, d\theta}{m_2 M_1} \end{aligned} \qquad (11\text{-}170)$$

where $\lambda = M_1/1000\Delta_1$ and $j = 1 - (\theta/\lambda m_2)$. Integration of Eq. (11-170) gives

$$\log \gamma_2 = -j - \int_{j=0}^{j} \frac{j}{m_2} dm_2 + O(\theta^2) + a(p) \qquad (11\text{-}171)$$

where $a(p)$ is a constant of integration. Equation (11-171) expresses the activity coefficient of the solute in terms of its molal concentration and the freezing-point depression.

In a dilute solution, $x_2 \ll 1$, we may write

$$\log (f_1 x_1) = \log x_1 + \log f_1 = -x_2 + O(x_2^2) \qquad (11\text{-}172)$$

where we have used Eq. (11-140) and the expansion for log $(1 - x_2)$. Substitution of Eq. (11-172) into Eq. (11-154) and neglect of terms of $O(x_2^2)$ result in

$$x_2 = \frac{L_f^\circ \theta}{RT_1^2} \tag{11-173}$$

or

$$\theta = \lambda m_2 \tag{11-174}$$

Thus, $j = 0$ for an infinitely dilute solution when $\gamma_2 = 1$ and the constant of integration in Eq. (11-171) is zero.

In practice, the integral in Eq. (11-171) is evaluated numerically by plotting j/m_2 versus m_2. The experimental quantity measured is the depression of the freezing point as a function of the molarity of the solute. It is found experimentally that

$$j \simeq m_2 + Cm_2^2 \tag{11-175}$$

In the approximation of Eq. (11-175), Eq. (11-171) becomes

$$\log \gamma_2 \simeq -2j \tag{11-176}$$

Measurements of the freezing-point depression are often utilized in the determination of the solution molecular weight of the solute. In the dilute-solution approximation,

$$\frac{L_f^\circ \theta}{RT_1^2} = x_2 \simeq \frac{n_2}{n_1} = \frac{w_2/M_2}{w_1/M_1} \tag{11-177}$$

where w_i is the number of grams of component i in the solution. Equation (11-177) can be rearranged to yield

$$M_2 = \frac{w_2}{w_1/M_1} \frac{1}{K\theta} \tag{11-178}$$

where $K = L_f^\circ/RT_1^2$ is a constant, dependent only on the solvent and the pressure, and M_2 is the solution molecular weight of component 2.

A similar analysis with L_f replaced by L_v, the molar heat of vaporization of the pure solvent, relates the boiling-point elevation for non-volatile solutes to the activity coefficients and the solution molecular weight of the solute. Although more accurate results are obtained by use of freezing-point determination, the boiling-point method is often used when only a small quantity of the solution is available.

11-7c. Solubility

It is possible to determine the activity coefficients of solute species in a given solvent by measuring their solubilities in that solvent. We consider a system in which pure solid component 2 is in equilibrium with a liquid solution in which 2 is a solute. A condition of equilibrium between solid 2 and the liquid solution is

$$\mu_2^{(s)}(T,p) = \mu_2^\circ(T,p) + RT \log (f_2 x_2) \tag{11-179}$$

where we have used the convention of Eq. (11-8). We consider the equilibrium between solid 2 and liquid solution at pressure p and at such a temperature T_0 that component 2 is very slightly soluble. Under these conditions, the equilibrium condition becomes

$$\mu_2^{(s)}(T_0,p) = \mu_2^\circ(T_0,p) + RT_0 \log x_2^\circ \tag{11-180}$$

where $x_2^\circ \ll 1$ is the mole fraction of 2 in solution in equilibrium with solid 2 at T_0 and p and where we have assumed that f_2° is approximately unity. Division of Eq. (11-179) by T, Eq. (11-180) by T_0, subtraction of the results, and use of Eq. (11-151) result in

$$\log (f_2 x_2) - \log x_2^\circ = \int_{T_0}^{T} \frac{h_2^\circ - h_2^{(s)}}{R(T')^2}\, dT' = \int_{T_0}^{T} \frac{L_f^*\, dT'}{R(T')^2} \tag{11-181}$$

where L_f^* is the molar heat of fusion of pure solid 2 into the infinitely dilute solution. Equation (11-181) relates the activity coefficient of component 2 at T to measurements of the solubility of component 2 at temperature T.

It is sometimes useful to measure the change of solubility of one component on addition of other components to the solvent. The equilibrium condition between pure solid 2 and the initial liquid solution is given by Eq. (11-179). After the addition of other components to the solvent the equilibrium condition between pure solid 2 and the liquid solution becomes

$$\mu_2^{(s)}(T,p) = \mu_2^\circ(T,p) + RT \log (f_2' x_2') \tag{11-182}$$

where x_2' is the new mole fraction of component 2 and f_2' is the new activity coefficient. If the other components have been added while T and p were held fixed, Eqs. (11-182) and (11-179) may be equated to yield, after some rearrangement,

$$f_2 x_2 = f_2' x_2' \tag{11-183}$$

Thus, the activity coefficient of component 2 in a liquid solution in equilibrium with solid 2 can be easily determined from knowledge of the activity coefficient of component 2 in a liquid solution of different composition in equilibrium with solid 2 and from the solubilities of 2 in the two solutions, assuming that the solvents, T, and p are the same in the two systems.

11-7d. Partition Coefficient

Measurements of partition coefficients are frequently used to determine activity coefficients of solute species. We consider a system consisting of two immiscible solvents, phases 1 and 2 and a solute component 2. At equilibrium,

$$\mu_2^{(1)} = \mu_2^{(2)} \tag{11-184}$$

Substitution of Eq. (11-11) into Eq. (11-184) yields

$$\mu_2^{(1)\circ} + RT \log (\gamma_2^{(1)} m_2^{(1)}) = \mu_2^{(2)\circ} + RT \log (\gamma_2^{(2)} m_2^{(2)}) \tag{11-185}$$

Rearrangement of Eq. (11-185) results in

$$RT \log \frac{\gamma_2^{(1)} m_2^{(1)}}{\gamma_2^{(2)} m_2^{(2)}} = \mu^{(2)\circ} - \mu^{(1)\circ} \tag{11-186}$$

or

$$\frac{\gamma_2^{(1)} m_2^{(1)}}{\gamma_2^{(2)} m_2^{(2)}} = K = \exp\left(-\frac{\mu^{(1)\circ} - \mu^{(2)\circ}}{RT}\right) \tag{11-187}$$

where K, the partition coefficient, is a function of T, p, and the solvents. K is determined experimentally by extrapolating the partition ratio, $\gamma_2^{(1)} m_2^{(1)} / \gamma_2^{(2)} m_2^{(2)}$, to infinite dilution,

$$\lim_{m_2 \to 0} \frac{\gamma_2^{(1)} m_2^{(1)}}{\gamma_2^{(2)} m_2^{(2)}} = \frac{m_2^{(1)}}{m_2^{(2)}} = K \tag{11-188}$$

Knowledge of K and the activity coefficient of the solute in one solvent determines the activity coefficient of the solute in another solvent.

11-7e. Osmotic Pressure

Measurements of osmotic pressure are frequently used to determine activity coefficients and solution molecular weights. The measurements are particularly useful in the determination of the properties of polymer solutions.

The system under consideration consists of a liquid solution of r components (phase α) separated from pure liquid 1 (phase β) by a nondeformable, heat-conducting membrane permeable to component 1

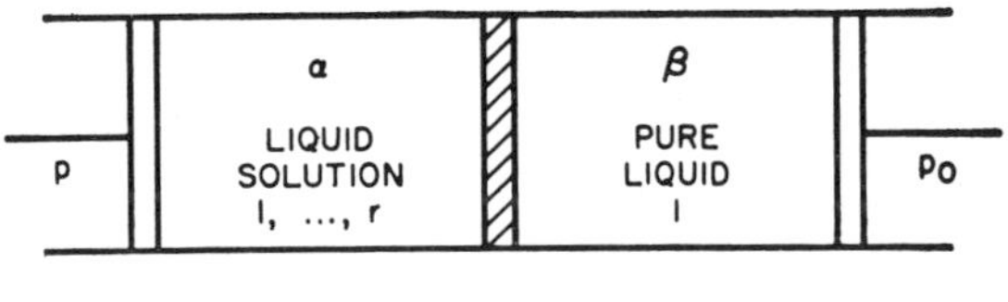

FIG. 11-1. System containing liquid solution (α) and pure liquid 1 (β) separated by nondeformable, heat-conducting membrane permeable, to component 1 alone.

alone (Fig. 11-1). The equilibrium conditions in this system are discussed in Sec. 6-3. They are

$$T^{(\alpha)} = T^{(\beta)} \tag{11-189}$$

and

$$\mu_1(T,p,x_1, \ldots ,x_{r-1}) = \mu_1^{(l)}(T,p_0) \tag{11-190}$$

where $\mu_1(T,p,x_1, \ldots ,x_{r-1})$ is the chemical potential of component 1 in phase α and p is the pressure on phase α required to achieve equilibrium between it and phase β at pressure p_0. The quantity $\pi = p - p_0$ is called the osmotic pressure. Since

$$\left(\frac{\partial \mu_1}{\partial p}\right)_{T,x} = \bar{v}_1 \tag{11-191}$$

we may write

$$\mu_1(T,p,x) - \mu_1(T,p_0,x) = \int_{p_0}^{p_0+\pi} \bar{v}_1(p')\, dp' \tag{11-192}$$

where the symbol x stands for the set of mole fractions $x_1, \ldots, x_{r-1}$. Substitution of Eq. (11-190) into Eq. (11-192) results in

$$\mu_1^{(l)}(T,p_0) - \mu_1(T,p_0,x) = \int_{p_0}^{p_0+\pi} \bar{v}_1\, dp' \tag{11-193}$$

Comparison of Eq. (11-193) with Eq. (11-4) yields an explicit expression for the logarithm of the activity coefficient of the solvent in the form

$$RT \log (f_1 x_1) = -\int_{p_0}^{p_0+\pi} \bar{v}_1\, dp' \tag{11-194}$$

If we assume that $\bar{v}_1(p,T,x)$ is an analytic function of p, we may expand it about $\bar{v}_1^\circ = \bar{v}_1(p_0)$, in the form

$$\bar{v}_1(p) = \bar{v}_1^\circ + (p - p_0)\left(\frac{\partial \bar{v}_1}{\partial p}\right)_{\substack{T,x\\ p=p_0}} + O(p - p_0)^2 \tag{11-195}$$

or

$$\bar{v}_1(p) = \bar{v}_1^\circ[1 - \bar{\kappa}_1^\circ(p - p_0) + O(p - p_0)^2] \tag{11-196}$$

where

$$\bar{\kappa}_1^\circ = -\frac{1}{\bar{v}_1^\circ}\left(\frac{\partial \bar{v}_1}{\partial p}\right)_{T,x} \tag{11-197}$$

is the partial molal compressibility of component 1 evaluated at the pressure p_0. Substitution of Eq. (11-196) into Eq. (11-193) and integration of the resulting equation lead to

$$\mu_1^{(l)}(T,p_0) - \mu_1(T,p_0,x) = \pi \bar{v}_1^\circ\left[1 - \frac{\bar{\kappa}_1^\circ \pi}{2} + O(\pi^2)\right] \tag{11-198}$$

In the incompressive approximation,

$$\bar{v}_1(p) = \bar{v}_1^\circ \tag{11-199}$$

and Eq. (11-198) reduces to

$$\pi\bar{v}_1^\circ = \mu_1^{(l)}(T,p_0) - \mu_1(T,p_0,x) \tag{11-200}$$

Equations (11-198) and (11-200) provide explicit expressions for f_1 in terms of the experimentally measured osmotic pressures. If equilibrium exists between the liquid and vapor phases, the osmotic pressure can be related to the vapor fugacities by the expression

$$\pi\bar{v}_1^\circ = RT \log \frac{p_1^{\circ *}}{p_1^*} \tag{11-201}$$

where we have used Eq. (11-200) and the equilibrium condition [Eq. (11-143)].

Equation (11-200) can be utilized to obtain an expression for the osmotic coefficient of component 1 in the form

$$\pi\bar{v}_1^\circ = -g_1 RT \log x_1 \tag{11-202}$$

where Eq. (11-31) has been used. In a binary solution Eq. (11-202) may be rewritten

$$\pi\bar{v}_1^\circ = -g_1 RT \log (1 - x_2) = g_1 RT x_2 + O(x_2^2) \tag{11-203}$$

An expression for the total volume of the solution, V, is given by

$$V = n_1 v_1 + n_2 v_2 = (n_1 + n_2)\bar{v}_1 \left[1 + \frac{x_2}{\bar{v}_1}(\bar{v}_2 - \bar{v}_1)\right] \tag{11-204}$$

Multiplication of Eq. (11-204) by π and use of Eq. (11-203) yield, in the incompressive approximation,

$$\pi V = g_1 RT n_2 \left[1 + \frac{x_2}{\bar{v}_1}(\bar{v}_2 - \bar{v}_1)\right][1 + O(x_2)] = n_2 g_1 RT[1 + O(x_2)] \tag{11-205}$$

In the zero approximation, neglecting terms of $O(x_2)$, Eq. (11-205) becomes

$$\pi = c_2 g_1 RT \tag{11-206}$$

where

$$c_2 = \frac{n_2}{V} \tag{11-207}$$

For an ideal solution, Eq. (11-206) reduces to

$$\pi = c_2 RT \tag{11-208}$$

Equation (11-208) is the van't Hoff law; its similarity to the perfect-gas law is superficial.

In the treatment of nonideal solutions, expansions of a form similar to the virial expansion for gases [Eq. (7-14)] are introduced. The osmotic coefficient of 1 can be expanded in a power series in concentration of component 2 in the form

$$g_1 = 1 + B_1 c_2 + B_2 c_2^2 + \cdots \tag{11-209}$$

where $B_1, B_2, \ldots$ are functions of T and p only. Substitution of Eq. (11-209) into Eq. (11-206) yields

$$\pi = RTc_2(1 + B_1 c_2 + B_2 c_2^2 + \cdots) \tag{11-210}$$

Equation (11-210) is used in the determination of the molecular weights of high polymers from osmotic-pressure measurements.

11-7f. Light Scattering

We shall now present a brief résumé of the formulas necessary for the computation of activity coefficients from light-scattering measurements. The method is practicable only for species of high molecular weight.

We consider a binary solution and take into account only Rayleigh scattering. Using Boer's law, we have

$$\frac{I}{I_0} = e^{-\tau x} \tag{11-211}$$

where I_0 = intensity of incident radiation
I = intensity of transmitted radiation
x = thickness of sample
τ = turbidity of sample

The turbidity due to composition fluctuations, with neglect of density fluctuations, as calculated by statistical theory, is

$$\tau = \frac{8\pi^3 RT}{3\lambda^4 N\rho_1}\left(\frac{\partial n^2}{\partial C_2}\right)^2_{T,p} \frac{M_2}{(\partial\mu_2/\partial C_2)_{T,p}} \tag{11-212}$$

where λ = wavelength of incident light
n = refractive index of solution
$C_2 = w_2/w_1$
ρ_1 = density of component 1 in solution

Since

$$C_2 = \frac{M_2 m_2}{1000} \tag{11-213}$$

we can write the chemical potential of component 2 in the form

$$\mu_2 = RT \log(\gamma_2 C_2) + \mu_2'^{\circ}(T,p) \tag{11-214}$$

where

$$\mu_2'^{\circ} = \mu^{(m)\circ} + RT \log \frac{M_2}{1000} \tag{11-215}$$

Thus the derivative of μ_2 with respect to C_2 is given by

$$\left(\frac{\partial \mu_2}{\partial C_2}\right)_{T,p} = \frac{RT}{C_2} + RT\left(\frac{\partial \log \gamma_2}{\partial C_2}\right)_{T,p} \tag{11-216}$$

Substitution of Eq. (11-216) into Eq. (11-212) and rearrangement result in

$$\frac{1}{M_2}\left[1 + \left(\frac{\partial \log \gamma_2}{\partial \log C_2}\right)_{T,p}\right] = \frac{HC_2}{\tau} \tag{11-217}$$

where

$$H = \frac{8\pi^3}{3\lambda^4 N\rho_1}\left(\frac{\partial n^2}{\partial C_2}\right)^2_{T,p} \tag{11-218}$$

A typical plot of experimental data is given in Fig. (11-2). In this graph, HC_2/τ is plotted against C_2. The curve intersects the ordinate at $1/M_2$ since

$$\lim_{C_2 \to 0} C_2\left(\frac{\partial \log \gamma_2}{\partial C_2}\right)_{T,p} = 0 \tag{11-219}$$

The deviation of HC_2/τ from the constant value $1/M_2$ is given by $(1/M_2)\,(\partial \log \gamma_2/\partial \log C_2)_{T,p}$. Thus light-scattering measurements yield information by which the solution molecular weights and the activity coefficient of the solute can be evaluated.

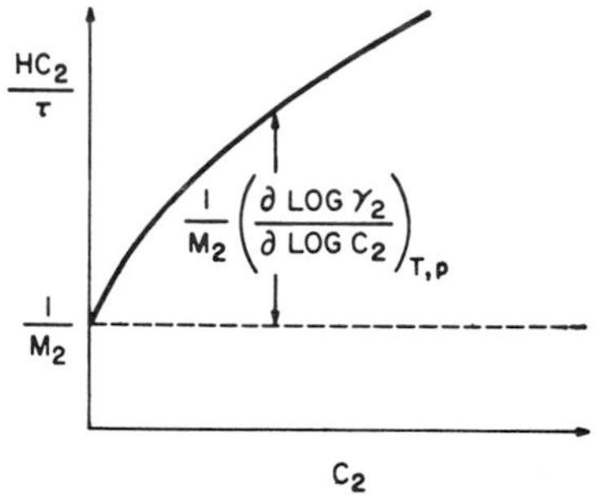

FIG. 11-2. Plot of HC_2/τ versus C_2.

Electromotive-force measurements are useful in the determination of activity coefficients in electrolyte solutions. These measurements will be discussed in Sec. 13-2.

This completes our discussion of chemical potentials of nonelectrolyte solutions.

12 CHEMICAL POTENTIALS OF ELECTROLYTE SOLUTIONS

There exist solutions whose properties, such as their electrical conductivity, indicate that the solute molecules are at least partially dissociated into ions. These solutions are termed *electrolyte solutions.* In general, solute molecules in which the chemical bonds have a large degree of ionic, rather than covalent, character will dissolve in polar solvents to yield electrolyte solutions. A solute is called a strong electrolyte if it completely dissociates into ions in solutions. Weak electrolytes are those for which an equilibrium is set up between undissociated molecules and constituent ions in solutions.

In this chapter we discuss some of the properties of electrolyte solutions. In Sec. 12-1, the chemical potential and activity coefficient of an electrolyte are expressed in terms of the chemical potentials and activity coefficients of its constituent ions. In addition, the zeroth-order approximation to the form of the chemical potential is discussed and the solubility product rule is derived. In Sec. 12-2, deviations from ideality in strong-electrolyte solutions are discussed and the results of the Debye-Hückel theory are presented. In Sec. 12-3, the thermodynamic treatment of weak-electrolyte solutions is given and use of strong-electrolyte and nonelectrolyte conventions is discussed.

12-1. CONVENTIONS

In principle, the conventions used for nonelectrolyte solutions developed in Chap. 11 could be employed for electrolyte solutions which are subject to the condition of electroneutrality. Agreement with experimental data could be obtained by choosing the molecular weight to be some fraction of the formula weight. However, these conventions generally lead to activity coefficients which are rapidly varying functions of composition. In order to avoid this, we formally define chemical potentials and activity coefficients for ionic components. The definition of chemical potentials for ionic components does not have operational significance since their concentrations cannot be varied independently.

The formula for a general electrolyte, Y_i, can be written

$$Y_i = \prod_{k=1}^{r} (X_k)_{\nu_k{}^i} \qquad (12\text{-}1)$$

Its formula weight is composed of $\nu_k{}^i$ formula weights of ions $X_k^{z_k\varepsilon}$ ($k = 1,2, \ldots, r$), where z_k is the charge number of ion k and ε is the protonic charge (4.8×10^{-10} esu). We thus introduce a new set of components, the ions, subject to the condition of electroneutrality,

$$\sum_{k=1}^{r} z_k \nu_k{}^i = 0 \tag{12-2}$$

The number of independent components in a solution composed of electrolyte Y_i dissolved in a nonelectrolyte solvent is determined by the restrictions placed on making up the solution. If it is specified that the electrolyte be added to the solvent, the number of independent components is 2; if the ions may be added independently, subject to the restraint of electroneutrality, the number of independent components is r (r-1 ionic components and the solvent).

The chemical potential of electrolyte Y_i can be written in terms of the chemical potentials of its constituent ions in the form

$$\mu_i = \sum_{k=1}^{r} \nu_k{}^i \mu_k \tag{12-3}$$

where μ_k is the chemical potential of ion component k. Equation (12-3) does not imply the existence of chemical equilibrium between the electrolyte and its ionic components; the equation states two equivalent ways of expressing the chemical potential of the electrolyte — one in terms of the electrolyte itself and the other in terms of the ionic components. Its lack of thermodynamic significance results from the impossibility of isolating individual ions in a system subject to the restraint of electroneutrality. Only the chemical potential of the electrolyte, μ_i, can be determined experimentally; it is measured by the methods employed for nonelectrolytes discussed in Sec. 11-3. In the discussion of electrolytes we assume that the condition of electroneutrality applies to the system. The condition of electroneutrality can be written in a number of ways,

$$\sum_{k=1}^{r} z_k n_k = \sum_{k=1}^{r} z_k c_k = \sum_{k=1}^{r} z_k m_k = 0 \tag{12-4}$$

depending on the mass units employed. In the electrochemical systems to be considered later the restraint is removed. We consider a system consisting of a mixture of s electrolytes, $i = 1, \ldots, s$, in a solvent. We write the chemical potential of ion component k in the form

$$\mu_k = RT \log (\gamma_k m_k) + \mu_k^\circ(T,p) \tag{12-5}$$

where γ_k is the activity coefficient, μ_k° is a reference value of the chemical potential, and where m_k, the molality of ion component k, is given by

$$m_k = \sum_{i=1}^{s} \nu_k{}^i m_i = \sum_{i=1}^{s} m_k{}^i \tag{12-6}$$

where m_i is the molality of electrolyte i and $m_k{}^i$ is the molality of ion component k from electrolyte i. Equation (12-5) is identical to Eq. (11-11) in which the chemical potential of a nonelectrolyte is written in terms of the molality as a composition variable. Equation (12-5) defines the activity coefficient with respect to molality, γ_k. We choose the reference value of the chemical potential of ion component k, μ_k°, by the convention of Eq. (11-13). Thus μ_k° is given by

$$\mu_k^\circ = \lim_{\substack{m_k \to 0 \\ \text{or } x_1 \to 0}} (\mu_k - RT \log m_k) \tag{12-7}$$

where x_1 is the mole fraction of solvent.

Substitution of Eq. (12-5) into Eq. (12-3) yields an expression for μ_i, the chemical potential of electrolyte i, in the form

$$\mu_i = \sum_{k=1}^{r} \nu_k{}^i RT \ln (\gamma_k m_k) + \mu_i^\circ(T,p) \tag{12-8}$$

where μ_i°, the reference value of the chemical potential of electrolyte i, is

$$\mu_i^\circ = \sum_{k=1}^{r} \nu_k{}^i \mu_k^\circ(T,p) \tag{12-9}$$

Rearrangement of Eq. (12-8) yields

$$\begin{aligned} \mu_i &= RT \log \left[\prod_{k=1}^{r} (\gamma_k m_k)^{\nu_k{}^i} \right] + \mu_i^\circ(T,p) \\ &= \nu_i RT \log \left[\prod_{k=1}^{r} (\gamma_k m_k)^{\nu_k{}^i} \right]^{1/\nu_i} + \mu_i^\circ(T,p) \\ &= \nu_i RT \log (\gamma_\pm{}^i m_\pm{}^i) + \mu_i^\circ(T,p) \end{aligned} \tag{12-10}$$

where

$$\nu_i = \sum_{k=1}^{r} \nu_k{}^i \tag{12-11}$$

$$\gamma_\pm{}^i = \left[\prod_{k=1}^{r} (\gamma_k)^{\nu_k{}^i} \right]^{1/\nu_i} \tag{12-12}$$

is the mean activity coefficient of electrolyte i,

$$m_\pm{}^i = \left[\prod_{k=1}^{r} (m_k)^{\nu_k{}^i} \right]^{1/\nu_i} \tag{12-13}$$

is the mean molality of electrolyte i, and

$$\mu_i^\circ = \lim_{x_1 \to 1} (\mu_i - \nu_i RT \ln m_\pm{}^i) \tag{12-14}$$

The limit in Eq. (12-14) exists if μ_i/ν_i is the partial free energy of M_i' grams of electrolyte i, where M_i' is the solution molecular weight of the electrolyte in the solvent under consideration. If μ_i is the partial free energy of M_i grams of electrolyte i, where M_i is an arbitrary formula weight, it is evident that ν_i is determined by the relation

$$\nu_i = \frac{M_i}{M_i'} \tag{12-15}$$

For example, the solution molecular weight of NaCl dissolved in water is 29. Thus, if we choose the arbitrary formula weight of NaCl to be 58, ν will be 2. In a solution of a single electrolyte or a mixture of electrolytes with no common ion

$$m_\pm{}^i = \left[\prod_{k=1}^{r} (m_k)^{\nu_k{}^i}\right]^{1/\nu_i} = \left[\prod_{k=1}^{r} (\nu_k^i)^{\nu_k{}^i}\right]^{1/\nu_i} m_i \tag{12-16}$$

and $m_\pm{}^i$ differs from m_i by a constant

$$m_\pm{}^i = Km_i \tag{12-17}$$

The existence of the limit in Eq. (12-14) is obvious in this case. In a mixture of electrolytes with common ions, the situation is not quite as simple. For example, in a mixture of NaCl and $BaCl_2$,

$$\begin{aligned} m_\pm{}^{\mathrm{NaCl}} &= (m_{\mathrm{Cl^-}} m_{\mathrm{Na^+}})^{\frac{1}{2}} = [(m_{\mathrm{NaCl}} + 2m_{\mathrm{BaCl_2}})m_{\mathrm{NaCl}}]^{\frac{1}{2}} \\ m_\pm{}^{\mathrm{BaCl_2}} &= (m_{\mathrm{Cl^-}}{}^2 m_{\mathrm{Ba^{++}}})^{\frac{1}{3}} = [(m_{\mathrm{NaCl}} + 2m_{\mathrm{BaCl_2}})^2 m_{\mathrm{BaCl_2}}]^{\frac{1}{3}} \end{aligned} \tag{12-18}$$

If it is assumed that

$$\lim_{x_1 \to 1} \frac{m_{\mathrm{NaCl}}}{m_{\mathrm{BaCl_2}}} = C \tag{12-19}$$

where $C \neq 0$ is finite, the limit in Eq. (12-14) exists.

It should be pointed out that the expression for $\gamma_\pm{}^i$ given in Eq. (12-12) is nonoperational since the individual γ_k cannot be measured. Equation (12-10) can be looked upon as providing a definition for $\gamma_\pm{}^i$ in terms of the measurable quantities μ_i and μ_i° and the calculable quantity $m_\pm{}^i$. The argument leading to Eq. (12-10) is presented as an aid to the understanding of the concepts involved. It is found experimentally that $\gamma_\pm{}^i$ is a slowly varying function of composition, not greatly different from unity, in dilute solutions for strong electrolytes. This statement could, of course, be used as a definition of strong electrolytes, if its somewhat qualitative nature were modified in a manner appropriate to the particular situation for which it was employed.

The zero approximation to Eq. (12-10) is often useful. In this approximation, $\gamma_\pm{}^i$ is set equal to 1, and Eq. (12-10) becomes

$$\mu_i = \nu_i RT \log m_\pm{}^i + \mu_i^\circ(T,p) \tag{12-20}$$

All the laws of elementary qualitative analysis may be derived by making use of this equation combined with the conditions for heterogeneous equilibrium. As an example, the solubility product rule will be discussed. We consider a two-phase system. Phase α is a solution of a set of electrolytes including i, and phase β is pure solid i. At equilibrium between phase α and phase β

$$\mu_i{}^{(\alpha)} = \mu_i{}^{(\beta)}(T,p) \tag{12-21}$$

where $\mu_i{}^{(\beta)}(T,p)$ is a function of T and p alone. Substitution of Eqs. (12-20) and (12-13) into Eq. (12-21) yields

$$\prod_{k=1}^{r} m_k{}^{\nu_k{}^i} = \exp\left[\frac{\mu_i{}^{(\beta)}(T,p) - \mu_i^\circ(T,p)}{RT}\right]$$
$$= K(T,p) \tag{12-22}$$

where $K(T,p)$ is a function of T and p alone. Equation (12-22) is an expression of the solubility product rule. It states that the product of the molalities of the ion components of electrolyte i, raised to the $\nu_k{}^i$ power, is constant at constant T and p in a solution in equilibrium with pure solid electrolyte.

In the zero approximation the electrolyte solution is treated as a mixture of ideal noninteracting ions. The fact that this approximation gives good results when applied to a dilute solution of, for example, NaCl is strong evidence for the structural hypothesis that NaCl dissociates into Na^+ and Cl^- ions in solution.

12-2. DEBYE-HÜCKEL THEORY

When deviations from the ideal zero-order theory of complete dissociation were noted in dilute solutions of strong electrolytes, attempts were made by Arrhenius and others to obtain agreement with experiment by assuming that the solution was ideal in all components, ionic as well as neutral, and that there was an equilibrium between undissociated electrolyte and dissociated ions. The theories based on these assumptions were of necessity unsuccessful. It has been experimentally determined that in very dilute solutions of strong electrolytes $RT \ln \gamma_\pm$ is proportional to the square root of the sum over species of the product of the concentration of an ion and the square of its charge number. Thus, a representation in terms of associating species, which corresponds to an expansion in a power series in concentrations beginning with a term linear in $\sum_k c_k$, is bound to lead to incorrect results. In contrast, a solution of nonelectrolytes can be treated as a mixture of ideal clusters because the activity coefficient can be expanded in terms of a power series in concentration, each term of which corresponds to the existence in solution of the appropriate n cluster.

The differences in behavior between electrolyte and nonelectrolyte solutions are due to the differences in the forces of interaction between ions on the one hand and between nonelectrolyte molecules on the other. The forces of interaction between nonelectrolyte molecules are short-range. The interaction force is repulsive when the molecules are very close together, because of the overlap of electron clouds, and is attractive at larger distances. The attractive force between two nonpolar molecules varies as $1/r^7$, where r is the distance between the molecules. These forces are important only when the molecules are close together. Thus, it is physically reasonable to speak of noninteracting clusters, and the properties of the system can be described in terms of power series in concentration. Statistical mechanical investigations substantiate this reasoning and present molecular expressions for the coefficients in the concentration power series.

In contrast, the force of interaction between two ions is long-range and at large distances is proportional to $1/r^2$, where r is the distance between the ions. Thus the solution cannot be considered to be composed of noninteracting clusters, and power series expansions in concentration are not possible. Statistical mechanical treatments of this problem demonstrate that the coefficients of the power series expansions diverge for coulomb forces and that another representation for the properties of the solution must be found. The rigorous molecular considerations confirm the results of the Debye-Hückel treatment for dilute solutions and demonstrate that the assumptions of the Arrhenius hypothesis are incorrect.

The beginning of the modern approach to strong-electrolyte solutions was G. N. Lewis' (1913) empirical observation that $\gamma_\pm^i$ depends approximately only on the total ionic strength, Γ, of the solution and not on the specific ions present. The total ionic strength is defined by the equation

$$\Gamma = \frac{1}{2} \sum_{k=1}^{r} c_k z_k^2 \tag{12-23}$$

The restricted applicability of this rule to solutions of low ionic strength can be seen from the tabulations of values of $\gamma_\pm$ for TlCl in the presence of other ions in Table 12-1.

Table 12-1
$\gamma_{\pm}$ *Values for* TlCl

Total m	KNO_3	KCl	HCl	$TlNO_3$
0.001	0.970	0.970	0.970	0.970
0.005	0.950	0.950	0.950	0.950
0.05	0.809	0.797	0.798	0.784
0.1	0.742	0.715	0.718	0.686

When the total molality m is 0.1, significant deviations from Lewis' rule are evident.

The treatment of strong-electrolyte solutions was greatly improved by the theory of Debye and Hückel (1925). Since their treatment is essentially nonthermodynamic, it will be discussed only briefly. The basic assumptions are as follows:

a. A solution of discharged ions is ideal; i.e., all departures from ideality in ionic solutions result from coulomb interactions. This assumption, though not rigorous, is a good approximation.

b. The solvent is a structureless dielectric continuum of dielectric constant D.

c. Each ion k is a cavity of radius a in the solvent, there being no space charge inside the cavity. a is the distance of closest approach of two ions and is often approximated by crystal radii.

On the basis of these assumptions and by integration of Poisson's equation with an approximate charge density, the potential at any distance from a given ion surrounded by an atmosphere of other ions is obtained. This potential is used together with a charging process on the ions to determine the excess chemical potential due to the electrostatic interactions. A major result of the theory is the determination of expression for single-ion activity coefficients in the form

$$\log \gamma_k = -\frac{z_k^2 \varepsilon^2}{2DkT} \frac{\kappa}{1 + \kappa a_k} \tag{12-24}$$

where

$$\kappa^2 = \frac{8\pi N \varepsilon^2}{1000DkT} \Gamma \tag{12-25}$$

$$\Gamma = \frac{1}{2} \sum_{k=1}^{r} c_k z_k^2 \tag{12-26}$$

a_k is the mean distance of closest approach of other ions to k, and k is Boltzmann's constant. The quantity κ^{-1} is the Debye radius. For a binary electrolyte $A_{\nu_A} B_{\nu_B}$, $\gamma_{\pm}$ may be written as

$$\gamma_{\pm} = (\gamma_{A^+}{}^{\nu_{A^+}} \gamma_{B^-}{}^{\nu_{B^-}})^{1/\nu} \tag{12-27}$$

where we have used Eq. (12-12). Substitution of Eq. (12-24) into Eq. (12-27) results in

$$\log_{10} \gamma_{\pm} = \frac{-S_{\gamma} z_A + |z_{B^-}| \sqrt{\Gamma}}{1 + \beta a \sqrt{\Gamma}} \tag{12-28}$$

where S_{γ} and β are functions of T and D only. In H_2O at 25°, $S_{\gamma} = 0.5056$ and $\beta = 0.329\text{A}^{-1}$. Although the Debye-Hückel expression [Eq. (12-24)] is often a good approximation up to ionic strengths of 0.1, it is rigorously correct only as a limiting law. Expansion of Eq. (12-24) in a power series in κ yields, in the limit as concentration goes to zero,

$$\log \gamma_k = -\frac{z_k^2 \varepsilon^2 \kappa}{2DkT} \tag{12-29}$$

Equation (12-29) provides a confirmation of Lewis' ionic-strength principle. (More details concerning the thermodynamic treatment of electrolyte solutions can be found in Falkenhagen, "Electrolyte," S. Hirzel Verlag, Leipzig, 1953, and H. S. Harned and B. B. Owen, "The Physical Chemistry of Electrolytic Solutions," Reinhold Publishing Corporation, New York, 1958.)

12-3. WEAK ELECTROLYTES

In this section, we discuss the thermodynamic treatment of weak-electrolyte solutions. In weak-electrolyte solutions, both undissociated molecules and ions exist. Thus, it may seem possible to describe the properties of these solutions by using the conventions developed either for nonelectrolyte or for electrolyte solutions. Our discussion will center around the usefulness of these conventions and the regions of concentration in which one may be more applicable than the other. For simplicity, our discussion will be restricted to the case of a weak electrolyte with the formula HA.

Application of the expression for the chemical potential of a strong electrolyte given by Eq. (12-10) to the system consisting of weak-electrolyte solute HA in a solvent yields the result

$$\mu_{\text{HA}} = 2RT \log (\gamma_{\pm} m_{\pm}) + \mu^{\circ}_{\text{HA}}(T,p) \tag{12-30}$$

The expression for the chemical potential of HA given by Eq. (12-30) can be rewritten in the form

$$\mu_{\text{HA}} = 2RT \log (\gamma_{\pm} m_{\text{HA}}) + \mu^{\circ}_{\text{HA}}(T,p) \tag{12-31}$$

where m_{HA} is the gross molality of HA and we have made use of Eq. (12-13) in the form

$$m_{\pm} = (m_{H^+} m_{A^-})^{\frac{1}{2}} = m_{HA} \tag{12-32}$$

In Eq. (12-32), we have made use of Eq. (12-6) which implies that

$$m_{H^+} = m_{A^-} = m_{HA} \tag{12-33}$$

Equation (12-33) is suitable for strong electrolytes but leads to difficulties in the treatment of weak electrolytes. Measurements of μ_{HA} by the usual experimental methods show that, as m_{HA} increases, $\gamma_{\pm}$ in Eq. (12-31) becomes a rapidly varying function of composition, deviating widely from unity. We therefore rearrange Eq. (12-31) to obtain

$$\mu_{HA} = RT \log [(\gamma_{\pm}{}^2 m_{HA}) m_{HA}] + \mu^{\circ}_{HA} \tag{12-34}$$

For large values of m_{HA}, we find by experiment that

$$\gamma_{\pm}{}^2 m_{HA} \to K(T,p)\gamma \tag{12-35}$$

where γ is a slowly varying function of composition.

Application of the conventions used for nonelectrolytes to the weak electrolyte HA yields an expression for the chemical potential of HA in the form

$$\mu_{HA} = RT \log (\gamma m_{HA}) + \mu^{\circ}_{HA}(T,p) \tag{12-36}$$

Equation (12-36) is similar to the expression given in Eq. (11-11) for the chemical potential of a nonelectrolyte solute. Comparison with experiment shows that

$$\lim_{m_{HA} \to 0} (\mu_{HA} - RT \log m_{HA}) \tag{12-37}$$

does not exist. Thus, γ is not equal to unity at infinite dilution.

Neither the strong-electrolyte nor the nonelectrolyte formulation is applicable to weak electrolytes throughout the entire range of concentration. At high molality a weak electrolyte behaves like a nonelectrolyte and at low molality it behaves like a strong electrolyte. In order to develop expressions for chemical potentials of weak electrolytes which may be used over the entire composition range it is customary to resort to a nonoperational treatment based on certain structural considerations which involve nonmeasurable quantities.

It is assumed that in a solution of HA there exists a chemical equilibrium between undissociated molecules HA and ions A^- and H^+ such that

$$HA \rightleftharpoons H^+ + A^- \tag{12-38}$$

At equilibrium,

$$\mu_{HA} = \mu_{H^+} + \mu_{A^-} \tag{12-39}$$

Here, in contrast to Eq. (12-3) in the strong-electrolyte case, the equality of chemical potentials is assumed to imply the existence of a chemical equilibrium. Since it is impossible to freeze the reaction [Eq. (12-38)] in order to study the components independently, the chemical-equilibrium assumption is nonoperational.

Expressions for the chemical potentials in Eq. (12-39) can be written in the form

$$\mu_{HA} = RT \log (\underline{\gamma}_{HA} c'_{HA}) + \mu^{\circ}_{HA}(T,p) \tag{12-40}$$

$$\mu_{H^+} = RT \log (\underline{\gamma}_{H^+} c'_{H^+}) + \mu^{\circ}_{H^+}(T,p) \tag{12-41}$$

$$\mu_{A^-} = RT \log (\underline{\gamma}_{A^-} c'_{A^-}) + \mu^{\circ}_{A^-}(T,p) \tag{12-42}$$

where c'_{HA}, c'_{H+}, and c'_{A-} represent the actual molarity of the components present in the solution at equilibrium and $\underline{\gamma}$ is the molar activity coefficient. Substitution of Eqs. (12-40) to (12-42) into Eq. (12-39) and rearrangement yield

$$\frac{\underline{\gamma}_{H^+} c'_{H^+} \underline{\gamma}_{A^-} c'_{A^-}}{\underline{\gamma}_{HA} c'_{HA}} = \exp\left(\frac{-\mu^{\circ}_{H^+} - \mu^{\circ}_{A^-} + \mu^{\circ}_{HA}}{RT}\right)$$

$$= K(T,p) \tag{12-43}$$

where $K(T,p)$ can be interpreted as being the equilibrium constant of the reaction Eq. (12-38). Use of the definition of $\gamma_{\pm}$ [Eq. (12-12)] in the form

$$\underline{\gamma}_{H^+} \underline{\gamma}_{A^-} = (\underline{\gamma}_{\pm})^2 \tag{12-44}$$

and substitution into Eq. (12-43) result in

$$K(T,p) = \frac{(\underline{\gamma}_{\pm})^2 c'_{H^+} c'_{A^-}}{\underline{\gamma}_{HA} c'_{HA}} \tag{12-45}$$

The concentrations appearing in Eq. (12-45) can be written in terms of the progress variable α and the total molarity of HA initially added to the solution c_{HA}. Thus, we can write

$$c'_{HA} = (1 - \alpha) c_{HA} \tag{12-46}$$

and

$$c'_{H^+} = c'_{A^-} = \alpha c_{HA} \tag{12-47}$$

Substitution of Eqs. (12-46) and (12-47) into Eq. (12-45) yields the expression

$$K(T,p) = \frac{(\underline{\gamma}_{\pm})^2 \alpha^2 c_{HA}}{\underline{\gamma}_{HA}(1 - \alpha)} \tag{12-48}$$

Since the standard chemical potentials of the components involved in the equilibrium cannot be measured, it is not possible to evaluate $K(T,p)$ by means of Eq. (12-43). In general, α is determined as a function of $(c_{HA})^{\frac{1}{2}}$ by some physical measurement. Substitution of experimentally determined values of α into Eq. (12-48), use of values of $\gamma_{\pm}$ determined by Debye-Hückel theory, and extrapolation to zero concentration, where γ_{HA} is unity, yield a value for $K(T,p)$. Utilization of Eq. (12-48) to determine values of α requires a knowledge of γ_{HA}, which is difficult to evaluate. In the usual application of Eq. (12-48), γ_{HA} is considered to be unity. Values of α obtained in this way compare well with those obtained by experiment.

In order to determine a value of α by a given measurement it is necessary to make a choice concerning which material in solution is to be considered dissociated and which undissociated. Thus each type of experiment may involve a different definition of α. Each definition of α leads to a different value of $K(T,p)$. The value of α can be determined by means of conductivity, spectroscopic, etc., measurements. The conductometric determination of α will be briefly discussed here. In this method, α is determined by the relation

$$\alpha = \frac{\Lambda}{\Lambda_e} \tag{12-49}$$

where Λ is the measured equivalent conductance and Λ_e is the equivalent conductance of the completely dissociated weak electrolyte. By the use of molecular theory, Λ_e can be expanded in a power series whose first term, $\Lambda°$, represents the conductance of a completely ionized solution in which the ionic components are ideal. Higher terms in the expansion correct for the electrostatic interaction among the ions. Thus Λ_e can be written in the form

$$\Lambda_e = \Lambda° - \beta(\alpha c_{HA})^{\frac{1}{2}} + \cdots \tag{12-50}$$

where

$$\beta = \theta\Lambda° + \sigma \tag{12-51}$$

and

$$\theta = \frac{8.159}{(DT)^{\frac{3}{2}}} \tag{12-52}$$

$$\sigma = \frac{81.96}{\eta(DT)^{\frac{1}{2}}} \tag{12-53}$$

where η is the viscosity coefficient. Substitution of Eq. (12-50) into Eq. (12-49) yields

$$\alpha = \frac{\Lambda/\Lambda°}{1 - (\beta/\Lambda°)(c_{HA}\alpha)^{\frac{1}{2}}} \tag{12-54}$$

In the ideal approximation, Eq. (12-54) becomes

$$\alpha = \frac{\Lambda}{\Lambda°} \tag{12-55}$$

For acetic acid, use of Eq. (12-54) yields $K(T,p) = 1.749 \times 10^{-5}$ while the ideal approximation [Eq. (12-55)] yields the value $K(T,p) = 1.80 \times 10^{-5}$.

The elementary physical chemistry treatment of weak-electrolyte solutions follows from the zero approximation to Eq. (12-48). In zero approximation, Eq. (12-48) becomes

$$K(T,p) = \frac{\alpha^2 c_{HA}}{1 - \alpha} = \frac{(\Lambda/\Lambda^\circ)^2 c_{HA}}{1 - \Lambda/\Lambda^\circ} \tag{12-56}$$

In this approximation, Eq. (12-40) becomes

$$\mu_{HA} = RT \log [(1 - \alpha)c_{HA}] + \mu_{HA}^\circ(T,p) \tag{12-57}$$

where we have made use of Eq. (12-46). It is clear from Eq. (12-56) that

$$\lim_{c \to \infty} \alpha = 0 \tag{12-58}$$

Thus, at high concentration we can formally associate $1 - \alpha$ with an activity coefficient. Equation (12-57) is an expression for the chemical potential of weak electrolyte HA using the nonelectrolyte convention of Eq. (12-36). An alternative expression for μ_{HA} in zero approximation can be obtained from Eq. (12-39) in the form

$$\mu_{HA} = 2RT \log (\alpha c_{HA}) + \mu_{H^+}^\circ + \mu_{A^-}^\circ \tag{12-59}$$

where we have used Eqs. (12-41), (12-42), and (12-47). It is clear from Eq. (12-56) that

$$\lim_{c \to 0} \alpha = 1$$

Thus it is useful to associate α with an activity coefficient at low concentrations. At low concentrations, it is useful to represent μ_{HA} by Eq. (12-59). Equation (12-59) is similar to Eq. (12-30) which expresses μ_{HA} in terms of strong-electrolyte conventions. This completes our discussion of weak-electrolyte solutions. [More details concerning computations involving Eq. (12-56) can be found in F. H. MacDougall, "Thermodynamics and Chemistry," chap. XV, 3d ed., John Wiley, & Sons, Inc., New York, 1939.]

13 THERMODYNAMIC THEORY OF ELECTROCHEMICAL SYSTEMS

In this chapter we consider heterogeneous systems that consist of electrically conducting, homogeneous parts between which ionic components can be transferred. A representative example is the galvanic cell.

The restraint of local electroneutrality has been removed from the systems of interest in this chapter. The magnitude of the composition fluctuations resulting from deviations from electroneutrality can be determined by a simple computation. Consider a spherical volume of radius 1 cm in a conducting medium. The electrostatic potential ϕ at the surface of this sphere is given by

$$\phi = \frac{q}{\varepsilon a} \tag{13-1}$$

where a = radius of sphere
q = spherically symmetric total charge in and on sphere
ε = permittivity of medium

One mole of univalent, positive ions has a charge of $\mathscr{F}$; $\mathscr{F} = 9.65 \times 10^4$ coulombs = 1 faraday. If, then, there is an excess of n moles of univalent, positive ions present in and on the sphere, the potential at the surface has the value

$$\phi = \frac{n9.65 \times 10^4}{(1.11 \times 10^{-10})(10^{-2})} = 9.5 \times 10^{16} n \text{ volts} \tag{13-2}$$

where we have assumed that the permittivity of the medium is the same as that of free space. The electrostatic potentials usually dealt with in electrochemical systems are less than 10^7 volts, and the excess concentration of charge associated with potentials of this order of magnitude is, by Eq. (13-2), less than 10^{-10} mole/cc. Thus, the deviation from electroneutrality produces macroscopically imperceptible composition changes. In the following treatment, two phases, identical in composition with respect to neutral components and differing in composition with respect to ionic components in amounts sufficient to produce electrostatic potentials of orders of magnitude lower than 10^7 volts, are considered to have the same chemical composition. In Sec. 13-1, we discuss the general thermodynamic theory of electrochemical systems. In Sec. 13-2, the results of Sec. 13-1 are applied to the treatment of galvanic cells without liquid junctions. In Sec. 13-3, the theory is extended to a treatment of galvanic cells with liquid junctions. In Sec. 13-4, the theory of the salt bridge is presented. In Sec. 13-5, the concept of pH is introduced and methods of measurement are discussed. Finally, in Sec. 13-6 membrane equilibrium between electrolyte solutions is treated.

13-1. GENERAL THEORY

In this section, we derive a necessary condition for equilibrium in homogeneous conducting systems. Then, we develop the thermodynamic theory of electrochemical systems.

We assume that the situations considered in this chapter are such that Ohm's law holds for homogeneous conducting systems. Thus, we may write

$$\mathbf{I} = \sigma \mathbf{E} \tag{13-3}$$

where $\mathbf{I}$ = current
σ = conductivity
$\mathbf{E}$ = electric field intensity

In the systems under consideration σ is finite and positive. At equilibrium, the current must be zero and thus $\mathbf{E}$ must be zero since σ is nonzero for conducting systems. The electrostatic potential is related to the electric field intensity by the relation

$$\mathbf{E} = -\nabla\phi \tag{13-4}$$

Thus, a necessary condition for equilibrium is that ϕ is constant throughout any homogeneous conducting system.

In principle, the electrostatic potential ϕ is measurable at any point in any homogeneous system. The measurement can be made by determining the electrostatic work done in transporting a unit test charge from infinity to the point in question. The evaluation of the difference of potential between two phases, differing in composition, is, however, extremely difficult. Since charge cannot be transported independent of mass (i.e., it is always associated with electrons, ions, etc.), the work done in transporting a charge across the phase boundary consists of two parts: electrical work against the electric field and nonelectrical work against the electromotive force due to the difference in the composition of the two phases. If the two phases have the same composition, it is possible to measure the electrostatic potential difference between them more easily since the nonelectrical work is equal to zero.

We consider a heterogeneous system consisting of ν phases and r components which may be charged or neutral. Since all charge transfer in the system implies mass transfer, the energy variations of the system due to the transport of charge across phase boundaries, from one electrostatic potential to another, are included in the chemical potential. Thus, the first law of thermodynamics applied to the open system consisting of phase α can be written in the form

$$dE^{(\alpha)} = T^{(\alpha)}\, dS^{(\alpha)} - p^{(\alpha)}\, dV^{(\alpha)} + \sum_{i=1}^{r} \bar{\mu}_i^{(\alpha)}\, dn_i^{(\alpha)} \qquad \alpha = 1, \ldots, \nu \tag{13-5}$$

where the symbol $\bar{\mu}_i^{(\alpha)}$ denotes the chemical potential of component i in phase α. Equation (13-5) is identical to Eq. (6-67) derived for general heterogeneous systems. The criteria for equilibrium in the heterogeneous system in which the phases and phase boundaries are heat-conducting, deformable, and permeable to all components are derived in Sec. 6-3 and are of the form

$$\begin{aligned} T^{(\alpha)} &= T \qquad \alpha = 1, \ldots, \nu \\ p^{(\alpha)} &= p \qquad \alpha = 1, \ldots, \nu \\ \bar{\mu}_i^{(\alpha)} &= \bar{\mu}_i \qquad \alpha = 1, \ldots, \nu \qquad i = 1, \ldots, r \end{aligned} \tag{13-6}$$

It is customary in the treatment of electrochemical systems to make a nonoperational decomposition of energy variations into two parts. We consider an open homogeneous system of r components at equilibrium. The differential change in the energy of the system can be written in the form

$$dE = dE' + dE_e \tag{13-7}$$

The term dE_e is associated with the differential change in the electrostatic energy of the system when there is a differential change in the charge distribution. We make use of electrostatic theory to write dE_e in the form

$$dE_e = \int_V (\phi\, d\rho)\, dV + \int_A (\phi\, d\sigma)\, dA \tag{13-8}$$

The first term on the right-hand side of Eq. (13-8) is an integral over the volume of the electrostatic potential ϕ times the change in the volume charge density $d\rho$. The second term is an integral over the surface of ϕ times the change in the surface charge density $d\sigma$. Since ϕ is constant in the homogeneous conducting system, Eq. (13-8) can be rewritten in the form

$$dE_e = \phi\, dq \tag{13-9}$$

where dq is the change in charge of the system. Substitution of Eq. (13-9) into Eq. (13-7) results in

$$dE = dE' + \phi\, dq \tag{13-10}$$

The decomposition of Eq. (13-10) does not imply that dE' is independent of the electrostatic potential. We shall, however, make the additional assumption that dE' depends only on the temperature, pressure, and composition of the system and not on its charge. Verification of this assumption, which is basic to all electrochemistry, has been obtained from experiment.

In order to obtain a decomposition of the chemical potential consistent with Eq. (13-10), we differentiate Eq. (13-10) with respect to the number of moles of component i at constant entropy, volume, and number of moles of all other components to obtain

$$\left(\frac{\partial E}{\partial n_i}\right)_{S,V,n_{j\neq i}} = \left(\frac{\partial E'}{\partial n_i}\right)_{S,V,n_{j\neq i}} + \phi\left(\frac{\partial q}{\partial n_i}\right)_{S,V,n_{j\neq i}} \tag{13-11}$$

The total charge of the system can be written in the form

$$q = \sum_{i=1}^{r} n_i z_i \mathscr{F} \tag{13-12}$$

where z_i is the charge number of the ith species and $\mathscr{F}$ is the charge of a mole of positive univalent ions. Differentiation of Eq. (13-12) with respect to n_i results in

$$\left(\frac{\partial q}{\partial n_i}\right)_{S,V,n_{j\neq i}} = z_i\mathscr{F} \tag{13-13}$$

Substitution of Eq. (13-13) into Eq. (13-11) yields

$$\left(\frac{\partial E}{\partial n_i}\right)_{S,V,n_{j\neq i}} = \left(\frac{\partial E'}{\partial n_i}\right)_{S,V,n_{j\neq i}} + z_i\mathscr{F}\phi \tag{13-14}$$

We can identify $\bar{\mu}_i$ with $(\partial E/\partial n_i)_{S,V,n_{j\neq i}}$ and μ_i with $(\partial E'/\partial n_i)_{S,V,n_{j\neq i}}$ and rewrite Eq. (13-14) in the form

$$\bar{\mu}_i = \mu_i + z_i\mathscr{F}\phi \tag{13-15}$$

In Eq. (15-15), $\bar{\mu}_i$ is the chemical potential and μ_i is a function of T, p, and composition alone. It is clear that for neutral particles

$$\bar{\mu}_i = \mu_i \tag{13-16}$$

It is unfortunately common practice to refer to $\bar{\mu}_i$ as the electrochemical potential and to μ_i as the chemical potential of component i. In the usual thermodynamic systems only $\bar{\mu}_i$ can be measured; thus, the separation of Eq. (13-15) is a nonoperational one. Although μ_i and ϕ cannot be determined separately by experiment, it is possible under special conditions to measure the electrostatic-potential difference across a phase boundary. We consider a constrained two-phase system. If the two phases (α and β) have the same pressure, temperature, and composition we can write

$$\mu_i^{(\alpha)} = \mu_i^{(\beta)} \tag{13-17}$$

Subtraction of $\bar{\mu}_i^{(\beta)}$ from $\bar{\mu}_i^{(\alpha)}$ and use of Eqs. (13-15) and (13-17) yield

$$\begin{aligned}\bar{\mu}_i^{(\alpha)} - \bar{\mu}_i^{(\beta)} &= z_i\mathscr{F}(\phi^{(\alpha)} - \phi^{(\beta)}) \\ &= z_i\mathscr{F}\Delta\phi\end{aligned} \tag{13-18}$$

Thus, $\Delta\phi$ can be evaluated from Eq. (13-18) since $\bar{\mu}_i^{(\alpha)}$ and $\bar{\mu}_i^{(\beta)}$ can be determined experimentally.

We now turn our attention to a study of the thermodynamic theory of galvanic cells. Galvanic cells are heterogeneous systems in which current is transmitted between the phases and in which chemical reactions may occur. The terminal phases of a galvanic cell are termed electrodes, and current passes from one electrode through the other phases to the other electrode.

We consider a closed system of ν phases and $r + 1$ components, of which r $(1, \ldots, r)$ are neutral and one $(r + 1)$ is ionic (the electron). Such a choice of components is always possible although it may require the use of negative masses; e.g., a system containing a mole of Ag^+ ions may be considered to be made up of a mole of Ag atoms and a negative mole of electrons, i.e.,

$$Ag^+ = Ag - e_- \tag{13-19}$$

where the symbol e_- denotes 1 mole of electrons.

The criteria for equilibrium in the system can be written in variational form

$$\delta E = \sum_{\alpha=1}^{\nu}\left(T^{(\alpha)}\,\delta S^{(\alpha)} - p^{(\alpha)}\,\delta V^{(\alpha)} + \sum_{i=1}^{r+1} \bar{\mu}_i^{(\alpha)}\,\delta n_i^{(\alpha)}\right) \geqslant 0 \tag{13-20}$$

where we have made use of Eq. (6-68). We consider a particular set of variations in which

$$\begin{aligned}
\delta S^{(\alpha)} &= 0 & \alpha &= 1, \ldots, \nu \\
\delta V^{(\alpha)} &= 0 & \alpha &= 1, \ldots, \nu \\
\delta n_i^{(\alpha)} &= \nu_i^{(\alpha)}\,\delta\lambda & i &= 1, \ldots, r \qquad \alpha = 1, \ldots, \nu \\
\delta n_{e_-}^{(1)} &= n\,\delta\lambda = -\delta n_{e_-}^{(\nu)} & & \\
\delta n_{e_-}^{(\alpha)} &= 0 & \alpha &= 2, \ldots, \nu - 1
\end{aligned} \tag{13-21}$$

In the set of variations described by Eq. (13-21), the total entropy and volume of the system are held constant, a heterogeneous reaction with progress variable $\delta\lambda$ is allowed to take place between the r neutral components, and $n\,\delta\lambda$ moles of electrons are transferred from phase ν to phase 1. There is no accumulation of charge in any of the phases except the two terminal phases, 1 and ν. Substitution of Eq. (13-21) into Eq. (13-20) yields the relation

$$\left[\sum_{\alpha=1}^{\nu}\sum_{i=1}^{r}\nu_i^{(\alpha)}\mu_i^{(\alpha)} + n(\bar{\mu}_{e_-}{}^{(1)} - \bar{\mu}_{e_-}{}^{(\nu)})\right]\delta\lambda \geqslant 0 \tag{13-22}$$

for this particular set of variations. We have made use of Eq. (13-16) in Eq. (13-22). Equation (13-22) must hold for both positive and negative variations of λ. Thus, we obtain the expression

$$\sum_{\alpha=1}^{\nu}\sum_{i=1}^{r}\nu_i^{(\alpha)}\mu_i^{(\alpha)} + n(\bar{\mu}_{e_-}{}^{(1)} - \bar{\mu}_{e_-}{}^{(\nu)}) = 0 \tag{13-23}$$

as a necessary condition for equilibrium. If the terminal phases of the system are identical in chemical composition and are at the same temperature and pressure, then

$$\bar{\mu}_{e_-}{}^{(1)} - \bar{\mu}_{e_-}{}^{(\nu)} = -\mathscr{F}(\phi^{(1)} - \phi^{(\nu)}) \tag{13-24}$$

where we have made use of Eq. (13-18). Substitution of Eq. (13-24) into Eq. (13-23) yields

$$n\mathscr{F}(\phi^{(1)} - \phi^{(\nu)}) = \sum_{\alpha=1}^{\nu}\sum_{i=1}^{r}\nu_i^{(\alpha)}\mu_i^{(\alpha)} \tag{13-25}$$

Equation (13-25) is a necessary condition for equilibrium in a galvanic cell for the process in which n moles of electrons are transported from phase ν to phase 1 and in which the heterogeneous chemical reaction

$$\sum_{\alpha=1}^{\nu}\sum_{i=1}^{r}\nu_i^{(\alpha)}X_i^{(\alpha)} = 0 \tag{13-26}$$

takes place.

The general criterion for heterogeneous equilibrium requires that

$$\bar{\mu}_{e_-}{}^{(1)} = \bar{\mu}_{e_-}{}^{(\nu)} \tag{13-27}$$

in an isolated system in which all phases and phase membranes are conducting. Thus, if the potential difference $\Delta\phi$ is to be nonzero at equilibrium, some of the phase boundaries must be impermeable to electrons. If phase 1 is a metal electrode and phase 2 is a solution, the boundary between these two phases will be impermeable to electrons to a high degree of approximation.

We have previously used the term electromotive force but have not rigorously defined it. The definition of the electromotive force can be given in terms of the equation

$$I_e = \frac{\Delta\phi - \varepsilon}{R} \tag{13-28}$$

where
$$\Delta\phi = \phi^{(\nu)} - \phi^{(1)} \tag{13-29}$$

and where I_e = electric current flowing in system
ε = electromotive force
R = resistance

At equilibrium, I_e is equal to zero, and Eq. (13-28) becomes

$$\varepsilon = \Delta\phi = \phi^{(\nu)} - \phi^{(1)} \tag{13-30}$$

Thus, the electromotive force in a galvanic cell at equilibrium is equal to the potential difference between the electrodes. Substitution of Eq. (13-30) into Eq. (13-25) results in

$$-n\mathcal{F}\varepsilon = \sum_{\alpha=1}^{\nu} \sum_{i=1}^{r} \nu_i^{(\alpha)}\mu_i^{(\alpha)} \tag{13-31}$$

The right-hand side of Eq. (13-31) represents the free-energy increment for the heterogeneous reaction

$$\sum_{i=1}^{r} \sum_{\alpha=1}^{\nu} \nu_i^{(\alpha)} X_i^{(\alpha)} = 0 \tag{13-32}$$

Consequently, Eq. (13-31) may be rewritten in the form

$$n\mathcal{F}\varepsilon = -\Delta F \tag{13-33}$$

where
$$\Delta F = \sum_{\alpha=1}^{\nu} \sum_{i=1}^{r} \nu_i^{(\alpha)}\mu_i^{(\alpha)} \tag{13-34}$$

Equation (13-33) is the fundamental equation for the thermodynamic study of galvanic cells. The chemical potential of component i in phase α is related to the corresponding activity $a_i^{(\alpha)}$ by the equation

$$\mu_i^{(\alpha)} = RT \log a_i^{(\alpha)} + \mu_i^{\circ(\alpha)}(T,p) \tag{13-35}$$

Substitution of Eq. (13-35) into Eq. (13-33) yields, after some transformation,

$$\varepsilon = \varepsilon^\circ - \frac{RT}{n\mathcal{F}} \log \left[\prod_{\alpha=1}^{\nu} \prod_{i=1}^{r} (a_i^{(\alpha)})^{\nu_i^{(\alpha)}} \right] \tag{13-36}$$

where ε°, the standard electromotive force of the system, is defined by the equation

$$n\mathcal{F}\varepsilon^\circ = -\Delta F^\circ \tag{13-37}$$

where
$$\Delta F^\circ = \sum_{\alpha=1}^{\nu} \sum_{i=1}^{r} \nu_i^{(\alpha)}\mu_i^{\circ(\alpha)} \tag{13-38}$$

It is often possible from an examination of the electrochemical system to determine in which phases the cell reaction is occurring. As a result, Eq. (13-32) is conventionally abbreviated in the form

$$\sum_{i=1}^{r} \nu_i X_i = 0 \tag{13-39}$$

Correspondingly, Eqs. (13-34) and (13-36) are written in the form

$$\Delta F = \sum_{i=1}^{r} \nu_i \mu_i \tag{13-40}$$

and

$$\varepsilon = \varepsilon^\circ - \frac{RT}{n\mathscr{F}} \log \left(\prod_{i=1}^{r} a_i^{\nu_i} \right) \tag{13-41}$$

This simplification of notation is possible only if, for each component i, ν_i is different from zero in at most one phase.

The theory developed here has its most important application in the study of reversible galvanic cells. Galvanic cells may be separated into two classes: those with and those without liquid junction. In Sec. 13-2, we consider a galvanic cell without liquid junction using the necessary criterion for equilibrium [Eq. (13-23)]. In Sec. 13-3, we discuss a cell with liquid junction in terms of the complete conditions for heterogeneous equilibrium.

13-2. GALVANIC CELLS WITHOUT LIQUID JUNCTIONS

In this section we apply the general results of Sec. 13-1 to a treatment of galvanic cells without liquid junctions. A representative example of cells without liquid junction is the following one, written in terms of conventional notation:

$$\begin{array}{ccccccc} & (1) & & (2) & & (3) & \\ M^{(1)} & ; & MCl^{(2)}(xm) & ; & AgCl^{(3)}(s) & ; & Ag^{(4)} \end{array} \tag{13-42}$$

In Eq. (13-42), the phases are denoted by symbols and numbers in parentheses and the phase boundaries by semicolons and numbers in parentheses. Phase 1 consists of an arbitrary monovalent metal M. Phase 2 consists of a solution of x molal metal chloride. Phase 3 consists of solid AgCl. Phase 4 consists of Ag metal. In order for the cell to be complete, the two terminals must be of the same composition. Thus, the cell represented by Eq. (13-42) is more completely represented by the notation

$$M^{(1)}; MCl^{(2)}(xm); AgCl^{(3)}(s); Ag^{(4)}; M^{(5)} \tag{13-43}$$

However, the requirement that the terminals be of the same composition is ignored in the usual notation. Since there is no liquid junction in this cell, it is possible for the metal chloride to react directly with the AgCl. It is, therefore, necessary to assume that because of the insolubility of AgCl the reaction does not occur at an appreciable rate.

An alternative possibility is to suppose that there is a liquid junction present, i.e., that the cell consists of the phases

$$M; MCl(xm)\colon AgCl(\text{sat}); AgCl(s); Ag; M \tag{13-44}$$

where the colon represents a liquid junction. In the presence of a liquid junction it is necessary to calculate the liquid-junction potential and to determine under what conditions it is negligible in comparison with the electromotive force. These calculations are described in Sec. 13-3.

The additional restraint prohibiting direct interaction between AgCl and MCl is not of great importance, since all galvanic cells are in partial equilibrium. This is due to the fact that the existence of an electrostatic-potential difference requires impermeability of some of the phase boundaries to the charged component. In the present case, boundary 1 is permeable only to M^+; boundary 2, only to Cl^-; and boundary 3, to electrons alone (not to Ag^+ ions). By inspection, we realize that the cell reaction for the cell represented by Eq. (13-42) is given by

$$M(s) + AgCl(s) = MCl(xm) + Ag(s);\ n = 1 \tag{13-45}$$

where $n = 1$ refers to the transfer of electrons. Equation (13-45) is a specific example of Eq. (13-32). The equation for partial equilibrium [Eq. (13-33)] becomes

$$\mathscr{F}\varepsilon = -\Delta F \tag{13-46}$$

where

$$\Delta F = \mu_{Ag(s)} + \mu_{MCl(xm)} - \mu_{AgCl(s)} - \mu_{M(s)} \tag{13-47}$$

Although the electromotive force ε is a scalar quantity, it has direction. The American convention is that, at equilibrium, ε is given by

$$\varepsilon = \phi^{(v)} - \phi^{(1)} \tag{13-48}$$

where $\phi^{(v)}$ is the electrostatic potential of the electrode written on the right and $\phi^{(1)}$ that of the electrode written on the left. In Europe, the convention employed for the definition of the electromotive force is the reverse; i.e., the electromotive force is given by

$$\text{Electromotive force} = \phi^{(1)} - \phi^{(v)} \tag{13-49}$$

Use of Eqs. (13-36) and (13-47) results in

$$\varepsilon = \varepsilon^\circ + \frac{RT}{\mathscr{F}} \log \frac{a_{AgCl(s)}a_{M(s)}}{a_{MCl(xm)}a_{Ag(s)}} \tag{13-50}$$

The activities of all pure solids are arbitrarily set equal to unity. Therefore, Eq. (13-50) reduces to

$$\begin{aligned} \varepsilon &= \varepsilon^\circ - \frac{RT}{\mathscr{F}} \log a_{MCl} \\ &= \varepsilon^\circ - \frac{2RT}{\mathscr{F}} \log (\gamma_\pm m_{MCl}) \end{aligned} \tag{13-51}$$

where we have made use of the strong-electrolyte convention to obtain

$$a_{MCl} = (\gamma_\pm m_{MCl})^2 \tag{13-52}$$

We define the quantity ε' by the relation

$$\varepsilon' = \varepsilon + \frac{2RT}{\mathscr{F}} \log m_{\mathrm{MCl}} \tag{13-53}$$

where ε and m_{MCl} are measurable quantities. The plot of ε' versus $(m)^{\frac{1}{2}}$ produces a graph of the form shown in Fig. 13-1. Use of Eqs. (13-51) and (13-53) yields the relation

$$\varepsilon' = \varepsilon^\circ - \frac{2RT}{\mathscr{F}} \log \gamma_\pm \tag{13-54}$$

Since $\lim_{m \to 0} \gamma_\pm = 1$, the intercept of the curve of ε' versus $(m)^{\frac{1}{2}}$ is ε°. The curve itself determines $\gamma_\pm$ as a function of $(m)^{\frac{1}{2}}$. Thus, galvanic cells can be used to determine values of activity coefficients of electrolytes.

Galvanic cells may also be analyzed by use of the so-called half-cell notation. In this method, Eq. (13-45) is replaced by the half-cell reactions

$$\begin{aligned} \mathrm{AgCl}(s)^{(3)} &= \mathrm{Ag}(s)^{(3)} + \mathrm{Cl}^{-(3)} - e_-{}^{(3)} \\ \mathrm{M}^{(1)} &= \mathrm{M}^{+(1)} + e_-{}^{(1)} \end{aligned} \tag{13-55}$$

Since it is often evident in which phases the reactions are occurring, the superscripts in Eq. (13-55) are omitted in the usual formulation. In using these conventions, it should be realized that the separation of the cell reaction into half-cell reactions is usually nonoperational.

Single-electrode potentials, corresponding to half-cell reactions, are often listed. These are actually potentials of the given electrodes relative to the normal hydrogen electrode as a standard. For example, in order to determine the electrode potential for the half-cell reaction

$$\mathrm{Ag}(s) + \mathrm{Cl}^- = \mathrm{AgCl}(s) + e_- \tag{13-56}$$

one would measure the electromotive force of the cell

$$\mathrm{Ag};\ \mathrm{AgCl}(s);\ \mathrm{HCl}(a = 1);\ \mathrm{H_2}(1\ \mathrm{atm});\ \mathrm{Pt} \tag{13-57}$$

where the symbol $a = 1$ implies that the activity of the HCl solution is unity. In order for ε to coincide with ε° for this cell, H_2 gas at a fugacity

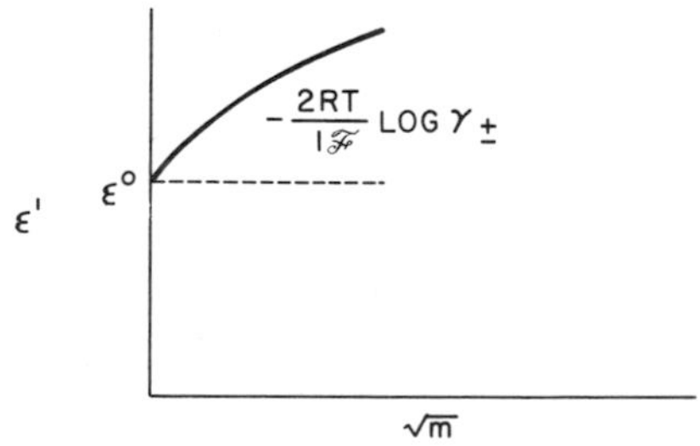

FIG. 13-1. Plot of ε' versus m.

of 1 atm should be used. However, H_2 gas at a pressure of 1 atm is usually employed as the standard.

We note that it is possible to measure absolute single-electrode potentials by nonthermodynamic techniques. In principle, the single-electrode potential can be determined from a measurement of quadrupole radiation from the oscillating electrode.

13-3. GALVANIC CELLS WITH LIQUID JUNCTIONS

In this section, we turn our attention to a discussion of cells with liquid junctions. We shall first determine the equilibrium conditions in a representative cell of the type

$$\mathrm{M_1}^{(1)} \overset{(1)}{;} \mathrm{M_1Cl}^{(2)}(xm) \overset{(2)}{:} \mathrm{M_2Cl}^{(3)}(ym) \overset{(3)}{;} \mathrm{M_2}^{(4)} \overset{(4)}{;} \mathrm{M_1}^{(5)} \qquad (13\text{-}58)$$

In agreement with our knowledge of the physical-chemistry properties of the system, we apply the following restraints to the phase boundaries of the cell: boundary 1 is permeable only to $M_1{}^+$; boundary 3 is permeable only to $M_2{}^+$; and boundary 4 is permeable only to electrons. A detailed discussion of boundary 2, the liquid junction, will be given below. The cell reaction is

$$\mathrm{M_1}^{(1)}(s) + \mathrm{M_2}^{+(3)} = \mathrm{M_1}^{+(2)} + \mathrm{M_2}^{(4)}(s);\ n = 1 \qquad (13\text{-}59)$$

Equation (13-59) can be written in terms of half-cell notation in the form

$$\begin{aligned} \mathrm{M_1}(s) &= \mathrm{M_1}^+ + e_- \\ \mathrm{M_2}^+ + e_- &= \mathrm{M_2}(s) \end{aligned} \qquad (13\text{-}60)$$

The conditions for heterogeneous equilibrium subject to the restraints listed above are

$$\bar{\mu}_{\mathrm{M_1}^+}{}^{(1)} = \bar{\mu}_{\mathrm{M_1}^+}{}^{(2)} \qquad (13\text{-}61)$$

$$\bar{\mu}_{\mathrm{M_2}^+}{}^{(3)} = \bar{\mu}_{\mathrm{M_2}^+}{}^{(4)} \qquad (13\text{-}62)$$

$$\bar{\mu}_{e-}{}^{(4)} = \bar{\mu}_{e-}{}^{(5)} \qquad (13\text{-}63)$$

$$T^{(\alpha)} = T \qquad \alpha = 1, \ldots, 5 \qquad (13\text{-}64)$$

$$p^{(\alpha)} = p \qquad \alpha = 1, \ldots, 5 \qquad (13\text{-}65)$$

It is useful to rewrite the conditions Eqs. (13-61) to (13-63) in terms of a set of components, all of which are neutral except for the electron. We make use of the relations

$$\mu_{\mathrm{M_1}} = \bar{\mu}_{\mathrm{M_1}} = \bar{\mu}_{\mathrm{M_1}^+} + \bar{\mu}_{e-} \qquad (13\text{-}66)$$

$$\mu_{\mathrm{M_2}} = \bar{\mu}_{\mathrm{M_2}} = \bar{\mu}_{\mathrm{M_2}} + \bar{\mu}_{e-} \qquad (13\text{-}67)$$

where the strong-electrolyte convention of Eq. (12-3) has been applied.

Substitution of Eqs. (13-66) and (13-67) into the equilibrium conditions yields

$$\mu_{M_1}{}^{(1)} - \bar{\mu}_{e_-}{}^{(1)} = \mu_{M_1}{}^{(2)} - \bar{\mu}_{e_-}{}^{(2)} \tag{13-68}$$

$$\mu_{M_2}{}^{(3)} - \bar{\mu}_{e_-}{}^{(3)} = \mu_{M_2}{}^{(4)} - \bar{\mu}_{e_-}{}^{(4)} \tag{13-69}$$

Addition of Eqs. (13-68), (13-69), and (13-63) results in

$$\mu_{M_1}{}^{(1)} + \bar{\mu}_{e_-}{}^{(5)} - \bar{\mu}_{e_-}{}^{(1)} + \mu_{M_2}{}^{(3)} - \bar{\mu}_{e_-}{}^{(3)} = \mu_{M_1}{}^{(2)} - \bar{\mu}_{e_-}{}^{(2)} + \mu_{M_2}{}^{(4)} \tag{13-70}$$

Since phases 1 and 5 are of the same chemical composition (the same metal) we obtain

$$\begin{aligned} \bar{\mu}_{e_-}{}^{(5)} - \bar{\mu}_{e_-}{}^{(1)} &= -(\phi^{(5)} - \phi^{(1)})\mathscr{F} \\ &= -\mathscr{F}\varepsilon \end{aligned} \tag{13-71}$$

where Eqs. (13-18) and (13-30) have been used. It follows from Eq. (13-15) that

$$\bar{\mu}_{e_-}{}^{(3)} - \bar{\mu}_{e_-}{}^{(2)} = \mu_{e_-}{}^{(3)} - \mu_{e_-}{}^{(2)} - \mathscr{F}(\phi^{(3)} - \phi^{(2)}) \tag{13-72}$$

The liquid-junction potential ε_L is defined by the relation

$$\varepsilon_L = \phi^{(3)} - \phi^{(2)} \tag{13-73}$$

Substitution of Eq. (13-73) into Eq. (13-72) yields

$$\bar{\mu}_{e_-}{}^{(3)} - \bar{\mu}_{e_-}{}^{(2)} = \mu_{e_-}{}^{(3)} - \mu_{e_-}{}^{(2)} - \mathscr{F}\varepsilon_L \tag{13-74}$$

Combination of Eqs. (13-71), (13-74), and (13-70) results in

$$-\mathscr{F}(\varepsilon - \varepsilon_L) + \mu_{M_1}{}^{(1)} + \mu_{M_2}{}^{(3)} - \mu_{e_-}{}^{(3)} = \mu_{M_1}{}^{(2)} - \mu_{e_-}{}^{(2)} + \mu_{M_2}{}^{(4)} \tag{13-75}$$

We make use of the relations

$$\begin{aligned} \mu_{M_2{}^+} &= \mu_{M_2} - \mu_{e_-} \\ \mu_{M_1{}^+} &= \mu_{M_1} - \mu_{e_-} \end{aligned} \tag{13-76}$$

which follow from Eqs. (13-66), (13-67), and (13-15) to rewrite Eq. (13-75) in the form

$$-\mathscr{F}(\varepsilon - \varepsilon_L) = \mu_{M_2}{}^{(4)} + \mu_{M_1{}^+}{}^{(2)} - \mu_{M_2{}^+}{}^{(3)} - \mu_{M_1}{}^{(1)} \tag{13-77}$$

The right-hand side of Eq. (13-77) is the free-energy increment of the cell reaction [Eq. (13-59)] and thus we can write

$$-\mathscr{F}(\varepsilon - \varepsilon_L) = \Delta F \tag{13-78}$$

where
$$\Delta F = \mu_{M_2}{}^{(4)} + \mu_{M_1{}^+}{}^{(2)} - \mu_{M_2{}^+}{}^{(3)} - \mu_{M_1}{}^{(1)} \tag{13-79}$$

Equation (13-78) is the fundamental equation for the study of the thermodynamic properties of galvanic cells with liquid junctions.

Evaluation of the liquid-junction potential requires a detailed consideration of the transition layer between the two phases, 2 and 3, which have different composition.

In this discussion, we consider a transition layer in which there is a continuous variation of composition in the x direction and no change of composition in the y and z directions. The system under consideration is in partial electrochemical equilibrium. Consequently, diffusion of components will be occurring across the boundary. It is, therefore, necessary to determine whether the theory of electrochemical equilibrium is applicable, i.e., whether it is possible to achieve an accurate measurement of the free-energy increment of the cell reaction by carrying it out in a manner that is reversible except for the concomitant irreversible diffusion. Comparison with experimental data shows that, during the short time in which the cell is studied, the effect of diffusion on the composition of the phases can be neglected and the equilibrium theory can be applied.

We consider a system in which the liquid junction consists of r ionic components and one neutral component, the solvent. The boundary is considered to be divided into ν compartments, in each of which the electrochemical potentials of all the components are uniform (see Fig. 13-2). A constant current is passed through the cell for the time required to transfer 1 faraday from one electrode to the other. During this process 1 mole of charge is transported across the liquid junction. The free-energy increment occurring in the boundary during this time can be written in the form

$$\Delta F = \sum_{\alpha=1}^{\nu} \sum_{i=1}^{r} \nu_i^{(\alpha)} \bar{\mu}_i^{(\alpha)} \tag{13-80}$$

where $\nu_i^{(\alpha)}$ represents the change in the number of moles of i in compartment α due to the transport of current. Since the condition of constant current has been placed on the system, there can be no accumulation of charge. Consequently, ions can move only in combinations such that

$$\sum_{i=1}^{r} \nu_i^{(\alpha)} z_i = 0 \tag{13-81}$$

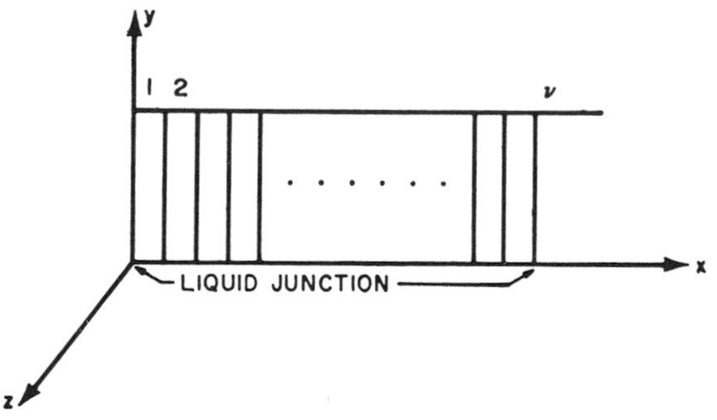

FIG. 13-2. The liquid junction.

Substitution of Eq. (13-15) into Eq. (13-80) results in

$$\Delta F = \sum_{\alpha=1}^{v} \sum_{i=1}^{r} \nu_i^{(\alpha)}(\mu_i^{(\alpha)} + z_i \mathscr{F} \phi^{(\alpha)}) \tag{13-82}$$

Equation (13-82) can be simplified to yield

$$\Delta F = \sum_{\alpha=1}^{v} \sum_{i=1}^{r} \nu_i^{(\alpha)} \mu_i^{(\alpha)} \tag{13-83}$$

where Eq. (13-81) has been used. Since no chemical reactions occur in the liquid junction, $\nu_i^{(\alpha)}$ must be equal to the number of moles of i that enter compartment α minus the number of moles of i that leave compartment α during the time interval considered. The quantity $\nu_i^{(\alpha)}$ may be calculated most easily by the use of transport numbers t_i, which represent the fraction of the current carried by ion species i. It should be pointed out that Hittorf transport numbers, which are measured relative to the solvent, must be used in this work; moving boundary numbers which are measured relative to a stationary frame of reference would lead to an incorrect result. (For details, see Duncan MacInnes, "Principles of Electrochemistry," chap. 4, Reinhold Publishing Corporation, New York, 1939.) Transport numbers are, in general, functions of composition and will change in the boundary as a function of x. We define $t_i^{(\alpha)}$ to be the transport number of component i at the left end of compartment α and $t_i^{(\alpha)} + \Delta t_i^{(\alpha)}$ to be the transport number at the right end of α. We may write the change in charge in compartment α due to ion species i when 1 faraday is passed, in the form

$$\mathscr{F} t_i^{(\alpha)} - \mathscr{F}(t_i^{(\alpha)} + \Delta t_i^{(\alpha)}) = -\mathscr{F} \Delta t_i^{(\alpha)} \qquad \alpha = 1, \ldots, v \tag{13-84}$$

The change in the number of moles of component i in compartment α can be obtained from Eq. (13-84) by dividing the change in charge in compartment α caused by component i by $z_i \mathscr{F}$. Thus, we may write

$$\nu_i^{(\alpha)} = -\frac{\Delta t_i^{(\alpha)}}{z_i} \qquad \alpha = 1, \ldots, v \tag{13-85}$$

Substitution of Eq. (13-85) into Eq. (13-83) yields the expression

$$\Delta F = -\sum_{i=1}^{r} \sum_{\alpha=1}^{v} \frac{\Delta t_i^{(\alpha)}}{z_i} \mu_i^{(\alpha)} \tag{13-86}$$

We wish to write Eq. (13-86) in a more general form which allows both continuous and discrete changes in t_i and μ_i as functions of the parameter x which denotes the position of a point in the liquid junction. In order to do this, we assume that the difference in x dimensions of the left-hand and right-hand boundaries of compartment α approaches zero;

that is, $\Delta x^{(\alpha)} \to 0$. In this case, the sum over α in Eq. (13-86) becomes a Stieltjes integral and we may rewrite Eq. (13-86) in the form

$$\Delta F = -\sum_{i=1}^{r} \int_{t_i(0)}^{t_i(L)} \frac{\mu_i(x)}{z_i}\, dt_i(x) \tag{13-87}$$

where the integration extends from $x = 0$, the x dimension of the left-hand boundary of the liquid junction to $x = L$, the x dimension of the right-hand boundary of the liquid junction. Equation (13-87) can be integrated by parts to yield

$$\Delta F = \sum_{i=1}^{r} \left[\int_{\mu_i(0)}^{\mu_i(L)} \frac{t_i(x)}{z_i}\, d\mu_i(x) + \frac{\mu_i(0)t_i(0)}{z_i} - \frac{\mu_i(L)t_i(L)}{z_i} \right] \tag{13-88}$$

Equation (13-88) for the free-energy change in the liquid junction during the reversible process in which 1 faraday is transferred from one electrode to another can be related to the liquid-junction potential. During the transfer of 1 mole of charge through the liquid junction, $t_i(0)/z_i$ moles of component i leave phase 2 to enter the liquid junction and $t_i(L)/z_i$ moles of i leave the liquid junction to enter phase 3. Since 1 mole of charge is transferred in the process considered,

$$-\sum_{i=1}^{r} \frac{t_i(0)}{z_i} = \sum_{i=1}^{r} \frac{t_i(L)}{z_i} = 1 \tag{13-89}$$

The free-energy change in phases 2 and 3 when 1 mole of charge is transferred from 2 to 3 via the liquid junction is given by

$$\sum_{i=1}^{r} \left[\frac{t_i(L)}{z_i}\, \bar{\mu}_i(L) - \frac{t_i(0)}{z_i}\, \bar{\mu}_i(0) \right] = \sum_{i=1}^{r} \left[\frac{t_i(L)}{z_i}\, \mu_i(L) - \frac{t_i(0)}{z_i}\, \mu_i(0) \right] + \mathscr{F}(\phi^{(3)} - \phi^{(2)}) \tag{13-90}$$

Since the process was carried out reversibly, the sum of free-energy changes in the liquid junction and in phases 2 and 3 in the process in which 1 mole of charge is transferred from 2 to 3 via the liquid junction must be zero. Addition of Eqs. (13-88) and (13-90) and rearrangement yield the expression

$$\mathscr{F}\varepsilon_L = -\sum_{i=1}^{r} \int_{\mu_i(0)}^{\mu_i(L)} \frac{t_i(x)}{z_i}\, d\mu_i(x) \tag{13-91}$$

where Eq. (13-73) has been used. Equation (13-91) is a fundamental equation for calculating liquid-junction potentials.

Equation (13-91) applies to a cell in which the only neutral component is the solvent. If neutral components other than the solvent are present, it is necessary to consider the changes in free energy due to the mass transport of these components in terms of the mass-transport numbers τ_i. In fact, as an alternative to the procedure outlined above, the calculation of ε_L can be made, considering the system to be made up of neutral components and one charged component, the electron, instead of r ionic components.

In order to illustrate the method of determining liquid-junction potentials, we shall apply it to a typical concentration cell of the form

$$\mathrm{M}^{(1)};\ \mathrm{MCl}^{(2)}(xm):\ \mathrm{MCl}^{(3)}(ym);\ \mathrm{M}^{(4)} \tag{13-92}$$

Since the cell of Eq. (13-92) is a special case of a galvanic cell with liquid junction, Eq. (13-78) is applicable, and we may write

$$-\mathscr{F}(\varepsilon - \varepsilon_L) = \mu_{\mathrm{M}^+}{}^{(2)} + \mu_{\mathrm{M}}{}^{(4)} - \mu_{\mathrm{M}}{}^{(1)} - \mu_{\mathrm{M}^+}{}^{(3)} \tag{13-93}$$

In Eq. (13-92), phases 1 and 4 are made up of the same metal. Consequently,

$$\mu_{\mathrm{M}}{}^{(4)} = \mu_{\mathrm{M}}{}^{(1)} \tag{13-94}$$

and Eq. (13-93) simplifies to

$$-\mathscr{F}(\varepsilon - \varepsilon_L) = \mu_{\mathrm{M}^+}{}^{(2)} - \mu_{\mathrm{M}^+}{}^{(3)} \tag{13-95}$$

For the cell under consideration, Eq. (13-91) specializes to

$$-\mathscr{F}\varepsilon_L = \int_{(2)}^{(3)} (t_{\mathrm{M}^+}\, d\mu_{\mathrm{M}^+} - t_{\mathrm{Cl}^-}\, d\mu_{\mathrm{Cl}^-}) \tag{13-96}$$

where the limits on the integration imply that we integrate across the liquid junction from phase 2 to phase 3. Substitution of Eq. (13-96) into Eq. (13-95) leads to the expression

$$-\mathscr{F}\varepsilon = \mu_{\mathrm{M}^+}{}^{(2)} - \mu_{\mathrm{M}^+}{}^{(3)} + \int_{(2)}^{(3)} (t_{\mathrm{M}^+}\, d\mu_{\mathrm{M}^+} - t_{\mathrm{Cl}^-}\, d\mu_{\mathrm{Cl}^-}) \tag{13-97}$$

We make use of the strong-electrolyte convention to write

$$\mu_{\mathrm{MCl}} = \mu_{\mathrm{M}^+} + \mu_{\mathrm{Cl}^-} \tag{13-98}$$

Differentiation of Eq. (13-98) and rearrangement result in

$$d\mu_{\mathrm{Cl}^-} = d\mu_{\mathrm{MCl}} - d\mu_{\mathrm{M}^+} \tag{13-99}$$

Since M^+ and Cl^- are the only charged components present, it follows that

$$t_{\mathrm{M}^+} + t_{\mathrm{Cl}^-} = 1 \tag{13-100}$$

Equation (13-97) can be simplified by use of Eqs. (13-99) and (13-100) to yield

$$-\mathscr{F}\varepsilon = \mu_{\mathrm{M}^+}{}^{(2)} - \mu_{\mathrm{M}^+}{}^{(3)} + \int_{(2)}^{(3)} d\mu_{\mathrm{M}^+} - \int_{(2)}^{(3)} t_{\mathrm{Cl}^-}\, d\mu_{\mathrm{MCl}} \tag{13-101}$$

The first integration in Eq. (13-101) can be trivially performed to yield terms which cancel the first two terms on the right-hand side of the equation. Thus, Eq. (13-101) becomes

$$\mathscr{F}\varepsilon = \int_{(2)}^{(3)} t_{\text{Cl}^-}\, d\mu_{\text{MCl}} \tag{13-102}$$

Equation (13-102) shows that, in agreement with the assumption of no accumulation of charge, the electromotive force of the galvanic cell depends on the chemical potential of neutral components only.

By the use of strong-electrolyte conventions, μ_{MCl} may be expanded in the form

$$\mu_{\text{MCl}} = 2RT \log (\gamma_{\pm} m_{\pm}) + \mu^{\circ}_{\text{MCl}} (T,p) \tag{13-103}$$

Differentiation of Eq. (13-103) at constant T, p, and solvent yields

$$d\mu_{\text{MCl}} = 2RT\, d \log (\gamma_{\pm} m_{\pm}) \tag{13-104}$$

Substitution of Eq. (13-104) into Eq. (13-102) results in

$$\mathscr{F}\varepsilon = 2 \int_{(2)}^{(3)} RT t_{\text{Cl}^-} d \log (\gamma_{\pm} m_{\pm}) \tag{13-105}$$

It is clear from Eq. (13-105) that a knowledge of ε and t_{Cl^-} permits evaluation of the activity coefficient $\gamma_{\pm}$. Comparison of results obtained by this method with those from other techniques yields excellent agreement. Thus, the applicability of thermodynamic theory to the case of partial equilibrium in a galvanic cell with liquid junction is demonstrated.

The exact integration of Eq. (13-105) requires a knowledge of the composition of the liquid-junction boundary and of the chemical potentials and transport numbers of all the ions as a function of composition. Since this information is normally not available, approximate integrations involving assumptions concerning the behavior of the electrolytes and the kind of phase boundary are usually performed. In the following we assume that the liquid junction exists between phases 1 and 2. The Planck method assumes that there is a constant steady-state concentration on the two sides of the boundary (Fig. 13-3). Such a situation can be closely approximated by using a boundary which consists of a membrane through which penetration is slow as compared with diffusion in the two liquid phases. [For details of the integration of Eq. (13-105) using this method see M. Planck, *Ann Physik*, vol. 40, p. 561, 1890, or MacInnes, *op. cit.*] The Henderson method assumes that, at $t = 0$, the concentration of the ionic components changes linearly across the boundary (Fig. 13-4). At later times, the distribution becomes

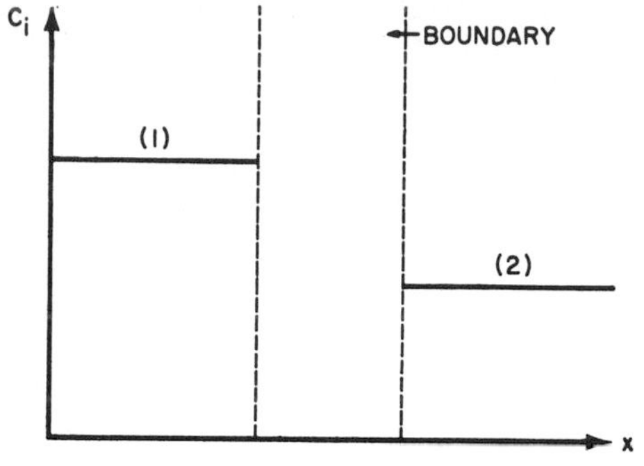

FIG. 13-3. Concentration of component i versus position in the Planck boundary.

distorted; this distortion can be calculated by the laws of diffusion. Boundaries approaching the conditions of the Henderson boundary are obtained by use of the shearing technique which is employed in many common experimental methods (e.g., electrophoresis). We present a detailed study of the integration of Eq. (13-105) using the Henderson method below.

When specialized for the Henderson boundary, Eq. (13-105) can easily be integrated if the ionic components are assumed to be ideal. This implies that the chemical potential of ion i is given by the expression

$$\mu_i = RT \log c_i + \mu_i^\circ(T,p) \tag{13-106}$$

Substitution of this expression into Eq. (13-91) yields

$$-\frac{\mathscr{F}\varepsilon_L}{RT} = \sum_{i=1}^{r} \int_{(1)}^{(2)} \frac{t_i}{z_i}\, d \log c_i \tag{13-107}$$

where the integration extends across the liquid junction from phase 1 to phase 2.

The evaluation of Eq. (13-107) is most readily accomplished when it is rewritten in terms of the equivalent conductances of the various ions involved. The transport number of component i is given by

$$t_i = \frac{I_i}{I} \tag{13-108}$$

where I_i is the current per square centimeter due to ion species i in an electric field E and where

$$I = \sum_{k=1}^{r} I_k \tag{13-109}$$

is the total current per square centimeter. The partial specific conductance of i, L_i, is defined by the relation

$$L_i = \frac{I_i}{E} \tag{13-110}$$

and the equivalent conductance of i, Λ_i, is defined by

$$\Lambda_i = \frac{1000L_i}{c_i} \tag{13-111}$$

Equation (13-108) can be rewritten in the form

$$t_i = \frac{\Lambda_i c_i}{\sum_{k=1}^{r} \Lambda_k c_k} \tag{13-112}$$

where we have made use of Eqs. (13-108) to (13-111). In the ideal approximation,

$$\Lambda_i = \Lambda_i^\circ \tag{13-113}$$

where Λ_i° is the equivalent conductance of component i at infinite dilution. It must be emphasized that the assumption of the ideality of the ion components which was made in introducing Eqs. (13-106) and (13-113) is highly unrealistic. Use of Λ_i° in Eq. (13-112) and substitution of the resulting expression into Eq. (13-107) result in

$$-\frac{\mathscr{F}\varepsilon_L}{RT} = \sum_{i=1}^{r} \frac{1}{z_i} \int_{(1)}^{(2)} \frac{\Lambda_i^\circ}{\sum_k \Lambda_k^\circ c_k} \, dc_i \tag{13-114}$$

The path of integration of the line integral in Eq. (13-114) is specified by the assumption of a Henderson boundary. The Henderson boundary requires the concentration of component i in the boundary to be given as a function of x by the expression

$$c_i = c_i^{(1)} + (c_i^{(2)} - c_i^{(1)})x \qquad 0 \leqslant x \leqslant 1 \tag{13-115}$$

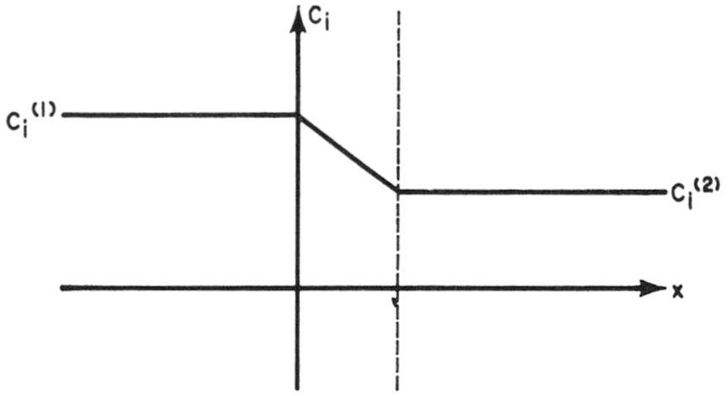

FIG. 13-4. Concentration of component i versus position in the Henderson boundary.

where $x = 0$ is the coordinate of the left-hand boundary of the liquid junction and $x = 1$ is the coordinate of the right-hand boundary of the liquid junction. Substitution of Eq. (13-115) into Eq. (13-114) yields

$$-\frac{\mathscr{F}\varepsilon_L}{RT} = \sum_{i=1}^{r} \frac{1}{z_i} \int_0^1 \frac{\Lambda_i^\circ (c_i^{(2)} - c_i^{(1)})\,dx}{\sum_k \Lambda_k^\circ c_k^{(1)} + x \sum_k \Lambda_k^\circ (c_k^{(2)} - c_k^{(1)})} \tag{13-116}$$

We define the quantity L° by the relation

$$L^\circ = \sum_{k=1}^{r} L_k^\circ = \frac{1}{1000} \sum_{k=1}^{r} \Lambda_k^\circ c_k \tag{13-117}$$

Equation (13-116) may be rewritten in the form

$$-\frac{\mathscr{F}\varepsilon_L}{RT} = \sum_{i=1}^{r} \frac{1}{z_i} \int_0^1 \frac{L_i^{\circ(2)} - L_i^{\circ(1)}}{L^{\circ(1)} + (L^{\circ(2)} - L^{\circ(1)})x}\,dx \tag{13-118}$$

where Eqs. (13-111) and (13-117) have been used. Integration of Eq. (13-118) yields

$$-\frac{\mathscr{F}\varepsilon_L}{RT} = \sum_{i=1}^{r} \frac{1}{z_i} \frac{L_i^{\circ(2)} - L_i^{\circ(1)}}{L^{\circ(2)} - L^{\circ(1)}} \log \frac{L^{\circ(2)}}{L^{\circ(1)}} \tag{13-119}$$

Equation (13-119) is the Henderson formula which is useful for order-of-magnitude estimates of ε_L.

In order to illustrate the use of this formula, we apply it to the computation of the liquid-junction potential between phases containing two electrolytes with a common ion, for example, $M_1CL^{(1)}(c)$: $M_2Cl^{(2)}(c)$. We assume that the two electrolytes are present in equal concentration. Equation (13-119) can be specialized for this case to yield

$$-\frac{\mathscr{F}\varepsilon_L}{RT} = \frac{[(\Lambda_{M_2^+}^\circ c_{M_2^+}{}^{(2)})/z_{M_2^+} + (\Lambda_{Cl^-}^\circ c_{Cl^-}{}^{(2)})/z_{Cl^-}] - [(\Lambda_{M_1^+}^\circ c_{M_1^+}{}^{(1)})/z_{M_1^+} + (\Lambda_{Cl^-}^\circ c_{Cl^-}{}^{(1)})/z_{Cl^-}]}{(\Lambda_{M_2^+}^\circ c_{M_2^+}{}^{(2)} + \Lambda_{Cl^-}^\circ c_{Cl^-}{}^{(2)}) - (\Lambda_{M_1^+}^\circ c_{M_1^+}{}^{(1)} + \Lambda_{Cl^-}^\circ c_{Cl^-}{}^{(1)})} \times \log \frac{\Lambda_{M_2^+}^\circ c_{M_2^+}{}^{(2)} + \Lambda_{Cl^-}^\circ c_{Cl^-}{}^{(2)}}{\Lambda_{M_1^+}^\circ c_{M_1^+}{}^{(1)} + \Lambda_{Cl^-}^\circ c_{Cl^-}{}^{(1)}} \tag{13-120}$$

Equation (13-120) reduces to

$$-\frac{\mathscr{F}\varepsilon_L}{RT} = \log \frac{\Lambda_{M_2^+}^\circ + \Lambda_{Cl^-}^\circ}{\Lambda_{M_1^+}^\circ + \Lambda_{Cl^-}^\circ} \tag{13-121}$$

since all the ions are univalent and all the concentrations are identical. We define Λ_{MCl}° by the relation

$$\Lambda_{MCl}^\circ = \Lambda_{M^+}^\circ + \Lambda_{Cl^-}^\circ \tag{13-122}$$

Table 13-1
Liquid-junction Potential of the Cell
$M_1Cl(0.1) : M_2Cl(0.1)$
ε_L in volts

Cell	Henderson	Planck	Experimental
HCl : KCl	28.52	26.78	26.78
HCl : NaCl	33.38	33.08	33.04
NaCl : NH_4Cl	−4.81	−4.30	−4.21
KCl : NaCl	4.86	6.30	6.42

Substitution of Eq. (13-122) into Eq. (13-121) results in

$$-\frac{\mathscr{F}\varepsilon_L}{RT} = \log \frac{\Lambda^\circ_{M_2Cl}}{\Lambda^\circ_{M_1Cl}} \tag{13-123}$$

If the Λ° of Eq. (13-123) are replaced by Λ we obtain the Lewis and Sargent formula which works well in practice.

The accuracy of the approximations inherent in the Planck and Henderson methods for the computation of liquid-junction potentials can be judged from the results tabulated in Table 13-1. The experimental values tabulated in Table 13-1 were measured in the cell

$$\text{Ag; AgCl}(s)\text{; } M_1Cl^{(1)}(c)\text{: } M_2Cl^{(2)}(c)\text{; AgCl}(s)\text{; Ag} \tag{13-124}$$

The cell reaction in the cell of Eq. (13-124) is

$$Cl^{-(1)} = Cl^{-(2)} \tag{13-125}$$

In this cell, Eq. (13-78) can be specialized to yield

$$-\mathscr{F}(\varepsilon - \varepsilon_L) = \mu_{Cl^-}{}^{(2)} - \mu_{Cl^-}{}^{(1)} \tag{13-126}$$

Since the ionic strength of solutions 1 and 2 is the same, the chemical potential of Cl^- is identical in the two solutions within the approximation of the Lewis rule [Eq. (12-29)]. Consequently, the measured electromotive force in the cell of Eq. (13-124) is identical to the liquid-junction potential.

13-4. THEORY OF THE SALT BRIDGE

Liquid-junction potentials introduce uncertainties in the results of certain physical measurements in which great accuracy is desired, for example, pH; membrane potentials. Thus, it is desirable to find methods for reducing the magnitude of liquid-junction potentials in various systems. Salt bridges containing saturated solutions of KCl are utilized for this purpose. The salt bridges are placed between liquid junctions which would otherwise give rise to large potential differences. The effectiveness of a salt bridge may be estimated by use of the Henderson method.

We consider the boundary

$$HCl(c_1)\colon KCl(4.2) \tag{13-127}$$

At 25°C, a saturated KCl solution is 4.2 normal. The application of Eq. (13-119) to the determination of the liquid-junction potential of the boundary of Eq. (13-127) results in

$$\varepsilon_L = -\frac{RT}{\mathscr{F}}\left[\frac{4.2(\Lambda^\circ_{K^+} - \Lambda^\circ_{Cl^-}) - c_1(\Lambda^\circ_{H^+} - \Lambda^\circ_{Cl^-})}{4.2(\Lambda^\circ_{K^+} + \Lambda^\circ_{Cl^-}) - c_1(\Lambda^\circ_{H^+} + \Lambda^\circ_{Cl^-})} \times \log\frac{4.2(\Lambda^\circ_{K^+} + \Lambda^\circ_{Cl^-})}{c_1(\Lambda^\circ_{H^+} + \Lambda^\circ_{Cl^-})}\right] \tag{13-128}$$

where we have used Eq. (13-111). Substitution of the values $\Lambda^\circ_{K^+} = 73.52$, $\Lambda^\circ_{Cl^-} = 76.34$, $\Lambda^\circ_{H^+} = 349.8$ into Eq. (13-128) and choice of the concentration $c_1 = 0.042$ yield the result $\varepsilon_L = 0.0035$ volt. Thus, for small values of c_1 and a saturated solution of KCl, ε_L is often negligible as compared with ε. A saturated solution of KCl is used in the salt bridge since the equivalent conductances of K^+ and Cl^- are large but are approximately equal. In principle, exclusion of the liquid-junction potential cannot be accomplished by this method. If the liquid-junction potential were zero, single-boundary potentials could be simply measured by direct methods.

13-5. pH: ITS DEFINITION AND MEASUREMENT

The quantity pH is best defined operationally in terms of the method used for its evaluation. In general, a cell of the form

$$\text{(Pt) } H_2 \text{ (1 atm); solution X} \overset{(1)}{:} \text{KCl (sat)} \overset{(2)}{:} \text{reference electrode} \tag{13-129}$$

is employed in the measurement of pH. Solution X contains hydrogen ions, and the pH of solution X is defined by the equation

$$\mathrm{pH} = \frac{\varepsilon - \varepsilon_0}{2.303RT/\mathscr{F}} \tag{13-130}$$

where ε is the measured electromotive force of the cell and ε_0 is assumed to be a constant which depends only on the reference electrode used.

A more exact analysis of the cell of Eq. (13-129) can be carried out by use of Eq. (13-78) in the form

$$-\mathscr{F}(\varepsilon - \varepsilon_L^{(1)} - \varepsilon_L^{(2)}) = \Delta F \tag{13-131}$$

The half-cell reaction occurring at the left electrode is

$$\tfrac{1}{2}H_2 = H^+ + e_- \tag{13-132}$$

Thus, the free-energy change for the cell reaction can be written

$$\Delta F = \Delta F_r + RT \log \frac{a_{H^+}}{(p^*_{H_2})^{\frac{1}{2}}} \tag{13-133}$$

where ΔF_r depends only on the reference electrode and T and p. Substitution of Eq. (13-133) into Eq. (13-131) and rearrangement yield

$$\varepsilon = \varepsilon_0 - \frac{RT}{\mathscr{F}} \log a_{H^+} \tag{13-134}$$

where
$$\varepsilon_0 = \varepsilon_L{}^{(1)} - \frac{\Delta F_r}{\mathscr{F}} + \varepsilon_L{}^{(2)} + \frac{RT}{\mathscr{F}} \log (p^*_{H_2})^{\frac{1}{2}} \tag{13-135}$$

The second, third, and fourth terms on the right-hand side of Eq. (13-135) are constants which depend only on T, p, and the type of reference electrode used. The quantity $\varepsilon_L{}^{(1)}$, however, is a function of the composition of solution X. Consequently ε_0 contains a variable quantity, $\varepsilon_L{}^{(1)}$, which can neither be measured nor calculated exactly.

In his original determination of pH, Sörenson assumed that the solution X was ideal and that the liquid-junction potential $\varepsilon_L{}^{(1)}$ was zero. He obtained the result that the electromotive force of the cell was

$$\varepsilon = \varepsilon_0 - \frac{RT}{\mathscr{F}} \log c_{H^+} \tag{13-136}$$

Thus, the quantity pH, defined by Eq. (13-130), becomes

$$\text{pH} = -\log_{10} c_{H^+} \tag{13-137}$$

In Sörenson's work, the reference electrode was a 0.1 normal calomel electrode of the form

$$\text{KCl}(0.1), \text{Hg}_2\text{Cl}_2(s), \text{Hg}(l) \tag{13-138}$$

The quantity ε_0 was obtained by measuring the electromotive force of cells containing standard solutions. The hydrogen ion concentration in these standard solutions was determined from conductance data, using the Arrhenius theory. Sörenson found the value

$$\varepsilon_0 = 0.3378 \text{ volt} \tag{13-139}$$

for the cell containing the reference electrode of Eq. (13-138) at 25°C. More modern measurements by MacInnes and others give the value

$$\varepsilon_0 = 0.3358 \text{ volt} \tag{13-140}$$

In recent work the assumption of the ideality of solution X is dropped and Eq. (13-134) is used. The quantity pH is then determined to be

$$\text{pH} = -\log_{10} a_{\text{H}^+} \tag{13-141}$$

where we have used the definition of Eq. (13-130). Although this procedure is formally exact, ε_0 is still uncertain since it contains $\varepsilon_L^{(1)}$. The quantity $\varepsilon_L^{(1)}$ is generally neglected; i.e., it is assumed to be zero. To reduce the uncertainty in ε_0, Guggenheim has suggested that pH be redefined by the expression

$$\text{pH} = \frac{\varepsilon - \varepsilon_0' - \varepsilon_L^{(1)}}{2.303(RT/\mathscr{F})} \tag{13-142}$$

where $\varepsilon_L^{(1)}$ is to be calculated from the Henderson boundary formula [Eq. (13-119)] and $\varepsilon_0' = \varepsilon_0 - \varepsilon_L^{(1)}$. MacInnes has proposed a method of adjusting ε_0 so that pH as defined by Eq. (13-130) is as close as possible to $-\log_{10}(\gamma_{\pm} c_{\text{H}^+})$. (For details, see MacInnes, *op. cit.*, chap. 15.)

In the measurement of pH a "glass electrode" is often used instead of the standard hydrogen gas, platinum electrode. The glass electrode consists of an electrode (for example, Ag, AgCl) dipping into a solution of HCl which is in contact with the unknown solution through a soft glass membrane permeable to hydrogen ions alone. To determine the range of applicability of the glass electrode it is necessary to measure its potential against that of a normal H_2 electrode in solutions in which the type of electrolyte and its concentration are varied. The electromotive force of the cell.

$$\text{Glass electrode; electrolyte solution; } H_2 \text{ (1 atm) (Pt)} \tag{13-143}$$

is found to have the constant value 0.352 volt for a large number of electrolytes when the pH is between 2 and 9 (Fig. 13-5). For this range of pH values, the glass electrode has several advantages over the normal H_2 electrode. One of the most important advantages is that the glass electrode yields accurate pH values in the presence of oxidizing or reducing agents; the H_2 electrode cannot be employed under such conditions since the tendency to oxidize H_2 or reduce H^+ may produce considerable changes in the electromotive force measured.

The quinhydrone electrode is sometimes substituted for the H_2 electrode in the measurement of pH. In its use a cell of the type

$$\text{Au; quinhydrone } (s)\text{; solution X: KCl (sat): reference electrode} \tag{13-144}$$

is usually employed. Quinhydrone is a solid-phase compound of an equimolar mixture of hydroquinone and quinone. The observed electromotive force arises from the reaction

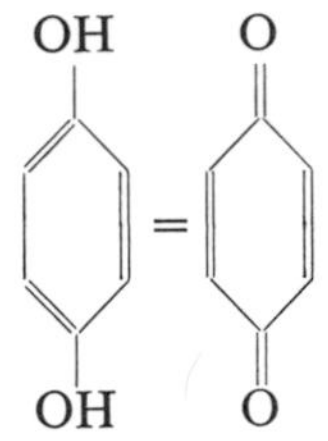

$$+ 2H^{+} + 2e_{-} \qquad (13\text{-}145)$$

The chemical reaction of Eq. (13-145) is an oxidation which involves direct transfer of the released electrons to the metal electrode. If the liquid-junction potential is neglected, the electromotive force of the cell of Eq. (13-144) may be written in the form

$$\varepsilon = \varepsilon^{\circ} - \frac{RT}{2\mathscr{F}} \log \frac{a_{Q}(a_{H^+})^2}{a_{Hy}} \qquad (13\text{-}146)$$

where a_Q is the activity of quinone, a_{Hy} is the activity of hydroquinone, and ε° includes the constant emf of the reference electrode and the standard emf of the quinhydrone electrode. It is frequently assumed in the application of Eq. (13-146) that the activities of quinone and hydroquinone are equal. In this case, the pH of solution X is given by

$$\text{pH} = \frac{\varepsilon - \varepsilon^{\circ}}{2.303(RT/\mathscr{F})} = -\log_{10} a_{H^+} \qquad (13\text{-}147)$$

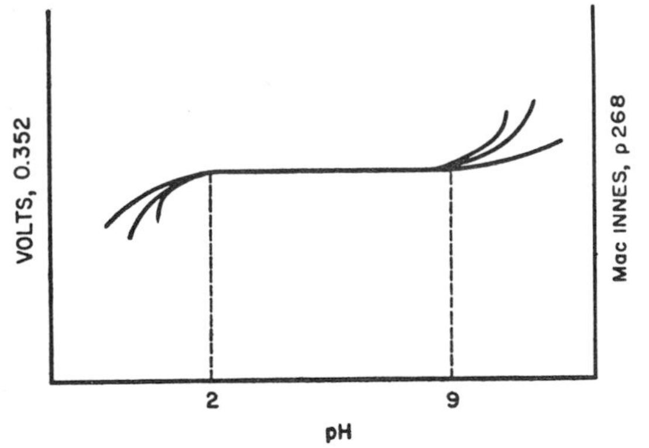

FIG. 13-5. Plot of emf of glass electrode versus pH.

Since excess solid quinhydrone is present in the system, its activity is constant. The activities of quinone and hydroquinone are related to that of quinhydrone by the equation

$$K = \frac{a_{\mathrm{Hy}} a_{\mathrm{Q}}}{a_{\mathrm{qh}}} \tag{13-148}$$

where $K(T,p)$ is an equilibrium constant and where a_{qh} is the activity of quinhydrone. If a_{qh} is kept constant, the product $a_{\mathrm{Hy}} a_{\mathrm{Q}}$ is constant. In the ideal approximation, Eq. (13-148) requires that

$$a_{\mathrm{Hy}} = a_{\mathrm{Q}} \tag{13-149}$$

as is assumed in Eq. (13-147). In real solutions, γ_{Hy} and γ_{Q} are not exactly equal and have a different dependence on the electrolytes present. Consequently, a salt error appears in the measured electromotive force. To obtain accurate values of the pH, an empirical salt correction has to be applied. In spite of this complication, the quinhydrone electrode is often used because of its ease of preparation and its applicability in the presence of O_2.

13-6. MEMBRANE EQUILIBRIUM

In this section, we present a discussion of the phenomena observed when a rigid, heat-conducting membrane separating two electrolyte solutions is permeable to some of the components but not to others. We restrict our attention to systems in which the electrolytes on the two sides of the membrane are dissolved in the same solvent.

A typical example of the systems under consideration is the cell

Ag; AgCl(*s*), KCl (sat.) $\overset{(1)}{\text{⌐:⌐}}$ solution (1), membrane, solution (2) $\overset{(2)}{\text{⌐:⌐}}$ KCl (sat.), AgCl(*s*); Ag (13-150)

Since the electrodes are identical, the measured emf of the cell of Eq. (13-150) is given by

$$\varepsilon = \varepsilon_L^{(1)} + \varepsilon_m + \varepsilon_L^{(2)} \tag{13-151}$$

where ε_m represents the electromotive force due to the presence of the semipermeable membrane.

We consider the system

Solution (1), membrane, solution (2) (13-152)

At equilibrium

$$T^{(1)} = T^{(2)} \tag{13-153}$$

and

$$\bar{\mu}_i^{(1)} = \bar{\mu}_i^{(2)} \tag{13-154}$$

for all components to which the membrane is permeable. By use of Eq. (13-15), Eq. (13-154) may be rewritten in the form

$$\mu_i^{(2)} - \mu_i^{(1)} = -z_i\mathcal{F}(\phi^{(2)} - \phi^{(1)}) = -z_i\mathcal{F}\,\Delta\phi \tag{13-155}$$

At equilibrium no current flows through the membrane, and the membrane potential is equal to the electromotive force by Eq. (13-30). Under these conditions, Eq. (13-155) becomes

$$\mu_i^{(2)} - \mu_i^{(1)} = -z_i\mathcal{F}\varepsilon_m \tag{13-156}$$

Equation (13-156) holds for all ions to which the membrane is permeable. Therefore we may write

$$\frac{\mu_i^{(2)} - \mu_i^{(1)}}{z_i\mathcal{F}} = \frac{\mu_k^{(2)} - \mu_k^{(1)}}{z_k\mathcal{F}} = \varepsilon_m \tag{13-157}$$

The existence of a membrane potential implies that the membrane must be impermeable to some of the components.

If the membrane is permeable to the solvent, the equilibrium conditions will, in general, require a pressure difference between the two sides of the membrane. Such membrane equilibria are called Donnan equilibria. In this case, Eq. (13-155) can be rewritten to yield

$$\Delta\phi = \frac{1}{z_i\mathcal{F}}\left[\mu_i^{(1)}(p + \pi, T, x^{(1)}) - \mu_i^{(2)}(p, T, x^{(2)})\right] \tag{13-158}$$

where $x^{(1)}$ stands for the set of mole fractions in phase 1, $x^{(2)}$ stands for the set of mole fractions in phase 2, and $p + \pi$ is the pressure of phase 1. The chemical potential $\mu_i^{(1)}(p + \pi, T, x^{(1)})$ can be expanded in a powers series in π of the form

$$\mu_i^{(1)}(p + \pi, T, x^{(1)}) = \mu_i^{(1)}(p, T, x^{(1)}) + \bar{v}_i^{(1)}(p, T, x^{(1)})\pi + O(\pi^2) \tag{13-159}$$

where we have used the equation

$$\bar{v}_i = \left(\frac{\partial \mu_i}{\partial p}\right)_{T,x} \tag{13-160}$$

Substitution of Eq. (13-159) into Eq. (13-158) and retention of first-order terms in π result in

$$\Delta\phi = \frac{1}{z_i\mathcal{F}}\left[\mu_i^{(1)}(p, T, x^{(1)}) - \mu_i^{(2)}(p, T, x^{(2)}) + \pi\bar{v}_i^{(1)}\right] \tag{13-161}$$

As discussed in Chaps. 11 and 12, the chemical potential can be written in the form

$$\mu_i = \mu_i^\circ + RT \log a_i \tag{13-162}$$

where μ_i° is a function of T, p, and the solvent. Substitution of Eq. (13-162) into Eq. (13-161) yields

$$\Delta\phi = \frac{RT}{z_i\mathscr{F}}\left(\log\frac{a_i^{(1)}}{a_i^{(2)}} + \frac{\pi\bar{v}_i^{(1)}}{RT}\right) \tag{13-163}$$

where we have used the fact that

$$\mu_i^{\circ(1)}(T,p) = \mu_i^{\circ(2)}(T,p) \tag{13-164}$$

since the solvent is the same on both sides of the membrane. Rearrangement of Eq. (13-163) gives

$$\frac{a_i^{(2)}}{a_i^{(1)}} = \exp\left(\frac{-z_i\mathscr{F}\Delta\phi + \pi\bar{v}_i^{(1)}}{RT}\right) \tag{13-165}$$

Equation (13-165) holds for all components to which the membrane is permeable. In the case of neutral components, z_i is zero, and the only term occurring in the exponential is that containing the osmotic pressure.

The equilibrium distribution of a permeant electrolyte consisting of ν_A cations, $A^{z_A e}$, and ν_B anions, $B^{z_B e}$, is determined by the equation

$$\left(\frac{a_A^{(2)}}{a_A^{(1)}}\right)^{\nu_A}\left(\frac{a_B^{(2)}}{a_B^{(1)}}\right)^{\nu_B} = \exp\left[\frac{\pi}{RT}(\nu_A\bar{v}_A + \nu_B\bar{v}_B)\right] \tag{13-166}$$

where we have used the fact that

$$\nu_A z_A + \nu_B z_B = 0$$

At high dilutions, the argument of the exponential in Eq. (13-166) is small and we may approximate Eq. (13-166) by

$$\left(\frac{a_A^{(2)}}{a_A^{(1)}}\right)^{\nu_A} = \left(\frac{a_B^{(1)}}{a_B^{(2)}}\right)^{\nu_B} \tag{13-167}$$

In the ideal approximation, Eq. (13-167) becomes

$$\left(\frac{c_A^{(2)}}{c_A^{(1)}}\right)^{\nu_A} = \left(\frac{c_B^{(1)}}{c_B^{(2)}}\right)^{\nu_B} \tag{13-168}$$

Frequently, experiments are performed in which the pressures on the two sides of the membrane are specified to be the same at equilibrium. In this case, or in the case that the membrane is impermeable to the solvent and there is no initial pressure difference, nonosmotic membrane equilibria exist; i.e., the osmotic pressure is zero. When the osmotic pressure is zero, Eq. (13-165) reduces to

$$\frac{a_i^{(2)}}{a_i^{(1)}} = \exp\left(-\frac{z_i \mathscr{F} \Delta\phi}{RT}\right) \tag{13-169}$$

Nonosmotic and osmotic equilibria are essentially equivalent for dilute solutions.

To illustrate the case of nonosmotic equilibria, we discuss a simple example. We consider two solutions which are initially isolated but are then brought into contact through a semipermeable membrane. There is no initial pressure difference. Solution 1 is initially comprised of a concentration $c_2^{(1)}$ of strong electrolyte NaR and a concentration $c_3^{(1)}$ of strong electrolyte NaCl dissolved in water. Solution 2 is initially comprised of a concentration $c_2^{(2)}$ of NaR and a concentration $c_3^{(2)}$ of NaCl dissolved in water. Since NaR and NaCl are strong electrolytes, solution 1 initially consists of Na^+(concentration $c_1^{(1)}$), $Cl^-(c_3^{(1)})$, $R^-(c_2^{(1)})$, and H_2O. Similarly, solution 2 initially consists of $Na^+(c_1^{(2)})$, $Cl^-(c_3^{(2)})$, $R^-(c_2^{(2)})$, and H_2O. It is clear that

$$c_1^{(1)} = c_2^{(1)} + c_3^{(1)} \tag{13-170}$$

and

$$c_1^{(2)} = c_2^{(2)} + c_3^{(2)} \tag{13-171}$$

We assume the membrane to be impermeable to R^- and H_2O.

We wish to calculate the equilibrium concentrations of the components and also to determine the membrane potential of the system. To do this, we assume that the electroneutrality condition is applicable, as discussed at the beginning of this chapter. At equilibrium,

$$\bar{\mu}_{Na^+}{}^{(1)} = \bar{\mu}_{Na^+}{}^{(2)} \tag{13-172}$$

and

$$\bar{\mu}_{Cl^-}{}^{(1)} = \bar{\mu}_{Cl^-}{}^{(2)} \tag{13-173}$$

Equations (13-172) and (13-173) are equivalent to Eq. (13-169) which leads to

$$\frac{a_{Na^+}{}^{(1)}}{a_{Na^+}{}^{(2)}} = \frac{a_{Cl^-}{}^{(2)}}{a_{Cl^-}{}^{(1)}} \tag{13-174}$$

In the ideal approximation for dilute solutions, Eq. (13-174) becomes

$$\frac{c_{Na^+}{}^{(1)}}{c_{Na^+}{}^{(2)}} = \frac{c_{Cl^-}{}^{(2)}}{c_{Cl^-}{}^{(1)}} \tag{13-175}$$

We assume that the solutions are dilute enough for Eq. (13-175) to apply. To achieve equilibrium, transfer of salts through the membrane must occur unless the amounts added initially satisfy Eq. (13-175). In accord with the restraint of electroneutrality, we assume that only neutral salts can be transferred. Suppose that n moles of NaCl per liter of solution moved from phase 1 to 2 in the attainment of equilibrium. Then, Eq. (13-175) can be written in the form

$$\frac{c_{\mathrm{Na}^+}{}^{(1)}}{c_{\mathrm{Na}^+}{}^{(2)}} = \frac{c_1{}^{(1)} - n}{c_1{}^{(2)} + n} = \frac{c_2{}^{(1)} + c_3{}^{(1)} - n}{c_2{}^{(2)} + c_3{}^{(2)} + n} = \frac{c_3{}^{(2)} + n}{c_3{}^{(1)} - n} \tag{13-176}$$

where we have used Eqs. (13-170) and (13-171). Equation (13-176) can be solved for n in terms of $c_2{}^{(1)}$, $c_2{}^{(2)}$, $c_3{}^{(1)}$, and $c_3{}^{(2)}$ to yield

$$n = \frac{(c_3{}^{(1)})^2 - (c_3{}^{(2)})^2 + c_2{}^{(1)}c_3{}^{(1)} - c_2{}^{(2)}c_3{}^{(2)}}{2(c_3{}^{(1)} + c_3{}^{(2)}) + c_2{}^{(1)} + c_2{}^{(2)}} \tag{13-177}$$

Expressions for the equilibrium concentrations of the various ions follow immediately from Eq. (13-177) and the relations

$$\begin{aligned} c_{\mathrm{Na}^+}{}^{(1)} &= c_1{}^{(1)} - n \\ c_{\mathrm{Na}^+}{}^{(2)} &= c_1{}^{(2)} + n \\ c_{\mathrm{Cl}^-}{}^{(1)} &= c_3{}^{(1)} - n \\ c_{\mathrm{Cl}^-}{}^{(2)} &= c_3{}^{(2)} + n \\ c_{\mathrm{R}^-}{}^{(1)} &= c_2{}^{(1)} \\ c_{\mathrm{R}^-}{}^{(2)} &= c_2{}^{(2)} \end{aligned} \tag{13-178}$$

Substitution of Eq. (13-177) into Eq. (13-176) results in

$$\frac{c_{\mathrm{Na}^+}{}^{(1)}}{c_{\mathrm{Na}^+}{}^{(2)}} = \frac{c_{\mathrm{Cl}^-}{}^{(2)}}{c_{\mathrm{Cl}^-}{}^{(1)}} = \frac{c_3{}^{(1)} + c_3{}^{(2)} + c_2{}^{(1)}}{c_3{}^{(1)} + c_3{}^{(2)} + c_2{}^{(2)}} \tag{13-179}$$

Use of Eq. (13-179) and Eq. (13-169) results in an explicit expression for ε_m in terms of the initial concentrations in the form

$$\varepsilon_m = \frac{RT}{\mathscr{F}} \log \frac{c_3{}^{(1)} + c_3{}^{(2)} + c_2{}^{(1)}}{c_3{}^{(1)} + c_3{}^{(2)} + c_2{}^{(2)}} \tag{13-180}$$

The measurement of membrane potentials is accomplished by use of cells of the type of Eq. (13-150). The measured emf of this system is given by Eq. (13-151). Usually, the assumption is made that $\varepsilon_L{}^{(1)} = \varepsilon_L{}^{(2)} = 0$. The error involved in this approximation can be roughly determined by use of the Henderson formula [Eq. (13-119)]. In general, it is found that the sum $\varepsilon_L{}^{(1)} + \varepsilon_L{}^{(2)}$ is small compared with ε_m.

14 ELECTRIC AND MAGNETIC FIELDS

In this chapter, we study the effects of uniform static electric and magnetic fields on the thermodynamic properties of material. The source of the fields may be in the surroundings or included in the system of interest. In either case, the properties of the material affect the value of the effective field at any point in the material. It is for this reason that the study of electric and magnetic fields is more complicated than the study of gravitational and centrifugal fields presented in the next chapter.

In Sec. 14-1, we discuss the thermodynamic properties of uniform, homogeneous dielectric material in an electrostatic field. In Sec. 14-2, a brief résumé of the properties of material in a magnetic field is presented.

14-1. ELECTRIC FIELDS

We now turn our attention to the study of the thermodynamic properties of substances in an electrostatic field. In particular, we consider the case of a homogeneous, constant electric field such as exists between the plates of a parallel-plate capacitor, with neglect of edge effects. The system to be studied consists of the battery, capacitor, dielectric, and wires of Fig. 14-1. The uniform, homogeneous, deformable dielectric fills the region between the plates of the capacitor and is assumed to be ideal; i.e., its conductivity is zero. The battery remains in a constant state in the following considerations; its only function is to maintain a constant potential.

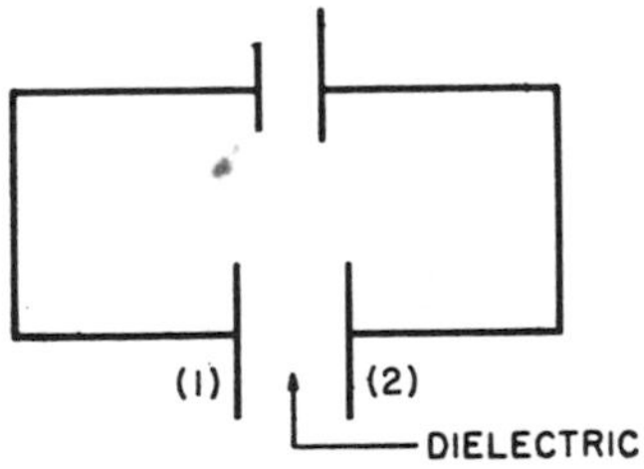

FIG. 14-1. System consisting of battery, wires, capacitor, and dielectric.

It is convenient to list the definitions of a number of quantities which will be useful in the following discussion:

a is the area of each plate of the capacitor.
l is the distance between the plates of the capacitor.
σ is the surface charge density on plate 2 of the capacitor.
$-\sigma$ is the surface charge density on plate 1 of the capacitor.
$\Delta\phi = \phi^{(2)} - \phi^{(1)}$ is the potential difference between the plates.

$\mathsf{E} = \Delta\phi/l$ is the homogeneous electric field between the plates.
ρ is the space charge density.
P is the total polarization of the dielectric.
$p^{(v)} = P/V$ is the polarization density of the dielectric.
ε is the dielectric constant of the insulator.
$\chi^{(v)}$ is the electric susceptibility of the dielectric per unit volume.
$\chi = V\chi^{(v)}$ is the total electric susceptibility of the dielectric.
E is the internal energy of the system in the presence of the electric field.

Some of the quantities listed above are related by definition or by the equations of electrostatics. In particular, we may write

$$\mathsf{E} + 4\pi p^{(v)} = \varepsilon\mathsf{E} = 4\pi\sigma \tag{14-1}$$

and

$$p^{(v)} = \chi^{(v)}\mathsf{E} \tag{14-2}$$

Use of Eqs. (14-1) and (14-2) yields the relation

$$\chi^{(v)} = \frac{\varepsilon - 1}{4\pi} \tag{14-3}$$

The total differential of the internal energy of a system of r components in an electrostatic field is given by

$$dE = dE' + \int^{a} \phi \, d\sigma \, da + \int^{V} \phi \, d\rho \, dV \tag{14-4}$$

where

$$dE' = T\,dS - p\,dV + \sum_{i=1}^{r} \mu_i \, dn_i \tag{14-5}$$

and where

$$\int^{a} \phi \, d\sigma \, da \qquad \text{and} \qquad \int^{V} \phi \, d\rho \, dV$$

are terms arising from electrostatic theory. The first term is the work done on the system when the surface charge distribution is altered. The second term represents the work done on the system when the volume charge distribution is altered. If no isolated charges are present, this term is zero for conductors and dielectrics in electrostatic equilibrium.

In the system under consideration the surface integral of Eq. (14-4) is taken over the faces of the capacitor. The potential is constant on the surface of a conductor in equilibrium. The surface charge density on each plate of the capacitor is constant if we neglect end effects. Thus we may write

$$\begin{aligned}\int^{a} \phi \, d\sigma \, da &= \int^{a(2)} \phi^{(2)} \, d\sigma^{(2)} \, da + \int^{a(1)} \phi^{(1)} \, d\sigma^{(1)} \, da \\ &= a(\phi^{(2)} - \phi^{(1)}) \, d\sigma = V\mathsf{E} \, d\sigma \end{aligned} \tag{14-6}$$

where
$$V = al \tag{14-7}$$

is the volume of the dielectric. We assume that the electric field in the dielectric is held constant by the battery when the volume of the dielectric is fixed. Under these conditions the total derivative of Eq. (14-1) becomes

$$4\pi\, dp^{(v)} = \mathsf{E}\, d\varepsilon = 4\pi\, d\sigma \tag{14-8}$$

or
$$dp^{(v)} = d\sigma \tag{14-9}$$

Use of Eq. (14-9) and the definition of P, the total polarization of the dielectric, results in

$$V\, d\sigma = dP \tag{14-10}$$

at constant volume. The quantity $\mathsf{E}\, dP$ then is the work done on the system by the constant, homogeneous field E when the polarization of the dielectric is changed from P to $P + dP$.

In this treatment we shall allow variation of the entropy, volume, and mass of components in the dielectric phase only. Use of Eqs. (14-4), (14-5), (14-6), and (14-10) yields

$$dE = T\, dS - p\, dV + \sum_{i=1}^{r} \mu_i\, dn_i + \mathsf{E}\, dP \tag{14-11}$$

We note that different forms of the first law have been promulgated by various authors. Equation (14-11) is the correct form in the general case in which the dielectric is deformable. We define the Helmholtz and Gibbs free energies of the system by the relations

$$A = E - TS \tag{14-12}$$

and
$$F = E + pV - TS \tag{14-13}$$

respectively, in analogy to the definition of these quantities in the absence of the field. The total differentials of these quantities can be obtained from Eqs. (14-11), (14-12), and (14-13) in the form

$$dA = -S\, dT - p\, dV + \sum_{i=1}^{r} \mu_i\, dn_i + \mathsf{E}\, dP \tag{14-14}$$

and
$$dF = -S\, dT + V\, dp + \sum_{i=1}^{r} \mu_i\, dn_i + \mathsf{E}\, dP \tag{14-15}$$

For convenience, we generalize the concept of the partial molal quantity defined in Eq. (2-5) to include the specification of constant electric field. Thus, we write

$$\bar{g}_i = \left(\frac{\partial G}{\partial n_i}\right)_{T,p,\mathsf{E},n_{j \neq i}} \tag{14-16}$$

It is found by experiment that an extensive variable G is a linear homogeneous function of the masses at constant T, p, and E. Use of the results of Sec. A-2 leads to the expression

$$G = \sum_{i=1}^{r} n_i \bar{g}_i \tag{14-17}$$

We note that the chemical potential of component i, μ_i, is not the partial molal free energy in the presence of an electric field.

To obtain the partial differential of the various thermodynamic quantities with respect to the field strength, it is convenient to consider the total differentials

$$d(A - \mathsf{E}P) = -S\,dT - p\,dV + \sum_{i=1}^{r} \mu_i\,dn_i - P\,d\mathsf{E} \tag{14-18}$$

and

$$d(F - \mathsf{E}P) = -S\,dT + V\,dp + \sum_{i=1}^{r} \mu_i\,dn_i - P\,d\mathsf{E} \tag{14-19}$$

Use of the Euler condition [Eq. (A-32)] and Eq. (14-19) results in

$$\left(\frac{\partial \mu_i}{\partial \mathsf{E}}\right)_{T,p,n} = -\left(\frac{\partial P}{\partial n_i}\right)_{T,p,\mathsf{E},n_{j\neq i}} \tag{14-20}$$

Equation (14-20) can be rewritten by use of Eq. (14-16) in the form

$$\left(\frac{\partial \mu_i}{\partial \mathsf{E}}\right)_{T,p,n} = -\bar{p}_i \tag{14-21}$$

where $\bar{p}_i$ is the partial molal polarization. Integration of Eq. (14-21) results in

$$\mu_i(T,p,x_1, \ldots ,x_{r-1},\mathsf{E}) = \mu_i' - \int_0^{\mathsf{E}} \bar{p}_i\,d\mathsf{E}' \tag{14-22}$$

where

$$\mu_i' = \mu_i(T,p,x_1, \ldots ,x_{r-1},0) \tag{14-23}$$

is the chemical potential in the absence of the field and the integration is performed along a path of constant temperature, pressure, and composition.

Further use of the Euler condition and Eqs. (14-18) and (14-19) results in the following interesting relations:

$$\bar{s}_i = -\left(\frac{\partial \mu_i}{\partial T}\right)_{p,\mathsf{E},n} \tag{14-24}$$

$$\bar{v}_i = \left(\frac{\partial \mu_i}{\partial p}\right)_{T,\mathsf{E},n} \tag{14-25}$$

$$\left(\frac{\partial \bar{s}_i}{\partial \mathsf{E}}\right)_{T,p,n} = \left(\frac{\partial \bar{p}_i}{\partial T}\right)_{p,\mathsf{E},n} \tag{14-26}$$

$$\left(\frac{\partial \bar{v}_i}{\partial \mathsf{E}}\right)_{T,p,n} = -\left(\frac{\partial \bar{p}_i}{\partial p}\right)_{T,\mathsf{E},n} \tag{14-27}$$

and

$$\left(\frac{\partial p}{\partial \mathsf{E}}\right)_{T,V,n} = \left(\frac{\partial P}{\partial V}\right)_{T,\mathsf{E},n} \tag{14-28}$$

In order to compute the explicit dependence of the various thermodynamic quantities on the magnitude of the electric field, it is necessary to utilize molecular theory or experiment. It is found that the electric susceptibility can be expanded in powers of the field except in the case of ferroelectrics. Thus we may write

$$\chi = \chi^\circ + O(\mathsf{E}) \tag{14-29}$$

and

$$\chi^{(v)} = \chi^{\circ(v)} + O(\mathsf{E}) \tag{14-30}$$

At low fields, where electric saturation can be neglected, χ and $\chi^{(v)}$ are essentially independent of the field. Use of the definitions and Eq. (14-2) yields

$$P = \chi \mathsf{E} \tag{14-31}$$

and thus

$$\bar{p}_i = \left(\frac{\partial \chi}{\partial n_i}\right)_{T,p,\mathsf{E},n_{j\neq i}} \mathsf{E} = \bar{\chi}_i \mathsf{E} \tag{14-32}$$

Substitution of Eqs. (14-32) and (14-29) into Eq. (14-22) results in

$$\mu_i = \mu_i' - \tfrac{1}{2}\bar{\chi}_i^\circ \mathsf{E}^2 + O(\mathsf{E}^3) \tag{14-33}$$

Similar calculations yield the expressions

$$\bar{s}_i = \bar{s}_i' + \frac{1}{2}\left(\frac{\partial \bar{\chi}_i^\circ}{\partial T}\right)_{p,\mathsf{E},n} \mathsf{E}^2 + O(\mathsf{E}^3) \tag{14-34}$$

$$\bar{v}_i = \bar{v}_i' - \frac{1}{2}\left(\frac{\partial \bar{\chi}_i^\circ}{\partial p}\right)_{T,\mathsf{E},n} \mathsf{E}^2 + O(\mathsf{E}^3) \tag{14-35}$$

and

$$\bar{h}_i = \bar{h}_i' + \frac{1}{2}\left[\bar{\chi}_i^\circ + T\left(\frac{\partial \bar{\chi}_i^\circ}{\partial T}\right)_{p,\mathsf{E},n}\right] \mathsf{E}^2 + O(\mathsf{E}^3) \tag{14-36}$$

where the primed quantities are the zero-field partial molal entropies, volumes, and enthalpies. Multiplication of Eq. (14-35) by n_i and summation over i from 1 to r result in

$$\Delta V = V(T,p,n,\mathsf{E}) - V(T,p,n,0) = -\frac{1}{2}\left(\frac{\partial \chi^\circ}{\partial p}\right)_{T,\mathsf{E},n} \mathsf{E}^2 \tag{14-37}$$

Equation (14-37) is the formula for electrostriction at constant T, p, and $n_1, \ldots, n_r$.

Of more interest is the electrostriction occurring at constant composition, chemical potential, and temperature. We consider a one-component, one-phase system and note that there are three degrees of freedom in this system. We may write the total differential of the chemical potential in the form

$$d\mu = -s\,dT + v\,dp - \mathsf{p}\,d\mathsf{E} \tag{14-38}$$

where

$$\mathsf{p} = \frac{P}{n} \tag{14-39}$$

and we have used Eqs. (14-21), (14-24), and (14-25). The total differential of the pressure is given by

$$dp = \left(\frac{\partial p}{\partial v}\right)_{T,\mathsf{E}} dv + \left(\frac{\partial p}{\partial \mathsf{E}}\right)_{T,v} d\mathsf{E} + \left(\frac{\partial p}{\partial T}\right)_{\mathsf{E},v} dT \tag{14-40}$$

where v, E, and T are the independent variables.

Substitution of Eq. (14-40) into Eq. (14-38) and specialization to the case of constant temperature result in

$$d\mu = v\left(\frac{\partial p}{\partial v}\right)_{T,\mathsf{E}} dv + \left[v\left(\frac{\partial p}{\partial \mathsf{E}}\right)_{T,v} - \mathsf{p}\right] d\mathsf{E} \tag{14-41}$$

At constant chemical potential, Eq. (14-41) may be rearranged to yield

$$v\left(\frac{\partial p}{\partial v}\right)_{T,\mathsf{E}} dv = \left[\mathsf{p} - v\left(\frac{\partial p}{\partial \mathsf{E}}\right)_{T,v}\right] d\mathsf{E} \tag{14-42}$$

We generalize the notion of the coefficient of isothermal compressibility to a system in an electric field by writing

$$\kappa_v = -\frac{1}{v}\left(\frac{\partial v}{\partial p}\right)_{T,\mathsf{E}} \tag{14-43}$$

Equation (14-28) can be rewritten in the form

$$\left(\frac{\partial p}{\partial \mathsf{E}}\right)_{T,v} = \left(\frac{\partial \mathsf{p}}{\partial v}\right)_{T,\mathsf{E}} \tag{14-44}$$

Substitution of the definition

$$\mathsf{p} = \frac{P}{n} = \frac{Vp^{(v)}}{n} = vp^{(v)} \tag{14-45}$$

into Eq. (14-44) results in

$$\left(\frac{\partial p}{\partial \mathsf{E}}\right)_{T,v} = v\left(\frac{\partial p^{(v)}}{\partial v}\right)_{T,\mathsf{E}} + p^{(v)} \tag{14-46}$$

Substitution of Eqs. (14-43) and (14-46) into Eq. (14-42) gives rise to

$$\frac{dv}{\kappa_v} = v^2 \left(\frac{\partial p^{(v)}}{\partial v}\right)_{T,\mathsf{E}} d\mathsf{E} \tag{14-47}$$

Integration of Eq. (14-47) along a path at constant T and μ yields

$$\Delta v = v(T,\mu,\mathsf{E}) - v(T,\mu,0) = \int_0^{\mathsf{E}} \kappa_v v^2 \left(\frac{\partial p^{(v)}}{\partial v}\right)_{T,\mathsf{E}'} d\mathsf{E}' \tag{14-48}$$

If we expand $p^{(v)}$ in a power series in E and neglect terms of $O(\mathsf{E}^2)$ we obtain from Eqs. (14-2) and (14-3)

$$p^{(v)} = \frac{\varepsilon - 1}{4\pi} \mathsf{E} \tag{14-49}$$

where ε is considered to be independent of the field. Substitution of Eq. (14-49) into (14-48) yields the result

$$\begin{aligned} v(T,\mu,\mathsf{E}) - v(T,\mu,0) &= \frac{\kappa_v v^2 (\partial\varepsilon/\partial v)_{T,\mathsf{E}} \mathsf{E}^2}{8\pi} \\ &= -\frac{v(\partial\varepsilon/\partial p)_{T,\mathsf{E}} \mathsf{E}^2}{8\pi} \end{aligned} \tag{14-50}$$

Equation (14-50) is the formula for electrostriction at constant T and μ. In general, $(\partial\varepsilon/\partial p)_{T,\mathsf{E}}$ is positive so that a system will contract when put into an electric field at constant T and μ. It is interesting to note that this theory, when applied on the molecular scale in the consideration of electrostriction of solvent in the field of an ion, qualitatively accounts for the decrease in volume resulting when some solutions are mixed.

We now turn our attention to the derivation of the expression governing the change in temperature of a system when the electrostatic field is varied at constant entropy and pressure. We again consider a one-component system. Equation (14-34) may be differentiated to yield

$$ds = ds' + \left(\frac{\partial \bar{\chi}^\circ}{\partial T}\right)_{p,\mathsf{E}} \mathsf{E}\, d\mathsf{E} \tag{14-51}$$

where

$$ds' = \frac{c_p}{T} dT + \left(\frac{\partial s}{\partial p}\right)_T dp \tag{14-52}$$

$$\bar{\chi}^\circ = \frac{\chi^\circ}{n} \tag{14-53}$$

and we have neglected terms of $O(\mathsf{E}^2)$. At constant pressure, Eq. (14-51) reduces to

$$ds = \frac{c_p}{T}\,dT + \left(\frac{\partial \bar{\chi}^\circ}{\partial T}\right)_{p,\mathsf{E}} \mathsf{E}\,d\mathsf{E} \tag{14-54}$$

If the entropy is held constant, Eq. (14-54) can be rearranged to yield

$$\left(\frac{\partial T}{\partial \mathsf{E}}\right)_{s,p} = -\frac{T}{c_p}\left(\frac{\partial \bar{\chi}^\circ}{\partial T}\right)_{p,\mathsf{E}} \mathsf{E} \tag{14-55}$$

The quantity $(\partial\bar{\chi}^\circ/\partial T)_{p,\mathsf{E}}$ is, in general, negative so that if the field is decreased adiabatically and reversibly (that is, isentropically) and at constant pressure the temperature of the system will decrease. However, the effect is so slight that extremely high fields in which dielectric breakdown would set in are necessary for any appreciable cooling of the system to result from decreases in the field.

In the remaining portion of this section we discuss the effect of uniform electrostatic fields on the properties of systems in heterogeneous or chemical equilibrium. A criterion for heterogeneous equilibrium in the presence of a uniform field is

$$(\delta E)_{S,V,n,P} \geqslant 0 \tag{14-56}$$

Thus, the conditions of heterogeneous equilibrium in the presence of a uniform field remain unchanged. It is sometimes useful, however, to maintain the volumes of the various phases of the system constant. In this case, the requirement of equality of pressures of the various phases is removed; the conditions of heterogeneous equilibrium are, then,

$$\mu_i^{(\alpha)} = \mu_i \qquad i = 1, \ldots, r \qquad \alpha = 1, \ldots, \nu \tag{14-57}$$

$$T^{(\alpha)} = T \qquad \alpha = 1, \ldots, \nu \tag{14-58}$$

We shall now discuss the effect of a uniform electric field on the transition temperature between two phases at a given pressure. We consider a heterogeneous system of two phases and one component in the presence of the field. At equilibrium

$$\mu^{(\alpha)} = \mu'^{(\alpha)} - \tfrac{1}{2}\bar{\chi}^{\circ(\alpha)}\,\mathsf{E}^2 = \mu^{(\beta)} = \mu'^{(\beta)} - \tfrac{1}{2}\bar{\chi}^{\circ(\beta)}\,\mathsf{E}^2 \tag{14-59}$$

where we have used Eq. (14-33) correct to order E^2. The quantities $\bar{\chi}^{\circ(\alpha)}$ and $\bar{\chi}^{\circ(\beta)}$ are defined by the relations

$$\bar{\chi}^{\circ(\alpha)} = \frac{\chi^{\circ(\alpha)}}{n^{(\alpha)}} \tag{14-60}$$

$$\bar{\chi}^{\circ(\beta)} = \frac{\chi^{\circ(\beta)}}{n^{(\beta)}} \tag{14-61}$$

where $n^{(\alpha)}$ is the number of moles in phase α and $n^{(\beta)}$ is the number of moles in phase β. Equation (14-59) can be rearranged to yield

$$\mu'^{(\alpha)} - \mu'^{(\beta)} = \tfrac{1}{2}(\bar{\chi}^{\circ(\alpha)} - \bar{\chi}^{\circ(\beta)})\mathsf{E}^2 \tag{14-62}$$

where

$$\mu'^{(\alpha)} = \mu'^{(\alpha)}(T,p,0) = \mu'^{(\alpha)}(T,p) \tag{14-63}$$

where T is the transition temperature, in the presence of the field, at pressure p.

If T_0 is the transition temperature between phases α and β at pressure p in the absence of the field, then

$$\mu'^{(\alpha)}(T_0,p) - \mu'^{(\beta)}(T_0,p) = 0 \tag{14-64}$$

We make use of Eq. (11-151) to write

$$\left(\frac{\partial}{\partial T}\frac{\mu'^{(\alpha)} - \mu'^{(\beta)}}{T}\right)_p = \frac{h'^{(\beta)} - h'^{(\alpha)}}{T^2} = -\frac{\Delta h'^{(\beta\alpha)}}{T^2} \tag{14-65}$$

where $h'^{(\alpha)}$ is the molal enthalpy of phase α in the absence of the field. Equation (14-65) can be integrated along a path at constant pressure to yield

$$\mu'^{(\alpha)}(T,p) - \mu'^{(\beta)}(T,p) = -T\int_{T_0}^{T}\frac{\Delta h'^{(\beta\alpha)}}{(T')^2}\,dT' \tag{14-66}$$

where we have used Eq. (14-64). Substitution of Eq. (14-66) into Eq. (14-62) results in

$$T\int_{T_0}^{T}\frac{\Delta h'^{(\alpha\beta)}}{(T')^2}\,dT' = \tfrac{1}{2}(\bar{\chi}^{\circ(\alpha)} - \bar{\chi}^{\circ(\beta)})\mathsf{E}^2 \tag{14-67}$$

If we assume that $\Delta T = T - T_0$ is small and that $\Delta h'^{(\alpha\beta)}$ does not depend strongly on the temperature, we may rewrite Eq. (14-67) in the form

$$\frac{T - T^\circ}{T^\circ} \approx \frac{\tfrac{1}{2}(\bar{\chi}^{\circ(\alpha)} - \bar{\chi}^{\circ(\beta)})\mathsf{E}^2}{h'^{(\beta)} - h'^{(\alpha)}} \tag{14-68}$$

Equation (14-68) can be rearranged to yield

$$T \approx T^\circ\left[1 + \frac{\mathsf{E}^2}{8\pi}\,\frac{v^{(\alpha)}(\varepsilon^{(\alpha)} - 1) - v^{(\beta)}(\varepsilon^{(\beta)} - 1)}{h'^{(\beta)} - h'^{(\alpha)}}\right] \tag{14-69}$$

since

$$\bar{\chi}^{\circ(\alpha)} = v^{(\alpha)}\chi^{\circ(v)(\alpha)} = \frac{v^{(\alpha)}(\varepsilon^{(\alpha)} - 1)}{4\pi} \tag{14-70}$$

The field-dependent term in Eq. (14-69) is usually small. In a two-component, two-phase system we could fix p and T; the compositions of the phases would then vary with the electric field.

The condition for chemical equilibrium in a homogeneous system remains unchanged in the presence of a uniform field. For chemical equilibrium,

$$\sum_{i=1}^{r} \nu_i \mu_i = 0 \tag{14-71}$$

Substitution of Eq. (14-33) into Eq. (14-71) results in

$$\sum_{i=1}^{r} \nu_i \mu_i' - \tfrac{1}{2}\,\Delta\chi \mathsf{E}^2 = 0 \tag{14-72}$$

where

$$\Delta\chi = \sum_{i=1}^{r} \nu_i \bar{\chi}_i \tag{14-73}$$

Equation (14-72) can be written more explicitly in the form

$$\sum_{i=1}^{r} \nu_i \mu_i^\circ(T,p) + \sum_{i=1}^{r} \nu_i RT \log a_i - \tfrac{1}{2}\,\Delta\chi \mathsf{E}^2 = 0 \tag{14-74}$$

where we have used Eqs. (11-4) and (11-5). The equilibrium constant for the reaction in the absence of the field is given by

$$K(T,p,0) = \exp\left(-\frac{\sum_{i=1}^{r} \nu_i \mu_i^\circ}{RT}\right) \tag{14-75}$$

Substitution of Eq. (14-75) into Eq. (14-74) and rearrangement result in

$$\sum_{i=1}^{r} a_i^{\nu_i} = K(T,p,0) \exp\left(\frac{\Delta\chi \mathsf{E}^2}{2RT}\right) \tag{14-76}$$

We define the quantity $K(T,p,\bar{\chi}_1, \ldots, \bar{\chi}_{r-1},\mathsf{E})$ by the relation

$$K(T,p,\bar{\chi}_1, \ldots, \bar{\chi}_{r-1},\mathsf{E}) = \sum_{i=1}^{r} a_i^{\nu_i} \tag{14-77}$$

The quantity $K(T,p,\bar{\chi}_1, \ldots, \bar{\chi}_{r-1},\mathsf{E})$ is not a true equilibrium constant since it may depend on the composition of the system. However, if the partial molal susceptibilities are independent of composition, it becomes a true equilibrium constant and we may write

$$K(T,p,\mathsf{E}) = K(T,p,0) \exp\left(\frac{\Delta\chi \mathsf{E}^2}{2RT}\right) \tag{14-78}$$

This completes our discussion of the influence of an electrostatic field on the thermodynamic properties of dielectrics.

14-2. MAGNETIC FIELDS

The effect of uniform static magnetic fields on the thermodynamic properties of materials can be described by considerations similar to those outlined in Sec. 14-1 for electrostatic fields. In this section, we briefly present one or two interesting thermodynamic relationships for systems in magnetic fields.

We consider a system in a uniform static magnetic field. The total differential of the internal energy of the system may be written in the form

$$dE = T\,dS - p\,dV + \sum_{i=1}^{r} \mu_i\,dn_i + \mathsf{H}\,dI \tag{14-79}$$

where H is the magnetic field intensity and I is the magnetization of the system.

In analogy to the formula for electrostriction [Eq. (14-50)], we have in the case of magnetostriction at constant T and μ:

$$\frac{\Delta v}{v} = -\frac{\mathsf{H}^2}{8\pi}\left(\frac{\partial \psi}{\partial p}\right)_{T,\mathsf{H}} \tag{14-80}$$

where ψ is the magnetic permeability.

For the change of temperature with magnetic field at constant entropy and pressure, we obtain in analogy to Eq. (14-55)

$$-\frac{1}{T}\left(\frac{\partial T}{\partial \mathsf{H}}\right)_{S,p} = \frac{1}{c_p}\left(\frac{\partial \bar{\chi}_M}{\partial T}\right)_{p,\mathsf{H}} \mathsf{H} \tag{14-81}$$

where $\bar{\chi}_M$ is the magnetic susceptibility per mole of the medium. This effect is of far greater importance than the corresponding one in the case of an electric field. Since $(\partial \bar{\chi}_M/\partial T)_{p,\mathsf{H}}$ is usually negative, an isentropic decrease in H will lead to a corresponding decrease in T. Equation (14-81) provides the theoretical basis of the important experimental production of low temperatures by adiabatic demagnetization.

15 GRAVITATIONAL AND CENTRIFUGAL FIELDS

In this chapter, we study the effects of gravitational and centrifugal fields on the thermodynamic properties of systems. We generalize many of the results obtained in previous chapters to include the effects of these fields.

The gravitational or centrifugal field may be characterized by a potential $\psi(\mathbf{R})$ which has a definite value at each point in space. We shall make the approximation that $\psi(\mathbf{R})$ is determined by masses or forces external to the system of interest. This approximation is valid for the gravitational field when the mass of the system of interest is small compared with the mass of the earth. In this case, the potential $\psi(\mathbf{R})$ can be written explicitly in the form

$$\psi(\mathbf{R}) = gz \tag{15-1}$$

where g is the acceleration due to gravity and z is the distance from the system to the center of the earth. The potential characterizing the centrifugal field can be written in the form

$$\psi(\mathbf{R}) = -\tfrac{1}{2}\omega^2 R^2 \tag{15-2}$$

where ω is the angular velocity of rotation and R is the distance of the system from the axis of rotation. The fact that $\psi(\mathbf{R})$ can be considered to be determined by masses or forces external to the system of interest distinguishes the discussion of this chapter from the treatment of electric or magnetic fields. The treatments of the thermodynamics of the gravitational and centrifugal fields are identical. Thus, in the following we discuss the effect of the field potential ψ on the properties of the system without specifying whether ψ is given by Eq. (15-1) or Eq. (15-2).

The total differential of the internal energy of a homogeneous system of r components in the presence of a field characterized by a potential ψ is given by

$$dE = dE' + \psi\, dm \tag{15-3}$$

where

$$dE' = T\, dS - p\, dv + \sum_{i=1}^{r} \mu_i'\, dn_i \tag{15-4}$$

and μ_i' is the chemical potential of component i in the absence of the gravitational field. The term $\psi\, dm$, in which m is the mass of the system, represents the work done against the field by increasing the mass of the system infinitesimally. The total mass of the system can be written in terms of the numbers of moles of the various components in the form

$$m = \sum_{i=1}^{r} M_i n_i \tag{15-5}$$

where n_i is the number of moles of component i and M_i is its molecular weight. Differentiation of Eq. (15-5) yields

$$dm = \sum_{i=1}^{r} M_i \, dn_i \tag{15-6}$$

Substitution of Eqs. (15-4) and (15-6) into Eq. (15-3) results in

$$dE = T\,dS - p\,dV + \sum_{i=1}^{r} (\mu_i' + M_i\psi)\,dn_i \tag{15-7}$$

The chemical potential of component i in the presence of the field is defined by the relation

$$\mu_i = \mu_i' + M_i\psi \tag{15-8}$$

Thus, Eq. (15-7) can be written in the form

$$dE = T\,dS - p\,dV + \sum_{i=1}^{r} \mu_i\,dn_i \tag{15-9}$$

We now consider the system, whether homogeneous or heterogeneous in the absence of the field, to be divided into an infinite number of homogeneous systems of fixed volume and of infinitesimal thickness in the direction of the field. In Fig. 15-1 we have drawn a sketch of a system divided into homogeneous phases, α, β, etc., of thickness dz in the direction of the field. The quantity dz is supposed to be infinitesimal from the macroscopic, thermodynamic point of view but is large compared with typical microscopic lengths such as the mean distance between molecules.

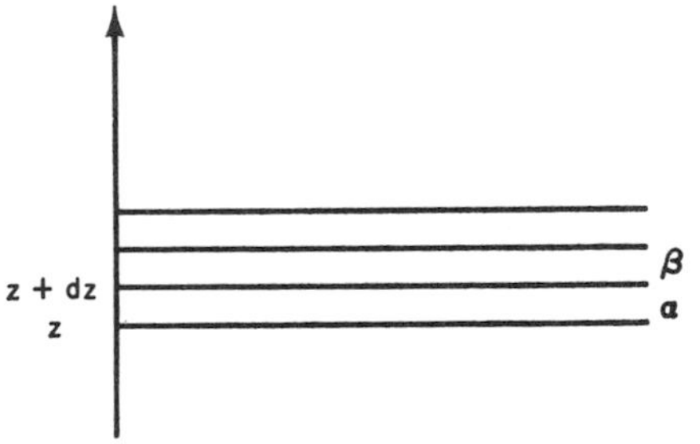

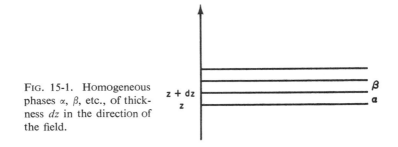

FIG. 15-1. Homogeneous phases α, β, etc., of thickness dz in the direction of the field.

Equation (15-9) applies to each of the homogeneous phases, α, β, etc., and thus we may write

$$dE^{(\alpha)} = T^{(\alpha)}\, dS^{(\alpha)} - p^{(\alpha)}\, dV^{(\alpha)} + \sum_{i=1}^{r} \mu_i^{(\alpha)}\, dn_i^{(\alpha)} \qquad \alpha = 1, \ldots \qquad (15\text{-}10)$$

A criterion for heterogeneous equilibrium in the gravitational field can be written in terms of a variation of the total energy of the system at constant total entropy, volume, and number of moles of each of the r components in the form

$$(\delta E)_{S,V,n} \geqslant 0 \qquad (15\text{-}11)$$

We assume that E, S, V, and n_i can be written as sums over α of $E^{(\alpha)}$, $S^{(\alpha)}$, $V^{(\alpha)}$, and $n_i^{(\alpha)}$, respectively. In this case we may use the results of the discussion in Sec. 6-3 to arrive at the conditions for heterogeneous equilibrium in a gravitational field in the form

$$T^{(\alpha)} = T \qquad \alpha = 1, \ldots \qquad (15\text{-}12)$$

$$\mu_i^{(\alpha)} = \mu_i'^{(\alpha)} + M_i\psi^{(\alpha)} = \mu_i \qquad \alpha = 1, \ldots \qquad i = 1, \ldots, r \qquad (15\text{-}13)$$

The condition of equality of pressures in the various phases does not appear because the phases are of fixed volume.

We allow the thickness of the various phases to shrink to zero and consider the thermodynamic variables to be functions of z. In this case we can write

$$\frac{d(\mu_i' + M_i\psi)}{dz} = 0 \qquad (15\text{-}14)$$

which follows from Eq. (15-13) as a condition for heterogeneous equilibrium. An expression for $d\mu_i'/dz$ can be obtained from Eq. (9-18) in the form

$$\frac{d\mu_i'}{dz} = -\bar{s}_i \frac{dT}{dz} + \bar{v}_i \frac{dp}{dz} + \sum_{k=2}^{r} G_{ik} \frac{dx_k}{dz} \qquad i = 1, \ldots, r \qquad (15\text{-}15)$$

where

$$G_{ik} = \left(\frac{\partial \mu_i'}{\partial x_k}\right)_{T,p,x_{j \neq k}}$$

Substitution of Eq. (15-15) into Eq. (15-14) yields

$$-\bar{s}_i \frac{dT}{dz} + \bar{v}_i \frac{dp}{dz} + \sum_{k=2}^{r} G_{ik} \frac{dx_k}{dz} + M_i \frac{d\psi}{dz} = 0 \qquad (15\text{-}16)$$

At equilibrium, Eq. (15-12) applies. Thus

$$\frac{dT}{dz} = 0 \qquad (15\text{-}17)$$

and Eq. (15-16) becomes

$$\bar{v}_i \frac{dp}{dz} + M_i \frac{d\psi}{dz} + \sum_{k=2}^{r} G_{ik} \frac{dx_k}{dz} = 0 \qquad i = 1, \ldots, r \tag{15-18}$$

Equation (15-18) is a set of r equations which determine the dependence of the r quantities p, x_k, $k = 2, \ldots, r$ on the parameter z.

At constant T, the Gibbs-Duhem equation [Eq. (6-59)] reduces to

$$\sum_{i=1}^{r} n_i \, d\mu_i' = V \, dp \tag{15-19}$$

Use of Eqs. (15-14) and (15-19) leads to

$$\sum_{i=1}^{r} n_i \frac{d\mu_i'}{dz} = -\sum_{i=1}^{r} M_i n_i \frac{d\psi}{dz} = V \frac{dp}{dz} \tag{15-20}$$

Equation (15-20) may be rewritten in the form

$$\frac{dp}{dz} = -\frac{m}{V}\frac{d\psi}{dz} = -\rho \frac{d\psi}{dz} \tag{15-21}$$

where we have used Eq. (15-5) and where ρ is the mean density of the system. Equation (15-21) is the condition for hydrostatic equilibrium.

Equations (15-18) and (15-21) are not independent. Multiplication of Eq. (15-18) by n_i and summation over i from 1 to r result in

$$V \frac{dp}{dz} + m \frac{d\psi}{dz} = 0 \tag{15-22}$$

where we have used Eq. (15-5) and the facts that

$$\sum_{i=1}^{r} n_i \bar{v}_i = V \tag{15-23}$$

and

$$\sum_{i=1}^{r} n_i G_{ik} = 0 \tag{15-24}$$

Equation (15-24) is an expression of the Gibbs-Duhem equation at constant T and p. Equations (15-22) and (15-21) are identical. Combination of Eqs. (15-18) and (15-21) yields a set of r independent equations which are an alternative equivalent set of equations to Eq. (15-18) for determining the dependence of p and x_k, $k = 2, \ldots, r$ on z. The equations obtained in this fashion are called the equilibrium sedimentation equations and can be written in the form

$$(M_i - \rho \bar{v}_i) \frac{d\psi}{dz} + \sum_{k=2}^{r} G_{ik} \frac{dx_k}{dz} = 0 \qquad i = 2, \ldots, r \tag{15-25}$$

$$\frac{dp}{dz} = -\rho \frac{d\psi}{dz} \tag{15-26}$$

Equations (15-25) and (15-26) can be obtained from hydrodynamic considerations. Equations (15-25) have a simple physical interpretation. The quantity

$$-\sum_{k=2}^{r} G_{ik}\frac{dx_k}{dz}$$

is a diffusion force on the ith component. The quantity $M_i - \rho\bar{v}_i$ is the mass of the ith component corrected for buoyancy (Archimedes correction). Thus, the quantity $(M_i - \rho\bar{v}_i)(d\psi/dz)$ is the external force produced by the field on the ith component. At equilibrium, the diffusion force must equal the external force and Eq. (15-25) results.

For a two-component system, Eqs. (15-25) and (15-26) become

$$(M_2 - \rho\bar{v}_2)\frac{d\psi}{dz} + G_{22}\frac{dx_2}{dz} = 0 \qquad (15\text{-}27)$$

$$\frac{dp}{dz} = -\rho\frac{d\psi}{dz} \qquad (15\text{-}28)$$

In the ideal-mixture approximation,

$$G_{22} = \frac{RT}{x_2}$$

$$\bar{v}_2 = v_2 \qquad (15\text{-}29)$$

$$\bar{v}_1 = v_1$$

and Eqs. (15-27) and (15-28) simplify to

$$\frac{d\log x_2}{dz} = -\frac{M_2 - \rho v_2}{RT}\frac{d\psi}{dz} \qquad (15\text{-}30)$$

$$\frac{dp}{dz} = -\frac{M_1x_1 + M_2x_2}{x_1v_1 + x_2v_2}\frac{d\psi}{dz} \qquad (15\text{-}31)$$

If we assume that the mixture is dilute,

$$\rho \simeq \rho_1 \qquad (15\text{-}32)$$

where ρ_1 is the density of the pure solvent. Under these conditions, Eq. (15-30) can be easily integrated to yield

$$x_2 = x_2^\circ \exp\left[-\frac{(M_2 - \rho_1 v_2)(\psi - \psi^\circ)}{RT}\right] \qquad (15\text{-}33)$$

where the superscript $^\circ$ refers to the value of the quantity at some fixed value of the coordinate $z = z^\circ$. If we further assume that the fluid mixture is incompressible, integration of Eq. (15-31) gives

$$p = p^\circ - \rho_1(\psi - \psi^\circ) \qquad (15\text{-}34)$$

For a system consisting of a pure ideal gas,

$$p = \frac{\rho}{M} RT \qquad (15\text{-}35)$$

and

$$dp = \frac{RT}{M}\, d\rho \qquad (15\text{-}36)$$

Substitution of Eq. (15-36) in Eq. (15-28) specialized for one component results in

$$\frac{d\rho}{M} RT = -\rho\, d\psi \qquad (15\text{-}37)$$

Integration of Eq. (15-37) yields

$$\rho = \rho^\circ e^{-(M/RT)(\psi - \psi^\circ)} \qquad (15\text{-}38)$$

Equation (15-38) is the familiar equation for determining the density of the atmosphere as a function of height. It resembles the equation for a Boltzmann distribution.

We turn our attention to a study of the effect of a gravitational or centrifugal field on chemical equilibrium. We consider a system in which the chemical reaction

$$\sum_{i=1}^{r} \nu_i X_i = 0 \qquad (15\text{-}39)$$

occurs. The condition for chemical equilibrium in a field described by the potential ψ is given by

$$\sum_{i=1}^{r} \nu_i \mu_i = 0 \qquad (15\text{-}40)$$

where

$$\mu_i = \mu_i' + M_i \psi \qquad (15\text{-}41)$$

Substitution of Eq. (15-41) into Eq. (15-40) yields

$$\sum_{i=1}^{r} \nu_i \mu_i' + \psi \sum_{i=1}^{r} \nu_i M_i = 0 \qquad (15\text{-}42)$$

The condition for the conservation of mass in the chemical reaction is

$$\sum_{i=1}^{r} \nu_i M_i = 0 \qquad (15\text{-}43)$$

Thus, Eq. (15-42) becomes

$$\sum_{i=1}^{r} \nu_i \mu_i' = 0 \qquad (15\text{-}44)$$

The presence of the field has no influence on the condition for chemical equilibrium and therefore does not affect the value of the equilibrium constant.

This completes our discussion of the thermodynamic properties of systems in gravitational or centrifugal fields.

APPENDIX: INTRODUCTORY MATHEMATICS

In this appendix we present a discussion of a few mathematical techniques frequently utilized in thermodynamics. We treat several topics in the analysis of real functions of several real variables. We assume that the functions considered have the continuity properties necessary for the operations performed upon them to be meaningful. In Sec. A-1, we discuss some of the properties of partial derivatives. In Sec. A-2 we define homogeneous functions and derive a useful relation. In Sec. A-3, we treat linear differential forms. Line integrals are discussed in Sec. A-4.

The topics treated here are covered more completely in books on advanced calculus. (See D. V. Widder, "Advanced Calculus," Prentice-Hall, Inc., Englewood Cliffs, N.J., 1947.)

A-1. PARTIAL DIFFERENTIATION

We consider a real function z which is a single-valued function of r real independent variables $x_1, x_2, \ldots, x_r$. We adopt the notation

$$z = z(x_1,x_2, \ldots ,x_r) = z(x^{(r)}) \tag{A-1}$$

where the symbol $x^{(r)}$ stands for the set of r variables $x_1, \ldots, x_r$. We shall use the notation $x_i^{(r-1)}$ to stand for the set of $r - 1$ variables $x_1, \ldots, x_{i-1}, x_{i+1}, \ldots, x_r$ and the notation $x_{ij}^{(r-2)}$ to stand for the set of $r - 2$ variables $x_1, \ldots, x_{i-1}, x_{i+1}, \ldots, x_{j-1}, x_{j+1}, \ldots, x_r$. The partial derivative of z with respect to x_i at constant x_j, $j = 1, \ldots, r \neq i$, is defined by the relation

$$\left(\frac{\partial z}{\partial x_i}\right)_{x_i^{(r-1)}} = (z_{x_i})_{x_i^{(r-1)}} = \lim_{\Delta x_i \to 0} \frac{z(x_i + \Delta x_i, x_i^{(r-1)}) - z(x_i, x_i^{(r-1)})}{\Delta x_i} \tag{A-2}$$

Since it is important to state which variables are held constant in the differentiation, the notation $(\partial z/\partial x_i)_{x_i^{(r-1)}}$ is employed; the subscript $x_i^{(r-1)}$ denotes the variables held constant. In a similar fashion we may write the formula for a second derivative of z with respect to x_j in the form

$$\left[\frac{\partial}{\partial x_j}\left(\frac{\partial z}{\partial x_i}\right)_{x_i^{(r-1)}}\right]_{x_j^{(r-1)}} = \lim_{\Delta x_j \to 0} \frac{z_{x_i}(x_j + \Delta x_j, x_j^{(r-1)}) - z_{x_i}(x_j, x_j^{(r-1)})}{\Delta x_j}$$

$$= \lim_{\substack{\Delta x_j \to 0 \\ \Delta x_i \to 0}} \left[\frac{z(x_i + \Delta x_i, x_j + \Delta x_j, x_{ij}^{(r-2)}) - z(x_i, x_j + \Delta x_j, x_{ij}^{(r-2)})}{\Delta x_i \, \Delta x_j} - \frac{z(x_i + \Delta x_i, x_j, x_{ij}^{(r-2)}) - z(x_i, x_j, x_{ij}^{(r-2)})}{\Delta x_i \, \Delta x_j}\right]$$

$$= \lim_{\Delta x_i \to 0} \frac{z_{x_j}(x_i + \Delta x_i, x_i^{(r-1)}) - z_{x_j}(x_i, x_i^{(r-1)})}{\Delta x_i}$$

$$= \left[\frac{\partial}{\partial x_i}\left(\frac{\partial z}{\partial x_j}\right)_{x_j^{(r-1)}}\right]_{x_i^{(r-1)}} \tag{A-3}$$

Equation (A-3) indicates that the partial differential operators commute when applied to a function with the proper continuity properties.

The total differential of z is defined by

$$dz = \sum_{i=1}^{r} \left(\frac{\partial z}{\partial x_i}\right)_{x_i^{(r-1)}} dx_i \tag{A-4}$$

We define the quantity Δz by the relation

$$\Delta z = z(x^{(r)} + \Delta x^{(r)}) - z(x^{(r)}) \tag{A-5}$$

It can be shown that

$$\lim_{\Delta x_i \to 0} \frac{dz}{\Delta z} = 1 \tag{A-6}$$

where $\Delta x_1/\Delta x_i$, $i = 1, \ldots, r$, is kept constant in the limiting operation. The quantity Δz can be interpreted geometrically as being the distance between two hyperplanes of n dimensions in an $(n + 1)$-dimensional Euclidean space.

Division of Eq. (A-4) by dx_j results in

$$\frac{dz}{dx_j} = \sum_{i=1}^{r} \left(\frac{\partial z}{\partial x_i}\right)_{x_i^{(r-1)}} \frac{dx_i}{dx_j} \tag{A-7}$$

At constant z and $x_{jk}^{(r-2)}$, Eq. (A-7) becomes

$$0 = \left(\frac{\partial z}{\partial x_j}\right)_{x_j^{(r-1)}} + \left(\frac{\partial z}{\partial x_k}\right)_{x_k^{(r-1)}} \left(\frac{\partial x_k}{\partial x_j}\right)_{z, x_{jk}^{(r-2)}} \tag{A-8}$$

which can be rearranged to yield

$$\left(\frac{\partial x_k}{\partial x_j}\right)_{z, x_{jk}^{(r-2)}} = -\frac{(\partial z/\partial x_j)_{x_j^{(r-1)}}}{(\partial z/\partial x_k)_{x_k^{(r-1)}}} \tag{A-9}$$

Equation (A-9) is the equation for implicit differentiation. For three variables, $z = z(x, y)$, it has the more familiar form

$$\left(\frac{\partial y}{\partial x}\right)_z = -\frac{(\partial z/\partial x)_y}{(\partial z/\partial y)_x} \tag{A-10}$$

Products of partial derivatives may be manipulated in the same fashion as products of total derivatives as long as the same variables are held fixed. Thus, we may write

$$\left(\frac{\partial z}{\partial x_i}\right)_{x_i^{(r-1)}}\left(\frac{\partial x_i}{\partial z}\right)_{x_i^{(r-1)}} = 1 \tag{A-11}$$

If $t = t(x^{(r)})$, then

$$\left(\frac{\partial z}{\partial x_i}\right)_{x_i^{(r-1)}} = \left(\frac{\partial z}{\partial t}\right)_{x_i^{(r-1)}}\left(\frac{\partial t}{\partial x_i}\right)_{x_i^{(r-1)}} \tag{A-12}$$

Use of Eq. (A-11) enables us to rewrite Eqs. (A-9) and (A-10) in the form

$$\left(\frac{\partial z}{\partial x_k}\right)_{x_k^{(r-1)}}\left(\frac{\partial x_k}{\partial x_j}\right)_{z,x_{jk}^{(r-2)}}\left(\frac{\partial x_j}{\partial z}\right)_{x_j^{(r-1)}} = -1 \tag{A-13}$$

and

$$\left(\frac{\partial y}{\partial x}\right)_z\left(\frac{\partial z}{\partial y}\right)_x\left(\frac{\partial x}{\partial z}\right)_y = -1 \tag{A-14}$$

We illustrate the use of the properties of partial derivatives described above by an example. We consider the functions $z = z(x,y)$, $u = u(x,y)$, and $v = v(x,y)$ and wish to compute $(\partial z/\partial u)_v$ in terms of derivatives of z, u, and v with respect to x at constant y and with respect to y at constant x. The total derivative of z is given by

$$dz = \left(\frac{\partial z}{\partial x}\right)_y dx + \left(\frac{\partial z}{\partial y}\right)_x dy \tag{A-15}$$

Division of Eq. (A-15) by du at constant v yields

$$\left(\frac{\partial z}{\partial u}\right)_v = \left(\frac{\partial z}{\partial x}\right)_y\left(\frac{\partial x}{\partial u}\right)_v + \left(\frac{\partial z}{\partial y}\right)_x\left(\frac{\partial y}{\partial u}\right)_v \tag{A-16}$$

Division of the total derivative of u by dx at constant v yields

$$\left(\frac{\partial u}{\partial x}\right)_v = \left(\frac{\partial u}{\partial x}\right)_y + \left(\frac{\partial u}{\partial y}\right)_x\left(\frac{\partial y}{\partial x}\right)_v \tag{A-17}$$

Substitution of Eq. (A-10) in the form

$$\left(\frac{\partial y}{\partial x}\right)_v = -\frac{(\partial v/\partial x)_y}{(\partial v/\partial y)_x} \tag{A-18}$$

into Eq. (A-17) results in

$$\left(\frac{\partial u}{\partial x}\right)_v = \left(\frac{\partial u}{\partial x}\right)_y - \left(\frac{\partial u}{\partial y}\right)_x \frac{(\partial v/\partial x)_y}{(\partial v/\partial y)_x} \tag{A-19}$$

Substitution of Eq. (A-19) for $(\partial u/\partial x)_v$ and a similar expression for $(\partial u/\partial y)_v$ into Eq. (A-16) results in

$$\left(\frac{\partial z}{\partial u}\right)_v = \frac{(\partial z/\partial x)_y(\partial v/\partial y)_x - (\partial z/\partial y)_x(\partial v/\partial x)_y}{(\partial u/\partial x)_y(\partial v/\partial y)_x - (\partial u/\partial y)_x(\partial v/\partial x)_y} = \frac{\begin{vmatrix} z_x & z_y \\ v_x & v_y \end{vmatrix}}{\begin{vmatrix} u_x & u_y \\ v_x & v_y \end{vmatrix}}$$

$$= \frac{\partial(z,v)/\partial(x,y)}{\partial(u,v)/\partial(x,y)} \tag{A-20}$$

where

$$\frac{\partial(z,v)}{\partial(x,y)} = z_x v_y - z_y v_x \tag{A-21}$$

The quantity $\partial(z,v)/\partial(x,y)$ is a Jacobian. (Jacobian methods of solution are discussed in H. Margenau and G. Murphy, "The Mathematics of Physics and Chemistry," chap. I, D. Van Nostrand Company, Inc., Princeton, N.J., 1943.)

A-2. HOMOGENEOUS FUNCTIONS

The transformation known as Euler's theorem which describes a property of homogeneous functions is of great use in thermodynamics. The function $f(x^{(r)})$ is called homogeneous of degree n if, and only if,

$$f(\lambda x^{(r)}) = \lambda^n f(x^{(r)}) \tag{A-22}$$

where λ is a constant. Euler's theorem states that a homogeneous function of degree n obeys the equation

$$nf(x^{(r)}) = \sum_{i=1}^{r} x_i \left(\frac{\partial f}{\partial x_i}\right)_{x_i^{(r-1)}} \tag{A-23}$$

The proof of Eq. (A-23) is straightforward. We define the set of variables $u^{(r)}$ by the relations

$$u_i = \lambda x_i \qquad i = 1, \ldots, r \tag{A-24}$$

Then, by definition,

$$f(u^{(r)}) = \lambda^n f(x^{(r)}) \tag{A-25}$$

Differentiation of Eq. (A-25) with respect to λ at constant $x^{(r)}$ results in

$$\left[\frac{\partial f(u^{(r)})}{\partial \lambda}\right]_{x^{(r)}} = n\lambda^{n-1} f(x^{(r)}) \tag{A-26}$$

Division of the total derivative of $f(u^{(r)})$ by $d\lambda$ at constant $x^{(r)}$ results in

$$\left[\frac{\partial f(u^{(r)})}{\partial \lambda}\right]_{x^{(r)}} = \sum_{i=1}^{r} \left[\frac{\partial f(u^{(r)})}{\partial u_i}\right]_{u_i^{(r-1)}} \left(\frac{\partial u_i}{\partial \lambda}\right)_{x^{(r)}} \qquad \text{(A-27)}$$

Differentiation of Eq. (A-24) with respect to λ at constant $x^{(r)}$ yields

$$\left(\frac{\partial u_i}{\partial \lambda}\right)_{x^{(r)}} = x_i \qquad \text{(A-28)}$$

Combination of Eqs. (A-26) to (A-28) gives

$$n\lambda^{n-1} f(x^{(r)}) = \sum_{i=1}^{r} x_i \left[\frac{\partial f(u^{(r)})}{\partial u_i}\right]_{u_i^{(r-1)}} \qquad \text{(A-29)}$$

Equation (A-29) holds for all values of λ. For $\lambda = 1$, Eq. (A-29) reduces to Eq. (A-23) and we have completed the proof of Euler's theorem. Equation (A-23) is of use in relating extensive thermodynamic properties to the corresponding partial molal properties.

A-3. LINEAR DIFFERENTIAL FORMS

The general expression for a linear differential form of r real independent variables is given by

$$L(x^{(r)}) = \sum_{i=1}^{r} M_i(x^{(r)})\, dx_i \qquad \text{(A-30)}$$

where the quantities $M_i(x^{(r)})$ are arbitrary functions of the variables $x^{(r)}$. A linear differential form is exact if it corresponds to the total derivative of some function $z = z(x^{(r)})$. Therefore, an exact linear differential form may be written

$$dz = \sum_{i=1}^{r} \left(\frac{\partial z}{\partial x_i}\right)_{x_i^{(r-1)}} dx_i \qquad \text{(A-31)}$$

The coefficients of dx_i in Eq. (A-31) obey the equation

$$\left(\frac{\partial M_i}{\partial x_k}\right)_{x_k^{(r-1)}} = \left(\frac{\partial M_k}{\partial x_i}\right)_{x_i^{(r-1)}} \qquad i, k = 1, \ldots, r \qquad \text{(A-32)}$$

which follows from Eq. (A-3). It can be shown that Eq. (A-32) is a set of necessary and sufficient conditions for Eq. (A-30) to be exact.

In thermodynamics, we deal with a number of linear differential forms, some of which are exact. The second law of thermodynamics is concerned with finding an integrating factor for the linear differential form $đq$ which transforms it into the exact differential form $dS = đq/T$ for reversible processes.

A-4. LINE INTEGRALS

The integral of a linear differential form [Eq. (A-30)] is uniquely determined only if the complete path of integration in the r-dimensional Euclidean space is specified. Thus we may write

$$I(x^{(r)},x^{(r)^\circ},c) = \int_{x^{(r)\circ},\,c}^{x^{(r)}} \sum_{i=1}^{r} M_i(x^{(r)})\, dx_i \tag{A-33}$$

where $x^{(r)\circ}$ denotes the initial point of the integration, $x^{(r)}$ denotes the final point of the integration, and c denotes the path of integration. An integral of the form of Eq. (A-33) is called a line integral.

The line integral of an exact differential form depends only on the initial and final points of integration and is independent of the path of integration. This can be easily seen by substituting Eq. (A-31) into Eq. (A-33). The result is

$$\begin{aligned} I(x^{(r)},x^{(r)^\circ},c) &= \int_{x^{(r)\circ},\,c}^{x^{(r)}} \sum_{i=1}^{r} \left(\frac{\partial z}{\partial x_i}\right)_{x_i^{(r-1)}} dx_i = \int_{z^\circ,\,c}^{z} dz \\ &= z - z^\circ \end{aligned} \tag{A-34}$$

which is independent of c. If the initial and final points of the integration are the same, Eq. (A-34) becomes

$$I(x^{(r)^\circ},x^{(r)^\circ}) = \oint dz = 0 \tag{A-35}$$

It can be shown that Eq. (A-35) is a sufficient as well as a necessary condition for the exactness of a linear differential form. We specialize Eq. (A-33) to the case of two independent variables and use Gauss's theorem to obtain

$$\oint (M_1\, dx_1 + M_2\, dx_2) = \int\left[\left(\frac{\partial M_1}{\partial x_2}\right)_{x_1} - \left(\frac{\partial M_2}{\partial x_1}\right)_{x_2}\right] dx_1\, dx_2 \tag{A-36}$$

The integration on the right-hand side of Eq. (A-36) is over the area of the surface enclosed by the line integral. If the line integral of a linear differential form vanishes for every arbitrarily chosen closed path, then Eq. (A-36) implies that

$$\left(\frac{\partial M_1}{\partial x_2}\right)_{x_1} = \left(\frac{\partial M_2}{\partial x_1}\right)_{x_2} \tag{A-37}$$

Equation (A-37) is a necessary and sufficient condition for the differential form to be exact.

The indefinite integrals of exact differential forms in thermodynamics are called functions of state since they do not depend on the path of integration.

INDEX